ELEMENTS OF ENERGY CONVERSION

ELEMENTS OF
ENERGY CONVERSION

BY

CHARLES R. RUSSELL

PERGAMON PRESS

OXFORD · LONDON · EDINBURGH · NEW YORK

TORONTO · SYDNEY · PARIS · BRAUNSCHWEIG

[1967]

Pergamon Press Ltd., Headington Hill Hall, Oxford
4 & 5 Fitzroy Square, London W.1

Pergamon Press (Scotland) Ltd., 2 & 3 Teviot Place, Edinburgh 1

Pergamon Press Inc., 44-01 21st Street, Long Island City, New York 11101

Pergamon of Canada, Ltd., 6 Adelaide Street East, Toronto, Ontario

Pergamon Press (Aust.) Pty. Ltd., 20-22 Margaret Street, Sydney, N.S.W.

Pergamon Press S.A.R.L., 24 rue des Écoles, Paris 5ᵉ

Vieweg & Sohn GmbH, Burgplatz 1, Braunschweig

First edition 1967

Library of Congress Catalog Card No. 66-17812

2562/67

Dedicated to
DOLORES RUSSELL
for patience and
encouragement

CONTENTS

vii

PREFACE

THE subject of energy conversion recently has been extended from conventional heat power engineering (steam and internal combustion engines) to include many energy conversion and storage principles. Information is now scattered under several titles through many publications including voluminous government reports. Many of these are difficult to obtain and use. This book has been written, therefore, to bring together this information and to present it in terms of the fundamental thermodynamics that apply to energy conversion by any process. Emphasis is given to the development of the theory of heat engines because these are and will remain most important power sources. Descriptive material is then presented to provide elementary information on all important energy conversion devices.

Many individuals and organizations contributed to the preparation of this text. The manuscript was edited by Martha Davis. Helpful suggestions were received from Mr. O. P. Prachar and others. Several industrial organizations generously have provided illustrations and data from current programs. The author is indebted particularly to the U.S. Air Force for permission to use extensive material from their publication *Energy Conversion Systems Reference Handbook*, prepared for them by Electro-Optical Systems, Inc.

However, any opinions that may be expressed or implied in the material presented in this publication are those of the author and are not necessarily the opinions of any other organization. In addition, whereas the author has endeavoured to make all content as up-to-date and as factual as possible, the author is neither responsible nor accepts responsibility for the safety of personnel following procedures described herein or for the losses and damages that may arise as a result of errors and omissions in the presented material. Neither does the author represent that the performance of any work or effort in accordance with the material or techniques referred to will produce the results herein described. A conscientious effort has been made to provide adequate references to original documents. These original works should be consulted whenever their content is involved.

CHAPTER 1

ENERGY

FORMS OF ENERGY

Energy is capacity for doing work. Power is the rate of doing the work. Energy is a scalar quantity expressed in terms of a force acting through a distance. Typical units for energy and work are foot-pounds, horsepower-hours, ergs, joules or kilowatt-hours. There are many forms of energy. Some of these are listed in Table 1-1 under the categories of potential, kinetic and electromagnetic. In addition there are heat and work. These are energy in the process of transfer from one body to another. After the transfer, the energy is designated again according to its nature as, for example, heat transferred may become thermal energy and work done may appear as mechanical energy.

Potential energy results from position or configuration. An elevated mass and a wound spring possess external potential energy relative to their normal states. This energy is equal just to the minimum work required to elevate the mass or to wind the spring. Fuels for an engine and the chemicals in a battery possess internal potential energy—chemical energy—as the result of forces between atoms and molecules. A nuclear fuel has internal potential energy associated with forces between subatomic particles.

Kinetic energy is associated with a moving mass and equals the minimum work required to produce the motion. The kinetic energy of a translating or vibrating body is classified as external kinetic energy. A material also possesses internal kinetic energy by virtue of motions of its molecules and motions within these molecules. These random motions are identified with thermal

1

TABLE 1-1   FORMS OF ENERGY

Potential energy

   (1) Mechanical (Position)
   (2) Chemical
   (3) Nuclear

Kinetic energy

   (1) Mechanical (Velocity)
   (2) Free Particles
   (3) Thermal

Electromagnetic energy

   (1) Radiant
   (2) Electrical
   (3) Magnetic

---

energy. A flowing gas has both internal random and externa directed kinetic energy.

Beta- and alpha-radiations emitted by radioisotopes possess large amounts of kinetic energy. These are high velocity electrons and helium nuclei respectively. In the fissioning of an atom of nuclear fuel, much of the energy appears initially as the kinetic energy of the two fission products released at high velocity. When these and other emissions are absorbed within a fuel element, their energy is transformed into thermal energy. Thus the energy released in radioactive decay and in nuclear fissioning appears as thermal energy although originating mostly as the energy of free particles.

Electromagnetic radiations extend from long radio-frequency waves to X-rays. Thermal radiation is intermediate, with longer wavelengths than visible light. An electromagnetic wave has electric and magnetic components normal to each other. An electric current is visualized as a stream of electrons flowing through a conductor under the force of a potential difference.

ENERGY CHANGES

Energy can be converted in form, but the total amount of energy in an isolated system remains unchanged. This is the basic principle that energy cannot be created or destroyed. Frequent use is made of this in energy conversion calculations accounting for the unchanging total amount of energy at each step in a process. For example, the potential chemical energy of a fuel plus the thermal energy of the fuel and air for combustion in an engine can be accounted for as the sum of the work delivered, the thermal energy released to the surroundings and the chemical energy remaining in the combustion products.

Although the total amount of energy remains unchanged, there is a great difference in the quality of different forms of energy. Potential mechanical energy can in theory be transformed completely into work or other forms of energy. This is true of all energy in forms that are completely directed such as electrical, mechanical and even chemical energy. The term "free energy" designates all forms of directed energy. The undirected random motions associated with thermal energy, however, are not completely available for conversion into directed energy. The part of thermal energy that is available for conversion at some elevated temperature depends upon this temperature and also upon the temperature at which the remainder of the energy is rejected. The energy may be rejected in the condenser of a steam turbine or in the exhaust products from an internal combustion engine. If the heat rejection temperature is postulated to be absolute zero, all the thermal energy in theory then could be transformed into directed energy, since molecular motions decrease with temperature and approach zero as the temperature approaches absolute zero.

At practical temperatures for exhausting heat from a thermal energy conversion device, there is a limiting theoretical maximum efficiency. Only a fraction of this efficiency is realized in actual engines. These efficiency limitations apply whenever thermal energy becomes an intermediate energy form. Although chemical potential energy can be converted directly into electrical energy in a battery or fuel cell at very high efficiency, the combustion of the fuel to produce thermal energy for a heat engine again imposes the efficiency limitation defined by the temperatures of heat addition and rejection. A quantitative description of these energy conversion processes is provided by the science of thermodynamics and its specialized branches such as thermochemistry.

CONVERSION METHODS

Many methods for energy conversion are known. A few are listed in Table 1-2. All of these have been studied as part of current power programs. Devices invented a century ago but put aside

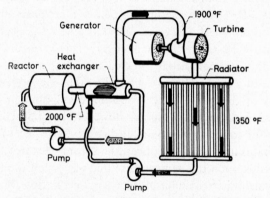

FIG. 1-1   Mercury turbine power system (NASA).

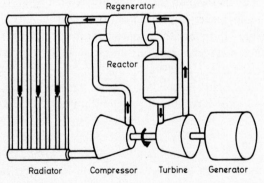

FIG. 1-2 Closed-cycle gas turbine power system (NASA).

for lack of a requirement or for some technical reason are now under active development. Direct energy conversion devices having no moving mechanical parts are of special interest because of their potential reliability and freedom from vibration and inertial forces. These include electrochemical combustion in fuel cells,

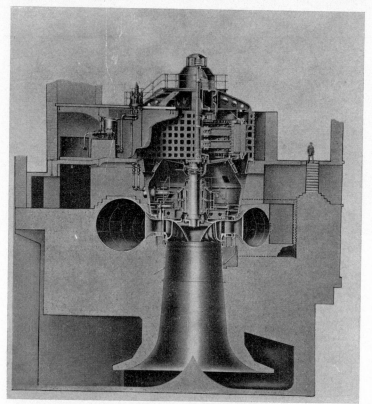

Fig. 1-3   Hydraulic turbine and generator in 1903 (Allis–Chalmers).

direct radiant energy conversion in solar cells, and thermal energy conversion in thermoelectric and thermionic generators.

Dynamic energy conversion devices are illustrated by the turbine and reciprocating internal combustion engine. The dynamic heat engines (Figs. 1-1 and 1-2) convert thermal energy into work through expansion of a fluid to exert a force against a turbine blade or piston. A gas can expand in a nozzle to produce

FIG. 1-4 Steam turbine generator unit (Allis–Chalmers).

FIG. 1-5 T 63-A-5 turboshaft engine (Allison Div. GMC).

FIG. 1-6   Rocket launch operations (U.S. Air Force).

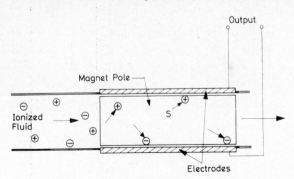

FIG. 1-7   Magnetohydrodynamic generator.

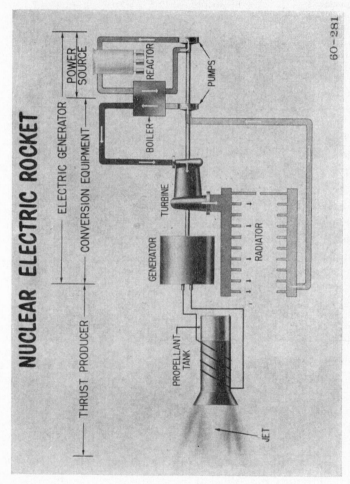

Fig. 1-8   Nuclear electric rocket (NASA).

TABLE 1-2 ENERGY CONVERSION TECHNIQUES

Thermal	Photon	Electrochemical

Thermoelectric
Thermionic
Dynamic heat engine
 	
Pyroelectric
Magnetohydrodynamic
Thermally regenerative
  fuel cells
	Photovoltaic
	Photoelectric
	Radiation regenera-
	  tive fuel cells
		Primary battery
		Secondary battery
		Fuel cells

thrust in a rocket or turbojet engine. Thus a fluid at a pressure above that of the surroundings can produce useful work in dynamic devices of several types.

A gas that is highly ionized to conduct electricity will generate electric power when flowing through a magnetic field. This is a magnetohydrodynamic generator (Fig. 1-7). In the reverse of this process (Fig. 1-8) electric power can accelerate a fluid to produce thrust in a nuclear electric rocket.

STATIC THERMAL CONVERTERS

Static thermal energy conversion devices can be considered to use electrons as the working fluid in place of a vapor or gas. These electrons are driven by thermal energy across a potential

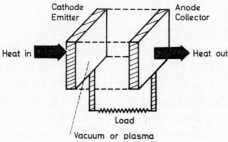

FIG. 1-9 Thermionic converter (NASA).

difference to produce electric energy. For example, in a thermionic generator (Fig. 1-9), electrons are first evaporated from a heated cathode and are then condensed or collected on a cooler anode. These electrons flow through an external circuit back to the cathode. Thus in a thermionic generator, thermal energy is converted directly into electricity through a process similar to that in a steam power plant where water is evaporated in a boiler and the steam is condensed after doing useful work in an engine.

Thomas Edison first observed an electric current between an incandescent filament and a cold electrode in an evacuated tube; however, not until recently (1958) has there been active develop-

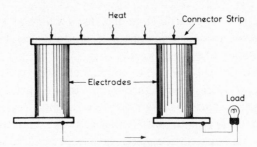

Fig. 1-10   Thermoelectric generator.

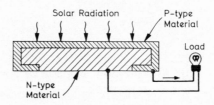

Fig. 1-11   Solar cell.

ment of thermionic generators. With the discovery of materials that provide adequate electron emission rates without melting and by the addition of cesium vapor to reduce the space charge, the performance of the system has been greatly improved. Now equipment is being designed for space power applications where the high temperature operation is advantageous. Thermionic generators are well suited for use with nuclear reactors or radio-isotope heat sources.

In thermoelectric generators (Fig. 1-10) and solar cells (Fig. 1-11) the electrons are driven across a potential difference at the junction within a solid of two materials. These are usually semiconductors. Again the electrons flow through an external circuit back to the positive electrode and can do useful work. The change of energy and the direction of electron flow across a junction depends upon the properties of the materials at the junction. This electron flow corresponds somewhat to that of the working fluid in a gas turbine power cycle since there is no change of state.

The thermoelectric effect resulting from a temperature difference between the junctions of dissimilar conductors in a circuit was observed in 1821 by Thomas Seebeck. He tested semiconductor materials that could have produced electricity with an efficiency of 3 percent long before the dynamo for generating electricity from mechanical power was developed. However, the usefulness of this discovery went unrecognized as a means for producing electricity because of interpretation as a magnetic effect caused by a difference in temperature. Not until recently have thermoelectric generators come into use for power production in special situations, although the thermoelectric effect has been used for measuring temperatures.

PHOTOVOLTAIC GENERATORS

Radiant energy can be converted directly into electrical energy by photovoltaic generators. This first was observed by W. G. Adams and R. E. Day with an illuminated selenium plate in a closed circuit. The development of the silicon solar cell was announced from the Bell Telephone Laboratories in 1952. This cell consists of a thin plate cut from a single crystal of silicon containing just a trace of an impurity. The plate is then treated with boron at an elevated temperature to diffuse this additional impurity into the top surface. After the other surfaces have been cleaned to remove any boron, metal contacts are soldered to the base and top. The impurities introduce extra positive and negative charges into the material on each side of the junction of the boron-contaminated surface layer with the base material. These extra charges remain in place until radiant energy causes migration. Then as long as the cell is illuminated, an electric current will flow through an external circuit connecting the metal contacts.

FIG. 1-12   Solar cell panels on NIMBUS meteorological satellite (NASA).

Solar cells vary so in efficiency that each cell of a production lot must be tested. A few will convert up to 14 percent of the incident radiant energy into electricity. A large fraction of the solar cells produced have an efficiency of at least 10 percent. Cells with lower efficiency are sold at reduced price for applications where efficiency is not critical. Efficiencies of 25 to 40 percent are possible for radiation within the limited range of wavelengths that the cell can best use. Solar cells are highly developed space power sources of proven reliability.

ELECTROCHEMICAL CELLS

Chemical free energy can be converted directly into electric energy in an electrochemical cell. Also energy can be stored in some reverse processes. Primary batteries, rechargeable (secondary) batteries, fuel cells and electrolytic units are all types of electrochemical cells. The theoretical efficiency of this method of energy conversion can be 100 percent and demonstrated efficiencies (at low current) have exceeded 80 percent.

Many different chemical systems can be used to generate electric energy. In a dry cell, a zinc electrode is oxidized by manganese dioxide. Hydrogen and oxygen will react on porous catalytic electrodes in contact with an electrolyte in a fuel cell (Fig. 1-13.) In these systems the fuel reacts to release electrons which flow through an external circuit back to the oxidizer electrode. There

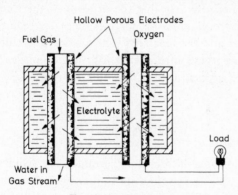

FIG. 1-13   Fuel cell.

the electrons are absorbed in reactions involving ions from the electrolyte. These ions are transported through the electrolyte to the fuel electrode to complete the circuit.

A fuel cell oxidizing carbon with nitric acid was studied by Sir Humphrey Davy in 1802. It has long been the dream of electrochemists that some day coal could be oxidized in a fuel cell to produce industrial electricity at high efficiency. Once there were plans for fuel cell power stations for street railways based on the oxidation of carbon. However, technical problems remained unsolved up to the time of the development of large central station steam power plants. Their success removed much of the incentive for further fuel cell development. This field then remained dormant until recently when new power requirements led to a major national effort to develop fuel cells for space power and other advanced applications.

Several types of regenerative fuel cells have been studied. In a thermally regenerative system the product of the electrochemical reaction such as lithium hydride is decomposed by thermal energy to regenerate the original reactants (hydrogen and lithium); these react again to produce electric energy. This overall process results in the conversion of thermal into electric energy. Then the efficiency limitation imposed by the temperatures of heat addition and rejection apply just as for any heat engine. Regenerative fuel cells based upon radiation-induced chemical reactions have also been proposed. By exposing the product of the electrochemical reaction (nitrosyl chloride for example) to radiation, this is decomposed and the reactants (nitric oxide and chlorine in this example) are regenerated. Reactants utilizing nuclear radiations, such as the decomposition of water by radiolysis, are also of interest.

OTHER CONVERSION DEVICES

A thermomagnetic generator produces a changing magnetic flux across a coil when the core is alternately heated and cooled. This results from variations in magnetic properties with temperature. The effect is the greatest at the Curie point — the temperature at which ferromagnetic materials such as iron lose most of their magnetic properties. When iron is in a weak magnetic field, the magnetic properties first increase with increasing temperature, and after passing through a maximum, drop suddenly to a small value. This point for iron is 1418 °F. Certain of the rare earth metals lose their magnetic properties at room temperature, while for some materials the Curie point is near absolute zero in temperature. Since the rate of flux change in a thermomagnetic generator depends upon the rate of temperature change, the power produced is a function of the rate of heating and cooling the magnet core. This is usually a relatively slow process so that thermomagnetic generators have low frequency and low output per unit mass. When some ingenious means for avoiding these limitations is found, it may be advantageous to combine a thermomagnetic generator with a nuclear reactor.

The ferroelectric converter is a close relative of the thermomagnetic generator. Here a ferroelectric material such as barium titan-

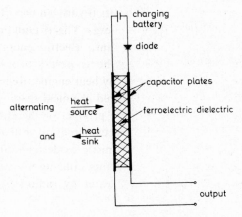

FIG. 1-14 Ferroelectric converter.

ate is used as the dielectric in a capacitor. When this is charged and then heated to the Curie point, the resulting change in capacitance forces an electric current through an external load at high potential. A battery can charge the capacitor at low voltage, and a diode will prevent reversal of the current during discharge. A possible circuit is shown in Fig. 1-14. Limitations on rates of heating and cooling also restrict the performance of this device.

Electricity can be produced in many other ways. Certain crystals, for instance, are known to produce a potential difference between crystal faces when heated or cooled. This effect is termed pyroelectricity. It is exhibited by tartaric acid and tourmaline crystals.

Piezoelectricity is derived from a mechanical force acting upon a crystal such as quartz or barium titanate. This phenomena is used to measure pressure and to generate high frequency sound. These crystals change in dimension when a potential difference is applied. This is a reversible process. A piezoelectric generator actuated by an explosive force or heavy impact has been studied as a source of single large power pulse.

Electricity can be produced by a photoelectric material such as selenium that emits electrons when illuminated. Unfurling a large surface of a photoelectric material has been considered for producing power in space from sunlight. A fluid passing through a porous plug can create a potential difference across the plug. This is observed sometimes in a gas flowing through an orifice. A spark can be produced under some conditions that may ignite an inflammable gas. Crystallization of a salt from a solution (the Workman–Reynolds effect) may generate a large potential difference. Practical applications for this and most every other possible power source will be found.

ENERGY SOURCES

The sun is a primary source of energy. This energy from the sun and other stars is released by thermonuclear reactions of hydrogen and other light elements. Electromagnetic radiations from the sun illuminate the earth and provide a convenient energy source in space. Thermal effects of solar energy in the earth's atmosphere create winds that can be used as a power source. Water power is produced more indirectly from solar radiation. Solar energy is available for conversion directly to power in amounts limited only by the area and cost of the collector. However, on earth there are usually less expensive ways to obtain electrical energy.

Photosynthesis converts solar energy into chemical energy and part of this energy has accumulated and been stored in coal, oil and gas reserves. These fuels supply most energy requirements of our civilization. However, the reserves of fossil fuels are not inexhaustible and many areas of the earth do not have adequate supplies. Therefore there is a strong incentive to develop other energy sources and particularly nuclear power. The estimated energy available from uranium and thorium supplies is about a hundred times that from coal reserves. Even so, the unlimited energy that can be obtained from heavy hydrogen in controlled thermonuclear reactions must eventually become the world's source of electricity. However, the reacting nuclei must be brough t to very high temperature and contained to initiate fusion. The development of controlled thermonuclear processes for power presents one of the most difficult technical problems ever undertaken. Fortunately, enough fossil and fission fuels are available to permit the orderly investigation of nuclear fusion power through several decades of years.

Progress in nuclear fission reactor development has made possible energy sources particularly suited for applications where atmospheric oxygen is not available for combustion or where large quantities of energy are required but with minimum fuel weight. These applications may range from nuclear auxiliary power units of a few watts to large generators for electric space propulsion. A radioisotope heat source is preferred as the energy source for small generators in the power range below a kilowatt; whereas nuclear reactors are required for large power units from a few kilowatts up to the megawatt range. The power requirements for many advanced space missions can be fulfilled only by nuclear energy.

ENERGY STORAGE

Capacity for energy storage is an essential part of many power systems. With stored energy available for peak power, the prime power source can be reduced in size and operate at a more favorable load. Also short-term emergency power can be provided from storage. Some equipment operates entirely from stored energy. Thus the development of efficient lightweight energy storage systems is a problem of equal importance with that of energy conversion. A high performance electric energy storage unit would make possible many technological advances ranging from improvements in transportation to more advanced space vehicles.

Most machines have provisions for potential or kinetic energy storage. A counterweight stores potential energy when lifted. Springs of all types are energy storage devices used in most mechanical systems. The flywheel on an engine stores and returns kinetic energy during the power cycle. Hydraulic power systems accumulate energy for peak loads by pumping the liquid into an elevated or high pressure reservoir. A compressed air tank stores energy between the prime mover and a pneumatic tool. Each of these systems for storing mechanical energy has characteristics that favor certain applications. For instance, springs are simple, reliable and efficient, but for storing large amounts of energy, some other systems are much lighter weight. There is an endless variety of requirements that are met by combinations of devices for storing mechanical energy.

Capacitors (condensers) are used in many circuits to store small amounts of electricity. However, the size and cost of capa-

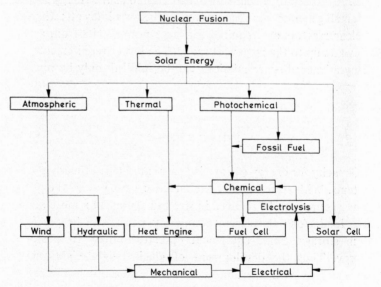

Fig. 1-15   Solar energy conversion.

citors become large for storing substantial amounts of energy.
Nevertheless, condenser banks until recently have been the only
practical means for producing high intensity power pulses of short
duration (milliseconds or microseconds). Condensers can be
recharged at a convenient rate and then connected in series to
produce a high potential discharge. Electric losses during charge
and storage periods depend on the dielectric material and operating conditions, but these losses are usually not excessive. Energy
is discharged from capacitors by closing a switch that connects
with the load.

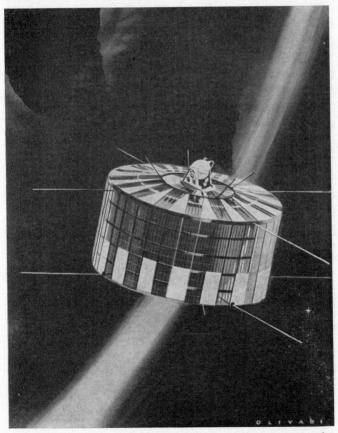

FIG. 1-16 TRANSIT satellite with nuclear auxiliary power and
solar cells (The Martin Company).

Electric energy can be stored also in a magnetic field. Air-core inductors that have an energy density a hundred times greater than that of capacitors are now possible. Also with superconductor materials at liquid helium temperatures, power losses during charging and storage become small. However, the liquid helium system is expensive and complex. Also to discharge the inductor, a contact must be opened in the circuit. This is a much more difficult

FIG. 1-17 Oak Ridge graphite reactor loading face (Oak Ridge National Laboratory).

problem in high energy systems than closing a contact. An inductor circuit stores electricity at low potential but with high current from a d.c. charging source.

Batteries will store even much larger amounts of energy than superconducting inductors. Also the charge and discharge processes in secondary batteries are efficient at low rates. However, batteries are not suitable for short (millisecond) power pulses at

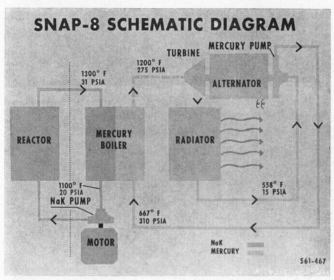

FIG. 1-18   Schematic arrangement of SNAP 8 (NASA).

very heavy current due to limitations on the rates of chemical reactions. Batteries will store energy for very long periods. Their unique and favorable characteristics are being utilized for more and more applications ranging from portable tools to space power systems.

Thermal energy can be stored by heating some suitable material to an elevated temperature. The steam and hot water in a large boiler, for example, represents a considerable inventory of thermal energy. The regenerator in a Stirling engine is a thermal storage device. For space applications, light elements and their com-

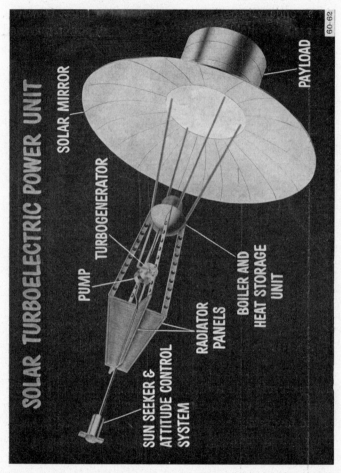

FIG. 1-19   Solar turboelectric power unit (NASA).

pounds with high heat capacities and large heats of fusion have been studied to provide energy storage. The most notable material is lithium hydride with a heat of fusion of over 300 Wh/lb—an exceptionally large value. Also the melting point of this compound (1272°F) is a convenient temperature for the operation of heat engines and thermoelectric generators. In the concept illustrated in Fig. 1-19, a container of this material is heated to its melting point with solar energy collected and focused by a large reflector unfurled in space. This system could provide power while a satellite is in the earth's shadow.

An efficient and convenient way to store large amounts of energy is in the form of the chemical energy of a fuel. The liquid hydrocarbons, for example, have the combined advantages of availability, high heat of combustion, and excellent handling and storage properties. However, oxygen or some other oxidizer is required to release chemical energy in combustion. The earth's atmosphere is an unlimited source of this oxygen. However, in space some oxidizer must be provided that considerably exceeds the fuel in mass. Liquid oxygen can be stored with low rates of evaporation in lightweight cryogenic containers and it is used in many space systems as the oxidizer. Hydrogen is a very high energy fuel that also can be stored as a liquid. Hydrogen can be used directly in a fuel cell producing electricity at high efficiency with potable water as a product. Electric energy can be converted into the chemical energy of a fuel for storage. The electrolysis of water to generate hydrogen and oxygen, for example, is a well-known process that can store electric energy as chemical energy efficiently. This is just the reverse of the fuel cell reaction. Other fuels can be produced with electric energy. Such chemical systems for electric energy storage will find important applications.

REFERENCES

1. C. J. LYNCH, "Unconventional Power Sources", *Prod. Engr.*, July 1961, pp. 616–18.
2. S. N. LEVINE, ed., *New Techniques for Energy Conversion*, New York, Dover Publications, 1961.

3. P. R. WIEDERHOLD, "Energy Storage for High-Power Discharges", *Astronautics and Aerospace Engr.* Vol. 1, No. 4, May 1963, pp. 104–6.
4. F. W. LAUCH, C. BUSCH, A. O. UYEHARA and P. S. MEYERS, "Portable Power from Nonportable Energy Sources", SAE Paper 608A, Nov. 1962.
5. W. LINVILLE, ed., *Proceedings of a Conference on Energy Storage and Conversion*, Oklahoma State University, Oct. 1963.
6. *Power for Spacecraft*, NASA SP-21, Washington, D.C., Dec. 1962.

CHAPTER 2

THERMAL PROPERTIES AND RELATIONS

INTRODUCTION

Relations between energy in various forms and the properties of matter are provided by the science of thermodynamics. This science is considered to have been founded, long after the development of the steam engine, with the publication by Carnot of a paper in 1824 on the ideal engine. He determined the relationship between the efficiency of this engine and the temperatures at which heat is added and rejected, although the conversion of heat into its equivalent of work was not recognized. This equivalence of heat and work and the important principle of the conservation of energy was established some nineteen years later by Joule. Other major contributions to this new science soon followed, and many of the concepts of thermodynamics were developed within the next several years. Thus, the conversion of thermal energy into work has been the subject of investigation over a long period of time by inventors of devices, experimenters, and by those who have searched for fundamental relations between the properties of matter. From their combined efforts have come the laws of thermodynamics explaining the observed behavior of energy conversion devices and providing relations between the physical properties of matter. New thermodynamic functions have been identified, such as entropy and free energy, to provide convenient descriptions of processes. Other functions also can be identified and given a special symbol or name as required for the study of some special problem. Although many mathematical manipulations are performed in deriving interrelations between equations, the science of thermodynamics is characterized by a few basic concepts that correlate a vast number of experimental observations, providing, therefore, a powerful analytical tool for the study of energy conversion.

TEMPERATURE

This science of thermodynamics is based upon measured changes in the properties of materials. For example, the fundamental concept of hot and cold comes from the observation that when a hot body and a cold body are brought into contact, the hot body cools and the cold body warms until there is no apparent further change; the two bodies are then in a state of thermal equilibrium. And when one body is in thermal equilibrium with two others, all the bodies then must be in thermal equilibrium with each other. These observations permit the establishment of a scale for measuring temperature, the degree of heat. The thermometer quantitatively measures the thermal state of other bodies.

The measurement of temperature is based conveniently upon some easily observed physical property, such as the expansion of a liquid in a thermometer bulb into a uniform capillary. The length of the liquid column is scaled in numbers and the thermometer can be calibrated by reference to two fixed points arbitrarily chosen (the freezing point and the boiling point of water, for example). On the Centigrade scale, the values of 0 and 100 are assigned these points with the intervening distance divided into 100 equal parts. On the Fahrenheit scale these two points are assigned values of 32 and 212 with 180 equal spaces between. Thus, the relations between the two temperature scales are

$$t°F = t°C \times 1.8 + 32$$

$$t°C = \frac{t°F - 32}{1.8}$$

Since these units of temperature are determined by the thermal expansion characteristics of the liquid selected for the thermometer, it would not be expected that an exact linear relation would exist necessarily with other thermodynamic properties. Therefore a thermodynamic temperature scale has been developed around the concept of measuring the pressure at the ice and the steam points in a gas-filled bulb of constant volume. The measurements are made at reduced pressure so that the expansion properties of the gas approach those of an ideal thermodynamic material. The thermodynamic temperatures T_1 and T_2 are defined in terms of the measured pressure ratios

$$\frac{T_1}{T_2} = \frac{p_1}{p_2}$$

With the temperature difference between the ice point and boiling point of water taken as 100 units for the Kelvin scale and 180 units for the Rankine scale, these temperatures are found to be related as follows:

$$T°K = t°C + 273.16$$

$$T°R = t°F + 459.69$$

$$0°K = 0°R$$

The temperature of 0 °K or 0 °R is termed absolute zero. From the kinetic theory of matter, molecular motion should approach zero as the temperature of the material approaches absolute zero.

EQUATIONS OF STATE

Equal volumes of ideal or perfect gases at the same temperature and pressure contain the same number of molecules. Therefore, many properties of materials can be correlated by using as a unit of mass a quantity equal to the molecular weight in grams or pounds (gram-moles or pound-moles). A gram-mole of any perfect gas contains 6.023×10^{23} molecules (Avogadro's number), and occupies a volume of 22,414 cm^3 at 0 °C and 760 mm of mercury pressure (standard temperature and pressure, STP); the volume of a pound-mole of any perfect gas is 359 ft^3 at STP (32 °F and 14.696 psia).

A fundamental property of matter is that the three parameters pressure, temperature, and volume are not independent. There always exists a relationship, the thermal equation of state, from which the third parameter can be determined, if any two are known. In the case of a perfect gas, the thermal equation of state is

$$pV = NRT$$

where N is the number of moles of material — the quantity divided by molecular weight (w/MW) — and R is the gas constant (1545.3 ft-lb/lb-mole °F). [*Note:* The gas constant, R, is expressed in units of energy per unit mass-degree of temperature. Values of this constant in various systems are given in Table 2-1.] This equation of state can be rewritten in the forms

$$pV = NRT = \frac{w}{MW} RT = w \frac{R}{MW} T = wR'T$$

Here R' is the gas constant for gas of a specific molecular weight. It is apparent from these relations that at constant volume, the pressure is proportional to the absolute temperature and at constant pressure the volume is proportional to the absolute temperature. Pressure and volume are inversely related at constant temperature. Many practical problems can be solved with reasonable accuracy using this simple equation of state.

TABLE 2-1   THE GAS CONSTANT R

1545.3	ft-lb/°F	lb-mole
82.06	atm cm³/°C	g-mole
1.987	Btu/°F	lb-mole
1.987	cal/°C	g-mole

EXAMPLE 2-1. Calculate the weight of hydrogen contained in a 4 ft³ cylinder at 1000 psia and 60 °F.

Solution: The absolute pressure in pounds per square foot is

$$p = 1000 \times 144$$

The absolute temperature in degrees Rankine, using the value of 460 instead of the more exact 459.69, is

$$°R = 460° + 60° = 520°$$

The molecular weight of hydrogen is 2.016. Then in consistent units, the mass, w, is found.

$$1000 \times 144 \times 4 = \frac{w}{2.016} \times 1545 \times 520$$

$$w = 1.45 \text{ lb hydrogen}$$

GAS MIXTURES

In a mixture of gases that do not react chemically, each gas behaves as though the others were not present (Dalton's law). Consequently, each gas may be considered as occupying the total volume and to exert a pressure, p_i, called the partial pressure. For a perfect gas, the partial pressure for the ith component is determined by the relation:

$$p_i = \frac{w_i}{MW_i} \frac{RT}{V}$$

The total pressure is the sum of the partial pressures and for n component gases

$$p = \sum_1^n p_i$$

An average molecular weight can be determined as the mass of gas divided by the number of moles, N, in this amount of gas, where

$$N = \sum_1^i \frac{w_i}{MW_i}$$

$$MW_{ave} = \frac{w}{N}$$

Using this average molecular weight, the simple gas law can be applied

$$pV = \frac{w}{MW_{ave}} RT$$

EXAMPLE 2-2. Calculate the average molecular weight of dry air from its composition of 75.5 percent nitrogen, 23.2 percent oxygen, and 1.3 percent argon by weight.

Solution: Taking 100 lb of air as a basis for calculation, the number of moles is

$$N = \frac{75.5}{28.016} + \frac{23.2}{32} + \frac{1.3}{39.944} = 3.45$$

$$MW_{ave} = \frac{100}{3.45} = 29$$

The mole fraction is the ratio of the number of moles of a component to the total number of moles in a quantity of material, and for a perfect gas the mole fraction and the volume fraction are equal. Also, the partial pressure p_i is the product of the mole fraction and the total pressure,

$$p_i = M_i p$$

where M_i is the mole fraction of the ith component.

The simple gas law is satisfactory for many gases at low density. A more accurate equation for gases at higher density is that of van der Waals,

$$\left(p + \frac{a}{v^2}\right)(v - b) = R'T$$

where v is the specific volume, b is a correction for the molecular volume, and a is related to the molecular attraction forces. Values of these constants may be found in Ref. 1 and other standard references. Although this equation is applicable over wider ranges of temperature and pressure than the simple gas law, there may be significant errors at low specific volumes, depending on the gas and its temperature.

COMPRESSIBILITY FACTOR

A more general equation for gas properties relates them to the properties at the critical temperature and pressure where the density and other properties of the liquid phase become identical to those of the vapor. Pressure can be expressed as the reduced pressure p_R, defined as the ratio of the absolute pressure p to the critical pressure p_c

$$p_R = p/p_c$$

The reduced temperature is the similar ratio

$$T_R = T/T_c$$

By the use of these parameters of reduced pressure and temperature it has been found possible to correlate data for most gases (except hydrogen and helium and the other noble gases). Correlations for hydrogen and these other gases can be obtained by the use of pseudocritical temperatures and pressures. A correction factor to the simple gas law, designated as the compressibility factor C, can be determined so that

$$pV = CNRT$$

This convenient relation can be used to estimate the properties of gases over a wide range of conditions and to extrapolate experimental data. For a perfect gas the value of C is unity. Applications of the reduced pressure and temperature to other correlations are described in Ref. 2.

EXAMPLE 2-3. Using the critical constants in Table 2-2, estimate the specific volume of steam at 5000 psia and 1000 °F.

Solution: The reduced temperature and pressure are determined

$$T_R = \frac{538 + 273}{647} = 1.25$$

$$p_R = \frac{5000}{14.7 \times 218} = 1.56$$

TABLE 2-2 CRITICAL CONSTANTS

Material	T_c °K	p_c, atm
Air	132.5	37.2
Butane, n	426.2	36.0
Carbon dioxide	304.3	73.0
Carbon monoxide	134.2	35.0
Chlorine	417.2	76.1
Ethane	305.3	48.8
Ethyl alcohol	516.3	63.1
Helium	5.3	2.26
Hydrogen	33.3	12.8
Methyl alcohol	513.2	78.7
Nitrogen	126.1	33.5
Octane, n	569.2	24.6
Oxygen	154.4	49.7
Propane, n	370.0	96.8
Water	647.2	217.7

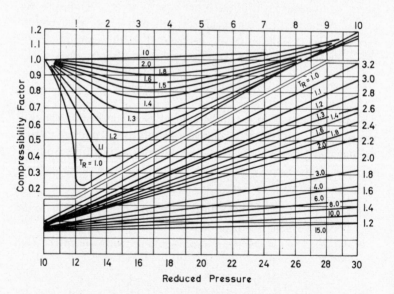

FIG. 2-1 Compressibility factor as a function of reduced pressure: intermediate and high pressure range. Reproduced from *Chemical Process Principles, Part Two: Thermodynamics*, Second Edition, Hougen, Watson and Ragatz. John Wiley, New York, 1959 with permission.

From Fig. 2-1 the compressibility factor is found to be 0.72 Then the volume of 1 lb of steam is

$$V = \frac{0.72 \times 1545 \times (459.7 + 1000)}{5000 \times 144 \times 18.016} = 0.125 \text{ ft}^3$$

Tables of gas properties are available for many of the fluids of interest in power generation and these tables should be used in preference to the above relations for calculations where accuracy is required. Also calculations using gas tables usually are more convenient and rapid.

KINETIC THEORY OF GASES

The properties of gases can be explained and a useful concept of thermal energy illustrated by the theory that gas molecules are in constant motion. Monatomic molecules such as helium behave as point masses with only random linear motion having significance, whereas more complicated molecules such as carbon dioxide have in addition, rotational motion of the whole molecule plus motion of the atoms within the molecule to consider. However, the average linear velocity of a gas molecule can be computed from the gas pressure and density, since the pressure exerted by the gas on the walls of a container is the result of gas molecules striking the walls and rebounding. The change in momentum of a molecule striking a wall and rebounding is

$$\text{momentum change} = 2mv_n$$

where v_n is the average velocity component normal to the surface and m is the mass of the molecule. A molecule will travel the distance $v_n t$ normal to the surface in the time interval t. Only half the molecules within a volume $v_n t$ above a unit surface area will be traveling toward the surface to strike it and rebound within the time interval t. The number of molecules with in this volume is

$$n = \frac{\varrho v_n t}{mg}$$

where ϱ is the gas density. Therefore the rate at which molecules strike this surface and rebound is

$$\text{rate} = \frac{\varrho v_n t}{mg} \times \frac{1}{2t}$$

The force exerted against a unit area—the pressure—is equal to the rate of change of momentum

$$p = \frac{\varrho v_n}{2mg} \times 2mv_n = \frac{\varrho v_n^2}{g}$$

Since the motion of the molecules is random in direction, the velocity components in each of three perpendicular directions are equal

$$v_x = v_y = v_z$$

The square of the total velocity is the sum of the squares of these normal components

$$v^2 = v_x^2 + v_y^2 + v_z^2 = 3v_n^2$$

Therefore the pressure is related to the gas density and average molecular velocity by the simple relation

$$p = \frac{\varrho v^2}{3g}$$

This velocity v is the root mean square of the molecular velocity. Also from the simple gas law

$$p = \frac{\varrho RT}{MW} = \frac{\varrho v^2}{3g}$$

The average velocity of a gas molecule is a function of temperature for conditions under which the gas follows this relation, since

$$v^2 = \frac{3RTg}{MW}$$

The molecules of a gas exchange energy with each other through collision and, as a result, at any instant some molecules may be at high velocities and others at low velocities. A definite distribution of velocities is established in a gas through molecular collision; however, as shown in Fig. 2-4, the number of molecules having velocity extremes is small.

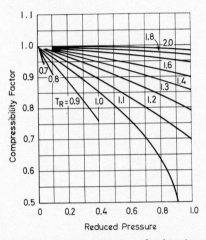

FIG. 2-2 Compressibility factor as a function of reduced pressure: low pressure range. Reproduced from *Chemical Process Principles. Part Two: Thermodynamics*, Second Edition, Hougen, Watson and Ragatz. John Wiley, New York, 1959 with permission.

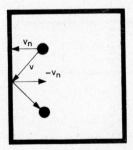

FIG. 2-3 Molecular impact on wall.

In these considerations of the velocity of gas molecules, it is assumed that the molecules are separated so that no significant forces exists between them. As the temperature of a gas is reduced, the average velocity of the molecules diminishes and at some point, attraction forces between molecules become sufficient for them to group together, forming a liquid phase. A rapid interchange of molecules continues between the liquid and the gas phases.

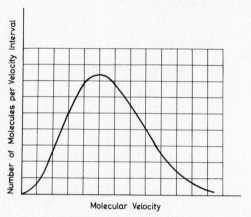

FIG. 2-4   Molecular velocity distribution in gas.

It is helpful to consider thermal energy in terms of the kinetic theory of matter. The molecules in a substance are in motion and the velocity increases with temperature. When two objects are brought into direct contact, the molecules at the contact surface

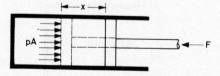

FIG. 2-5   Work from volume change.

exchange energy through collision, causing the temperatures to approach each other. Thermal energy is thus transferred from the material at higher temperature to the material at lower temperature. When the objects are at the same temperature, there is no net exchange of energy, since the molecules have the same average energy.

EXAMPLE 2-4. Calculate the average velocity of a nitrogen molecule at 60 °F.

Solution: The previous relation can be rearranged to give

$$v^2 = 3g \frac{RT}{MW}$$

$$v^2 = 3 \times 32.2 \times \frac{1545 \times (460 + 60)}{28}$$

$$v = 1660 \text{ ft/sec}$$

WORK

A system may do mechanical, electrical, or other work. The work done by the system on the surroundings is defined as being positive. Work done on the system from outside the system is negative work by definition and it is said that the surroundings have done work on the system.

An expanding gas can do mechanical work dW by exerting a force F through a distance dx, or

$$dW = Fdx$$

The force F on the inner face of a slowly moving piston in a cylinder containing gas at a pressure p above that of the surroundings is

$$F = pA$$

where A is the area of the piston. When the frictionless piston acts against an external force less than pA by only a negligible amount, the external work done is

$$dW = pAdx = pdV$$

The differential volume dV is Adx. It should be noted that a gas expanding into a vacuum has no resisting force and therefore no work is done. The maximum work is done when the resisting force is just slightly less than the force exerted by the gas on the piston.

When the relation between pressure and volume is known for the conditions of the expansion, the work done in an expansion from point 1 to point 2 can be found

$$W = \int_1^2 p\,dV$$

For an expansion at constant pressure from V_1 to V_2, the work becomes

$$W = p(V_2 - V_1)$$

THE FIRST LAW OF THERMODYNAMICS

Energy can be neither created nor destroyed but only can be changed in form; thus the total amount of energy in a system and its surroundings is unchanged by any process that may take place. According to this statement of the first law, an according system can be set up for the transfer of energy into different forms. The initial energy content of a system plus the energy added from the surroundings, minus the energy transferred to the surroundings in various forms must equal the final energy content of the system. Similar energy balances can be established for each component of the system.

The energy in the system may be in several forms including chemical, thermal, electrical and mechanical energy. The kinetic energy KE, of a mass moving at some velocity v, is

$$KE = \frac{1}{2} mv^2$$

The energy stored by lifting a mass is a form of potential energy. For example, in some large power systems, water is pumped up to an elevated reservoir during periods of low power requirement, and this stored potential energy is used to produce power during a peak load on the system. The amount of stored potential energy PE, at a height h is

$$PE = mgh$$

INTERNAL ENERGY

The part of the total energy of a material that depends upon the various modes of molecular motion together with the potential energy of intermolecular forces is termed internal energy and is designated as U. Where kinetic and potential energies are constant, the internal energy change for a system is determined from the first law of thermodynamics to be equal to the heat added to a system Q, minus the work done by the system or

$$\Delta U = Q - W$$

For a process involving no energy exchange with the surroundings, there must be no change in internal energy. Furthermore, since the internal energy of a material is a property of the material at any state of equilibrium, a change in internal energy is determined by the initial and final states. Thus the internal energy change is independent of the path or process involved.

The internal energy of a simple gas can be considered to consist of the kinetic energy of the molecules in random motion. For a molecule such as helium, the average (root mean square) molecular velocity is related to the gas properties by

$$pV = \frac{RT}{MW} = \frac{v^2}{3g}$$

Then the energy per mole of ideal gas is

$$U = \frac{1}{2} mv^2 = \frac{MWv^2}{2g} = \frac{3}{2} RT$$

HEAT CAPACITY

The rate of change of energy content with temperature is the heat capacity. At constant volume there is no interchange of mechanical work with the surroundings, so any change in energy content must equal the change in internal energy. Then the heat capacity at constant volume is the rate of change of internal energy with temperature. Therefore the heat capacity at constant volume of an ideal monatomic gas such as helium is

$$\left(\frac{\partial U}{\partial T}\right)_V = \frac{3}{2} R = C_{V_{He}}$$

Since the motion of a monatomic gas has components in each of three perpendicular directions, there are three degrees of freedom in this motion and each degree of freedom has associated with it a heat capacity at constant volume of $1/2R$. Using the approximate value, $R = 2$ Btu/°F lb-mole, the specific energy per degree of freedom becomes 1 Btu/F° lb-mole. The specific heat of monatomic gases at constant volume is thus 3 Btu/°F lb-mole over a wide range of temperatures. For diatomic gases such as nitrogen, the gas molecule can have two additional degrees of freedom in its motion associated with rotation about two perpendicular axes; hence, the heat capacity is larger by two units so that

$$C_{V_{N_2}} = \frac{5}{2} R = 5 \text{ Btu/°F lb-mole.}$$

There is additional energy from motion of the molecular components. The actual constant-volume heat capacity of diatomic gases is therefore greater than $\frac{5}{2} R$, increasing with temperature.

More complex molecules such as carbon dioxide have even larger heat capacity and temperature dependence as the result of other component motions.

Another important thermodynamic property is the heat capacity at constant pressure as in the heating of a gas in a cylinder with a frictionless piston to allow expansion at constant pressure. When an ideal gas is heated at constant pressure, the internal energy increases by the same amount as in a constant volume process, but work is done also as a result of the volume increase. The increase in heat capacity due to this volume change is

$$\left(\frac{\partial W}{\partial T}\right)_p = p \left(\frac{\partial V}{\partial T}\right)_p$$

From the simple gas law, $pV = RT$, this quantity is found to be

$$p\left(\frac{\partial V}{\partial T}\right)_p = R = 2 \text{ Btu/°F lb-mole}$$

Thus the molal heat capacity of a perfect gas at constant pressure is

$$C_p = C_V + 2$$

This relation is valid for all gases under conditions that permit application of the simple gas law. For other conditions, the value of

$$\left(\frac{\partial W}{\partial T}\right)_p = p\left(\frac{\partial V}{\partial T}\right)_p$$

must be determined. The molal heat capacities of several gases are plotted as a function of temperature in Fig. 2-6.

The ratio of heat capacity at constant pressure to the value at constant volume, C_p/C_V, designated by γ, is used in many thermo-

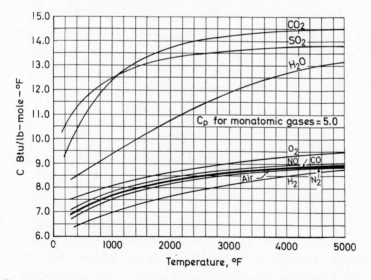

FIG. 2-6 True molal heat capacities of gases at constant pressure between 60 °F and abscissa temperature. Reproduced with permission from Sutton, *Rocket Propulsion Elements*, Second Edition, John Wiley, New York, 1956.

dynamic relations. The value of γ for monatomic gases is $5/3 =$ $=1.667$. For diatomic gases this value is approximately $7/5=1.40$, decreasing with temperature.

EXAMPLE 2-5. Determine the heat capacity ratio γ for steam at 2000 °F.
Solution: It is found from Fig. 2-6 that

$$C_p = 10.8 \text{ Btu/lb-mole}$$

Then from the above relations,

$$C_V = C_p - 2.0 = 8.8$$

and

$$\gamma = \frac{C_p}{C_V} = \frac{10.8}{8.8} = 1.23$$

ADIABATIC PROCESS

If no heat is exchanged with the surrounding in a process, it is termed an adiabatic process. The expansion of a gas in a well-insulated cylinder may closely approach this condition, and the

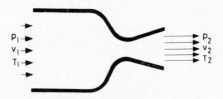

FIG. 2-7   Gas expansion in a nozzle.

work done must come from the internal energy of the gas. This decrease in internal energy corresponds to the change in kinetic energy of the gas molecules that strike the receding face of the piston and rebound with reduced velocity. The expansion of a gas through a nozzle also may approximate an adiabatic process. A gas expanding into an evacuated chamber does no external work. Therefore after the gas comes to rest, there is no decrease in internal energy and for a perfect gas, there is no temperature change. This was demonstrated experimentally by Joule in 1845. However, it was found that there is a significant temperature

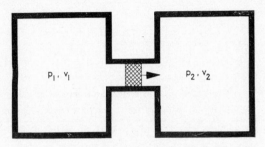

FIG. 2-8   Joule porous plug experiment.

change for most gases near their boiling points (the Joule–Thomson effect). This is due to intermolecular forces. The effect is used for cooling gases to low temperatures for liquefaction.

ENTHALPY

In a constant pressure process, the heat Q_p added to a system must equal the increase in internal energy, $U_2 - U_1$, plus the work, $p(V_2 - V_1)$, done by the system or

$$Q_p = U_2 - U_1 + p(V_2 - V_1)$$

A convenient thermodynamic function, the enthalpy H, is defined by the relations

$$H = U + pV$$
$$Q_p = H_2 - H_1$$

The heat capacity at constant pressure is then

$$C_p = \left(\frac{\partial H}{\partial T} \right)_p$$
$$dQ = C_p dT$$

Since the heat capacity $\bar{C}_p$ varies with temperature (except for monatomic gases), the change in enthalpy must be found by integration

$$Q_p = H_2 - H_1 = \int_1^2 C_p \, dT$$

An average heat capacity $\overline{C}_p$ can be computed from the enthalpy change between T_1 and T_2

$$\overline{C}_p = \frac{H_2 - H_1}{T_2 - T_1}$$

Values of the average heat capacity between 60 °F and t are given in Fig. 2-9 as a function of t. These values can be used to calculate the enthalpy change between two temperatures t_3 and t_4 since the enthalpy values ΔH_3 and ΔH_4 relative to 60 °F can be found

$$\Delta H_{3-4} = H_4 - H_3 = \overline{C}_p(t_4 - 60) - \overline{C}_p(t_3 - 60)$$

Values of the enthalpy of several gases are given in Table 2-3 for convenient and accurate calculation. The enthalpy and other thermodynamic functions for dry air are listed in Table 2-4.

EXAMPLE 2-6. Determine the average heat capacity of carbon dioxide over the temperature range 1000 °F to 2000 °F using values from Fig. 2-9 and Table 2-3.

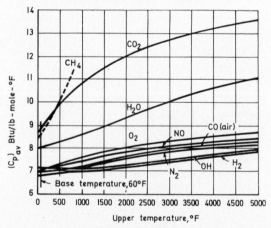

FIG. 2-9 Average molal heat capacities of gases at constant pressure between 60 °F and abscissa temperature. Reproduced with permission from Sutton, *Rocket Propulsion Elements*, Second Edition, John Wiley, New York, 1956.

Solution: The values of $\bar{C}_p$ are found for each temperature range to be

$$\bar{C}_{p1} = 10.8 \text{ Btu/lb-mole }°F \text{ from } 60° \text{ to } 1000 °F$$

$$\bar{C}_{p2} = 12.1 \text{ Btu/lb-mole }°F \text{ from } 60° \text{ to } 2000 °F$$

The enthalpies relative to 60 °F are

$$\Delta H_2 = (2000 - 60) \times 12.1 = 23,500 \text{ Btu/lb-mole}$$

$$\Delta H_1 = (1000 - 60) \times 10.8 = 10,200 \text{ Btu/lb-mole}$$

$$\bar{C}_{p12} = \frac{\Delta H}{\Delta T} = \frac{23,500 - 10,200}{1000} = 13.3 \text{ Btu/lb-mole }°F$$

Using values from Table 2-3, enthalpies of carbon dioxide at 2000 °F and 1000 °F are found

$$H_{2000} = 27,245 \text{ Btu/lb-mole}$$

$$H_{1000} = 14,077$$

$$\Delta H = 13,168$$

$$\bar{C}_p = \frac{13,168}{1000} = 13.17 \text{ Btu/lb-mole }°F$$

EXAMPLE 2-7. Determine the heat required to raise the temperature from 700 °R to 2000 °R of 500 ft^3 of a mixture of 50 percent by volume hydrogen and 50 percent carbon monoxide at a constant pressure of 1 atm.

Solution: The number of moles of each gas is found from the simple gas law to be

$$N_{H_2} = N_{CO} = \frac{500 \times 0.50 \times 492}{359 \times 700} = 0.49 \text{ moles}$$

From Table 2-3 the enthalpy of the gas mixture at 2000 °R is found

$$H_{CO} = 0.49 \times 14653.2 = 7180.1 \text{ Btu}$$

$$H_{H_2} = 0.49 \times 13980.1 = \underline{6850.2}$$

$$H_{2000} = 14,030.3 \text{ Btu}$$

TABLE 2-3   ENTHALPY PER MOLE OF GAS* (BTU/LB-MOLE)

T °R	t °F	CO_2 44.010	CO 28.010	H_2 2.016	N_2 28.016	O_2 32.000	H_2O 18.016	He 4.004
400	−59.7	2874.7	2776.9	2710.2	2777.0	2760.1	3163.8	1005.9
420	−39.7	3035.7	2916.0	2843.7	2916.1	2908.3	3323.2	
440	−19.7	3199.4	3055.0	2978.1	3055.1	3047.5	3482.7	
460	0.3	3365.7	3194.0	3113.5	3194.1	3186.9	3642.3	
480	20.3	3534.7	3333.0	3249.4	3333.1	3326.5	3802.0	
500	40.3	3706.2	3472.1	3386.1	3472.2	3466.2	3962.0	2482.4
520	60.3	3880.3	3611.2	3523.3	3611.3	3606.1	4122.0	
540	80.3	4056.8	3750.3	3660.9	3750.3	3746.2	4282.4	
560	100.3	4235.8	3889.5	3798.8	3889.5	3886.6	4442.8	
580	120.3	4417.2	4028.7	3937.1	4028.7	4027.3	4603.7	
600	140.3	4600.9	4168.0	4075.6	4167.9	4168.3	4764.7	2978.8
620	160.3	4786.8	4307.4	4214.3	4307.1	4309.7	4926.1	
640	180.3	4974.9	4446.9	4353.1	4446.4	4451.4	5087.8	
660	200.3	5165.2	4586.5	4492.1	4585.8	4593.5	5250.0	
680	220.3	5357.6	4726.2	4631.1	4725.3	4736.2	5412.5	
700	240.3	5552.0	4866.0	4770.2	4864.9	4879.3	5575.4	3475.3
720	260.3	5748.4	5006.1	4909.5	5004.5	5022.9	5738.8	
740	280.3	5946.8	5146.4	5048.8	5144.3	5167.0	5902.6	
760	300.3	6147.0	5286.8	5188.1	5284.1	5311.4	6066.9	
780	320.3	6349.1	5427.4	5327.6	5424.2	5456.4	6231.7	

800	340.3	6552.9	5568.2	5467.1	5564.4	5602.0	6396.9	3971.8
820	360.3	6758.3	5709.4	5606.7	5704.7	5748.1	6562.6	
840	380.3	6965.7	5850.7	5746.3	5845.3	5894.8	6728.9	
860	400.3	7174.7	5992.3	5885.9	5985.9	6041.9	6895.6	
880	420.3	7385.3	6134.2	6025.6	6126.9	6189.6	7062.9	
900	440.3	7597.6	6276.4	6165.3	6268.1	6337.9	7230.9	4468.2
920	460.3	7811.4	6419.0	6305.1	6409.6	6486.7	7399.4	
940	480.3	8026.8	6561.7	6444.9	6551.2	6636.1	7568.4	
960	500.3	8243.8	6704.9	6584.7	6693.1	6786.0	7738.0	
980	520.3	8462.2	6848.4	6724.6	6835.4	6936.4	7908.2	
1000	540.3	8682.1	6992.2	6864.5	6977.9	7087.5	8078.9	4964.7
1020	560.3	8903.4	7136.4	7004.4	7120.7	7238.9	8250.4	
1040	580.3	9126.2	7281.0	7144.4	7263.8	7391.0	8422.4	
1060	600.3	9350.3	7425.9	7284.4	7407.2	7543.6	8595.0	
1080	620.3	9575.8	7571.1	7424.5	7551.0	7696.8	8768.2	
1100	640.3	9802.6	7716.8	7564.6	7695.0	7850.4	8942.0	5461.2
1120	660.3	10030.6	7862.9	7704.7	7839.3	8004.5	9116.4	
1140	680.3	10260.1	8009.2	7844.9	7984.0	8159.1	9291.4	
1160	700.3	10490.6	8156.1	7985.2	8129.0	8314.2	9467.1	
1180	720.3	10722.3	8303.3	8125.5	8274.4	8469.8	9643.4	
1200	740.3	10955.3	8450.8	8265.8	8420.0	8625.8	9820.4	5957.6
1220	760.3	11189.4	8598.8	8406.2	8566.1	8782.4	9998.0	
1240	780.3	11424.6	8747.2	8546.7	8712.6	8939.4	10176.1	
1260	800.3	11661.0	8896.0	8687.3	8859.3	9096.7	10354.9	
1280	820.3	11898.4	9045.0	8828.0	9006.4	9254.6	10534.4	

TABLE 2-3 (cont.) ENTHALPY PER MOLE OF GAS (BTU/LB-MOLE)

T °R	t °F	CO_2 44.010	CO 28.010	H_2 2.016	N_2 28.016	O_2 32.000	H_2O 18.016	He 4.004
1300	840.3	12136.9	9194.6	8968.7	9153.9	9412.9	10714.5	6454.1
1320	860.3	12376.4	9344.6	9109.5	9301.8	9571.6	10895.3	
1340	880.3	12617.0	9494.8	9250.4	9450.0	9730.7	11076.6	
1360	900.3	12858.5	9645.5	9391.5	9598.6	9890.2	11258.7	
1380	920.3	13101.0	9796.6	9532.6	9747.5	10050.1	11441.4	
1400	940.3	13344.7	9948.1	9673.8	9896.9	10210.4	11624.8	6950.6
1420	960.3	13589.1	10100.0	9815.1	10046.6	10371.0	11808.8	
1440	980.3	13834.5	10252.2	9956.5	10196.6	10532.0	11993.4	
1460	1000.3	14080.8	10404.8	10098.0	10347.0	10693.3	12178.8	
1480	1020.3	14328.0	10557.8	10239.7	10497.8	10855.1	12364.8	
1500	1040.3	14576.0	10711.1	10381.5	10648.9	11017.1	12551.4	7447.1
1520	1060.3	14824.9	10864.9	10523.4	10800.4	11179.6	12738.8	
1540	1080.3	15074.7	11019.0	10665.5	10952.2	11342.4	12926.8	
1560	1100.3	15325.3	11173.4	10807.6	11104.3	11505.4	13115.6	
1580	1120.3	15576.7	11328.2	10950.0	11256.9	11668.8	13305.0	
1600	1140.3	15829.0	11483.4	11092.5	11409.7	11832.5	13494.9	7943.5
1620	1160.3	16081.9	11638.9	11235.1	11562.8	11996.6	13685.7	
1640	1180.3	16335.7	11794.7	11378.0	11716.4	12160.9	13877.0	
1660	1200.3	16590.2	11950.3	11521.0	11870.2	12325.5	14069.2	
1680	1220.3	16845.5	12107.5	11664.1	12024.3	12490.4	14261.9	

1700	1240.3	17101.4	12264.3	11807.4	12178.9	12655.6	14455.4	8440.0
1720	1260.3	17358.1	12421.4	11950.9	12333.7	12821.1	14649.5
1740	1280.3	17615.5	12579.0	12094.6	12488.8	12986.9	14844.3
1760	1300.3	17873.5	12736.7	12238.5	12644.3	13153.0	15039.8
1780	1320.3	18132.2	12894.9	12382.6	12800.2	13319.2	15236.1
1800	1340.3	18391.5	13053.2	12526.8	12956.3	13485.8	15433.0	8936.5
1820	1360.3	18651.5	13212.0	12671.2	13112.7	13652.5	15630.6
1840	1380.3	18912.2	13371.0	12815.3	13269.5	13819.6	15828.7
1860	1400.3	19173.4	13530.2	12960.7	13426.5	13986.8	16027.6
1880	1420.3	19435.3	13689.8	13105.7	13583.9	14154.4	16227.2
1900	1440.3	19697.8	13849.8	13250.9	13741.6	14322.1	16427.5	9432.9
1920	1460.3	19960.8	14009.9	13396.3	13899.5	14490.1	16628.5
1940	1480.3	20224.4	14170.3	13542.0	14057.8	14658.2	16830.0
1960	1500.3	20488.6	14331.0	13687.8	14216.4	14826.6	17032.4
1980	1520.3	20753.3	14492.0	13833.9	14375.2	14995.2	17235.3
2000	1540.3	21018.7	14653.2	13980.1	14534.4	15164.0	17439.0	9929.4
2020	1560.3	21284.4	14814.8	14126.5	14693.8	15332.9	17643.2
2040	1580.3	21550.7	14976.5	14273.2	14853.4	15502.1	17848.1
2060	1600.3	21817.6	15138.5	14420.1	15013.3	15671.5	18053.6
2080	1620.3	22084.9	15300.8	14567.2	15173.5	15841.1	18259.9
2100	1640.3	22352.7	15463.3	14714.5	15334.0	16010.9	18466.9	10425.9
2120	1660.3	22621.0	15626.1	14862.1	15494.7	16180.9	18674.4
2140	1680.3	22889.9	15789.0	15009.8	15655.6	16350.9	18882.5
2160	1700.3	23159.2	15952.3	15157.8	15816.8	16521.3	19091.2
2180	1720.3	23428.8	16115.7	15306.0	15978.2	16691.8	19300.7

TABLE 2-3 (cont.) ENTHALPY PER MOLE OF GAS (BTU/LB-MOLE)

T °R	t °F	CO_2 44.010	CO 28.010	H_2 2.016	N_2 28.016	O_2 32.000	H_2O 18.016	He 4.004
2200	1740.3	23699.0	16279.4	15454.4	16139.8	16862.6	19510.8	10922.3
2220	1760.3	23969.6	16443.2	15603.0	16301.7	17033.5	19721.6	
2240	1780.3	24240.6	16607.4	15751.9	16463.7	17204.5	19932.8	
2260	1800.3	24512.1	16771.6	15900.9	16626.0	17375.8	20144.8	
2280	1820.3	24784.0	16936.2	16050.2	16788.5	17547.2	20357.3	
2300	1840.3	25056.3	17101.0	16199.8	16951.2	17718.8	20570.6	11418.8
2320	1860.3	25329.1	17265.8	16349.5	17114.1	17890.6	20784.4	
2340	1880.3	25602.2	17431.0	16499.5	17277.2	18062.4	20998.7	
2360	1900.3	25875.7	17596.2	16649.6	17440.6	18234.5	21213.8	
2380	1920.3	26149.7	17761.8	16800.0	17604.1	18406.8	21429.4	
2400	1940.3	26424.0	17927.4	16950.6	17767.9	18579.2	21645.7	11915.3
2420	1960.3	26698.6	18093.4	17101.5	17931.9	18751.7	21862.4	
2440	1980.3	26973.7	18259.4	17252.6	18095.9	18924.4	22079.8	
2460	2000.3	27249.1	18425.7	17404.0	18260.3	19097.2	22297.8	
2480	2020.3	27525.0	18592.1	17555.5	18424.8	19270.3	22516.2	
2500	2040.3	27801.2	18758.8	17707.3	18589.5	19443.4	22735.4	12411.8
2520	2060.3	28077.6	18925.5	17859.3	18754.4	19616.8	22955.1	
2540	2080.3	28354.5	19092.5	18011.6	18919.4	19790.2	23175.3	
2560	2100.3	28631.8	19259.6	18164.0	19084.7	19963.8	23396.1	
2580	2120.3	28909.2	19426.9	18316.8	19250.1	20137.5	23617.5	

2600	12908.2	23839.5	20311.4	19415.8	18469.7	19594.3	29187.1	2140.3
2620		24061.9	20485.4	19581.5	18622.9	19762.0	29465.3	2160.3
2640		24284.8	20659.5	19747.5	18776.3	19929.7	29743.8	2180.3
2660		24508.4	20833.8	19913.6	18929.9	20097.7	30022.6	2200.3
2680		24732.6	21008.3	20079.9	19083.7	20265.7	30301.7	2220.3
2700	13404.7	24957.2	21182.9	20246.4	19237.8	20434.0	30581.2	2240.3
2720		25182.3	21357.6	20413.0	19392.1	20602.3	30860.9	2260.3
2740		25407.9	21532.5	20579.8	19546.7	20770.8	31141.0	2280.3
2760		25634.0	21707.4	20746.7	19701.5	20939.4	31421.3	2300.3
2780		25860.8	21882.6	20913.8	19856.5	21108.3	31702.0	2320.3
2800	13901.2	26088.0	22057.8	21081.1	20011.8	21277.2	31982.8	2340.3
2820		26315.6	22233.2	21248.4	20167.3	21446.2	32264.1	2360.3
2840		26543.8	22408.7	21416.0	20323.0	21615.4	32545.5	2380.3
2860		26772.5	22584.4	21583.6	20479.0	21784.7	32827.2	2400.3
2880		27001.6	22760.2	21751.5	20635.2	21954.1	33109.2	2420.3
2900	14397.6	27231.2	22936.1	21919.5	20791.5	22123.8	33391.5	2440.3
2920		27461.4	23112.2	22087.6	20948.1	22293.4	33674.0	2460.3
2940		27691.9	23288.3	22255.8	21104.9	22463.3	33956.8	2480.3
2960		27922.9	23464.7	22424.3	21262.0	22633.2	34239.8	2500.3
2980		28154.4	23641.1	22592.8	21419.3	22803.3	34523.1	2520.3
3000	14894.1	28386.3	23817.7	22761.5	21576.9	22973.4	34806.6	2540.3
3100		29552.8	23702.5	23606.8	22367.7	23826.0	36227.9	2640.3
3200	15887.0	30730.2	25590.5	24455.0	23164.1	24681.2	37654.7	2740.3
3300		31918.2	26481.6	25306.0	23539.5	25539.0	39086.7	2840.3
3400	16880.0	33116.0	27375.9	26159.7	24771.9	26399.3	40523.6	2940.3

* Abridged from *Gas Tables* by Joseph H. Keenan and Joseph Kay, Copyright 1948, John Wiley, New York.

At 700 °R the enthalpy is

$$H_{CO} = 0.49 \times 4866.0 = 2384.3 \text{ Btu}$$
$$H_{H_2} = 0.49 \times 4770.2 = \underline{2337.4}$$
$$H_{700} = 4721.7 \text{ Btu}$$

The heat required is then

$$Q = \Delta H = 14{,}030.3 - 4721.7 = 9308.6 \text{ Btu}$$

REVERSIBLE PROCESS

The expansion of a gas against an external force just equal to that exerted by the gas, will produce maximum work and therefore results in the maximum temperature drop for an adiabatic process. This process can be reversed at any point. Also as discussed previously, an expansion against no resisting force such as expansion into an evacuated chamber, does no work, and, for a perfect gas, there is no decrease in internal energy or temperature, after the gas comes to rest. This process is not reversible. The transfer of heat between two bodies approaches a reversible process when the temperature difference approaches zero.

A characteristic of reversible processes is that an infinitesimal change in the driving potential (temperature difference in heat conduction, or difference in force in gas expansion) can change the direction of the process. Furthermore, since the driving potential in a reversible process is infinitely small, the rate at which the process proceeds approaches zero. Even so, the concept of the reversible process is a useful basis for the development of many thermodynamic concepts, and many actual processes that take place at extremely high rates, such as the expansion of a gas through a nozzle, may closely approach the conditions predicted for a reversible process.

REVERSIBLE ADIABATIC PROCESS

According to the previous definition, in any adiabatic process, $dQ = 0$, and the work done by an expanding gas must equal the decrease in internal energy given by

$$dW = -dU$$

For a reversible process, the decrease in internal energy can be related to changes in temperature, pressure, and volume of a perfect gas by

$$dU = C_v dT = -p dV$$

By the substitution of $p = \dfrac{RT}{V}$, then

$$C_v \frac{dT}{T} = -\frac{R dV}{V}$$

This relation can be integrated, since R is a constant to give

$$\int_{T_1}^{T_2} C_v \frac{dT}{T} = -R \ln\left(\frac{V_2}{V_1}\right) = R \ln\left(\frac{T_1 p_2}{T_2 p_1}\right)$$

For a limited temperature range or for a gas where C_v can be considered a constant

$$C_v \ln\left(\frac{T_2}{T_1}\right) = R \ln\left(\frac{V_1}{V_2}\right) = (C_p - C_v) \ln\left(\frac{V_1}{V_2}\right)$$

Using $C_p/C_v = \gamma$ gives

$$\frac{T_2}{T_1} = \left(\frac{V_1}{V_2}\right)^{\gamma-1} = \frac{p_2 V_2}{p_1 V_1}$$

$$\frac{V_1}{V_2} = \left(\frac{p_2}{p_1}\right)^{\frac{1}{\gamma}}$$

$$\frac{T_2}{T_1} = \left(\frac{p_2}{p_1}\right)^{\frac{\gamma-1}{\gamma}}$$

It thus is found from these relations that for a reversible adiabatic process with a constant value of specific heat

$$p_1 V_1^\gamma = p_2 V_2^\gamma = \text{constant}$$

EXAMPLE 2-8. What pressure ratio is required for the adiabatic expansion of hydrogen through a nozzle so that the temperature of the gas drops from 3000 °R to 1000 °R? Use an average value for γ of 1.37.

Solution: From the relations for a reversible adiabatic process it is found that

$$\frac{p_1}{p_2} = \left(\frac{T_1}{T_2}\right)^{\frac{\gamma}{\gamma-1}} = \left(\frac{3000}{1000}\right)^{\frac{\gamma}{\gamma-1}} = 3^{\frac{1.37}{0.37}} = 58$$

If the exit pressure is 1 atm, 14.76 psia, the initial pressure must be

$$p_1 = p_2 \times 58 = 14.76 \times 58 = 856 \text{ psia.}$$

POLYTROPIC PROCESS

Any thermodynamic process is termed a polytropic process when the pressure–volume relation can be described by

$$pV^n = \text{constant}$$
$$n \neq \gamma$$

Values of n for various conditions are given in Table 2-4. The operation of compressors and turbines where there is some departure from the reversible adiabative process due to friction and heat exchange with the surroundings can be described accurately by the polytropic process relations. The value of n must be determined from test data. The work done is

$$W = \int_{V_1}^{V_2} p\,dV = \int_{V_1}^{V_2} \frac{k\,dV}{V^n} = \frac{1}{n-1}(p_1 V_1 - p_2 V_2) = \frac{R}{n-1}(T_1 - T_2)$$

Also Q the heat added to the system, must equal the sum of the work done and the increase in internal energy, or, provided $n \neq 1$,

$$Q = \frac{R}{n-1}(T_1 - T_2) + C_V(T_2 - T_1) = \left(\frac{n-\gamma}{n-1}\right) C_V(T_2 - T_1)$$

These relations cannot be applied to constant temperature expansions where $n = 1$, hence the following relation is derived for a constant temperature process of a perfect gas, where

$$pV = \text{constant} = RT$$

$$W_T = \int_{V_1}^{V_2} p\,dV = \int_{V_1}^{V_2} \frac{RT}{V}\,dV = RT \ln \frac{V_2}{V_1} = Q_T$$

These relations are summarized in Table 2-4. Note that for polytropic processes, the constant n may vary from a value greater than γ to less than unity.

TABLE 2-4   ENERGY RELATIONS FOR PERFECT GASES

Process	n	Work done (non-flow)	Heat added
Constant pressure	0	$p(V_2 - V_1)$	$NC_p(T_2 - T_1)$
Constant temperature	1	$NRT \ln\left(\frac{V_2}{V_1}\right)$	$NRT \ln\left(\frac{V_2}{V_1}\right)$
Constant volume	∞	0	$NC_v(T_2 - T_1)$
Reversible adiabatic	γ	$\frac{1}{\gamma - 1}(p_1 V_1 - p_2 V_2)$	0
Polytropic	$n \neq 1$	$\frac{1}{n-1}(p_1 V_1 - p_2 V_2)$	$\frac{(\gamma - n)}{(n-1)(\gamma - 1)}(p_1 V_1 - p_2 V_2)$

EXAMPLE 2-9. How much work can be done by the expansion of 1 lb of nitrogen at 60 °F from 200 psia to 10 psia in a polytropic process where the value of n is 1.2?

Solution: Since nitrogen closely approximates a perfect gas under these conditions, the simple gas law can be applied, and therefore

$$\frac{T_1}{T_2} = \left(\frac{p_1}{p_2}\right)^{\frac{n-1}{n}} = \left(\frac{200}{10}\right)^{\frac{0.2}{1.2}} = 1.647$$

$$T_2 = \frac{T_1}{1.647} = \frac{460+60}{1.647} = 316 \ °R$$

The polytropic non-flow work is then

$$W = \frac{1}{n-1}(p_1 V_1 - p_2 V_2) = \frac{NR}{n-1}(T_1 - T_2)$$

$$W = \frac{1545}{28 \times 0.2} \times (520 - 316) = 56,200 \ \text{ft-lb/lb } N_2$$

JET VELOCITY

The expansion of a gas through a nozzle converts part of the energy of the fluid into kinetic energy of the high velocity jet. With reference to Fig. 2-7, the total energies at the inlet and outlet are

$$\text{Inlet energy} = U_1 + p_1 V_1 + \frac{1}{2g}(v_1)^2$$

$$\text{Outlet energy} = U_2 + p_2 V_2 + \frac{1}{2g}(v_2)^2$$

The energy balance in terms of enthalpies becomes

$$H_1 + \frac{1}{2g}(v_1)^2 + Q = H_2 + \frac{1}{2g}(v_2)^2 + W$$

Usually there is no heat addition in the nozzle and heat losses can be neglected. Also no mechanical work is done by the gas in the nozzle so that both Q and W can be dropped. If the inlet to the nozzle is large, the inlet velocity v_1 will have an insignificant value so that the simple relation between the jet velocity and the enthalpy change can be used

$$H_1 - H_2 = \frac{1}{2g}(v_2)^2 = \bar{C}_p(T_1 - T_2)$$

$$v_2 = \sqrt{2g\Delta H}$$

SPECIFIC IMPULSE

The specific impulse of a propellant, I, is expressed in terms of pound-seconds of impulse per pound of propellant and is related to the jet velocity as

$$I = \frac{v}{g} = \sqrt{\frac{2}{g}(H_1 - H_2)}$$

EXAMPLE 2-10. Calculate the jet velocity and the specific impulse for the adiabatic expansion of hydrogen at 3000 °R through a nozzle to an exhaust temperature of 1000 °R.

Solution: The enthalpy change per mole for this expansion (Table 2-3) is found to be

$$H_1 = 21,576.9 \text{ Btu/mole}$$
$$H_2 = \underline{6,864.5}$$
$$\Delta H = 14,712.4 \text{ Btu/mole}$$

Since the molecular weight of hydrogen is 2.016 and there are 778.3 ft-lb/ Btu,

$$v^2 = 2 \times 32.2 \times \frac{778.3}{2.016} \times 14,712.4$$

Then

$$v = 19,130 \text{ ft/sec}$$

$$I = \frac{v}{g} = 594 \text{ lb-sec/lb, specific impulse}$$

Using these relations, an expression for the velocity and specific impulse of a gas jet can be obtained in terms of the initial gas temperature and the pressure ratio of the expansion. An average value of the specific heat of the gas over the temperature range of the expansion is used so that

$$\Delta H = \bar{C}_p(T_2 - T_1)$$

$$v^2 = -2g\bar{C}_p(T_2 - T_1) = 2g\bar{C}_p T_1\left(1 - \frac{T_2}{T_1}\right)$$

Since

$$\bar{C}_p = \frac{R\gamma}{1-\gamma}$$

and

$$\frac{T_2}{T_1} = \left(\frac{p_2}{p_1}\right)^{\frac{\gamma-1}{\gamma}}$$

the relation for the velocity becomes

$$v = \sqrt{\frac{2gRT_1}{MW} \frac{\gamma}{\gamma-1} \left[1 - \left(\frac{p_2}{p_1}\right)^{\frac{\gamma-1}{\gamma}}\right]}$$

EXAMPLE 2-11. Calculate the specific impulse for a propellant producing combustion products of average molecular weight of 32 at 5000 °R and 600 psia. The exhaust pressure is 15 psia and the average value of γ is 1.35.

Solution: The values are substituted into the velocity equation

$$v^2 = \frac{2 \times 32.2 \times 1545 \times 5000}{32} \times \frac{1.35}{1.35-1} \left[1 - \left(\frac{15}{600}\right)^{\frac{1.35}{1.35-1}}\right]$$

$$v^2 = 36.92 \times 10^6 \ \text{ft}^2/\text{sec}^2$$

$$v = 6076 \ \text{ft/sec}$$

$$I = \frac{v}{g} = \frac{6076}{32.2} = 189 \ \text{lb-sec/lb},$$

specific impulse.

FLOW PROCESS

Energy conversion devices such as turbines have a gas entering and leaving in steady flow with mechanical work being produced —this mechanical shaft work will be designated as W_s. The loss of thermal energy $(-Q)$ by radiation and convection from the engine to the surroundings may require consideration, and there will be a change in potential energy, if the inlet and outlet of the turbine are at different elevations. These effects are usually small. However, the difference in velocity between the inlet and outlet may produce appreciable energy changes. The total energy entering and leaving the system is

$$U_1 + p_1 V_1 + \frac{1}{2g} v_1^2 + Q = U_2 + p_2 V_2 + \frac{1}{2g} v_2^2 + W_s$$

$$H_1 + \frac{1}{2g} v_1^2 + Q = H_2 + \frac{1}{2g} v_2^2 + W_s.$$

Referring to Fig. 2-10, a unit mass of fluid entering the process at p_1 and V_1 can be imagined to be isolated by weightless pistons

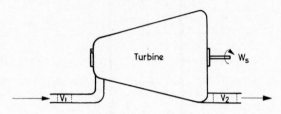

FIG. 2-10   Flow process.

in the inlet duct. Similarly at the outlet, this unit mass will be at p_2 and V_2. The work done against the surroundings by this change is $\Delta(pV)$ and the total work done by the fluid in a flow process is

$$W_{total} = W_s + \Delta(pV) = \int_{V_1}^{V_2} p \, dV$$

Thus the shaft reversible flow work W_s is less than the total work done by the gas or

$$dW_s = p \, dV - d(pV) = -V \, dp$$

$$W_s = -\int_{p_1}^{p_2} V \, dp = \int_{V_1}^{V_2} p \, dV - \Delta(pV).$$

The maximum shaft work done by a gas in reversible polytropic flow is also given by

$$W_s = \frac{n}{n-1} R(T_1 - T_2) = \frac{n}{n-1} RT_1 \left[1 - \left(\frac{p_2}{p_1} \right)^{\frac{n-1}{n}} \right] =$$

$$= \frac{n}{n-1} (p_1 V_1 - p_2 V_2)$$

These relations apply for perfect gases where the differences
between inlet and outlet velocities and elevations (potential

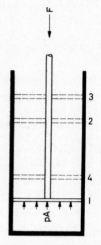

FIG. 2-11   Carnot's engine.

energy) are negligible. Note that flow work differs from that for
non-flow conditions by the value of n in the numerator. Also

$$C_p = \frac{\gamma R}{\gamma - 1}$$

and for an adiabatic flow process, $n = \gamma$

CARNOT CYCLE

The concept that reversible processes produce maximum work
is the basis for a thermodynamic cycle defining the maximum
possible conversion of thermal energy into mechanical work in an
engine operating between a higher-temperature heat source and a
lower-temperature heat sink. This cycle was described by Carnot
in 1824 and can be illustrated by a gas-filled cylinder fitted with a

frictionless piston. The cylinder is considered to be a perfect insulator except when brought into contact with a heat source or a heat sink, and these thermal reservoirs have such large heat capacities that they remain at constant temperature when placed in contact with the cylinder. With the higher-temperature body in contact with the cylinder, a reversible expansion process is started by an infinitesimal decrease in the force that resists motion of the piston. During this expansion, heat flows from the heat reservoir into the gas to maintain a constant temperature, T_1. This process is reversible since the temperature differences between the expanding gas and the heat source is very small. When the gas has expanded from the initial pressure p_1 to the final pressure p_2, contact with the heat source is removed and an adiabatic reversible expansion is allowed to proceed with decreasing temperature until a lower temperature T_3 is reached. At this point, the piston motion is reversed by an infinitesimal increase in external force – this starts the compression of the gas. The temperature of the gas is maintained at T_3 during this compression by contacting the cylinder with the heat sink (also at T_3) so that heat can flow from the gas into this reservoir. Finally, to restore the gas to its original condition, the heat sink is removed and the gas is compressed adiabatically and reversibly to its original temperature T_1 and original pressure p_1 as illustrated in Fig. 2-12. More work is done in the expansion than is the compression processes and this net work must equal the difference between the quantity of heat Q_1 provided from the heat source at T_1, and the quantity of heat $\frac{1}{m} Q_2$ rejected to the heat sink at T_3.

This cycle was conceived by Carnot as an illustration of a perfectly reversible engine, since at all times the temperature differences are infinitesimal where there is heat flow. Carnot concluded that the efficiency of this or any other perfectly reversible cycle is the maximum possible for the conversion of thermal energy into work, and that this efficiency is determined only by the temperature limits between which the cycle operates. The efficiency is independent of the type of fluid used in the cycle.

The efficiency of the Carnot engine can be derived conveniently by using the assumption of a perfect gas with constant heat capacity for the working fluid (the results are not limited to this assumption but are valid for any substance). With reference to Fig. 2-12, in the process from point 1 to point 2—a constant temperature

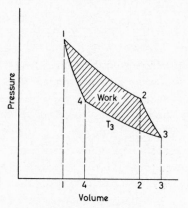

FIG. 2-12   Carnot cycle.

expansion at T_1 from V_1 to V_2—the heat added just equals the work done. Since the perfect gas law is assumed $\left(p = \dfrac{RT_1}{V}\right)$ then,

$$Q_{1-2} = W_{1-2} = \int_{V_1}^{V_2} p\,dV = RT_1 \int_{V_1}^{V_2} \frac{dV}{V} = RT_1 \ln\left(\frac{V_2}{V_1}\right)$$

In the reversible adiabatic expansion of a perfect gas from point 2 to point 3, the work done equals the decrease in internal energy, or

$$W_{2-3} = C_v(T_1 - T_3)$$

Also, from the relation derived previously for an adiabatic process

$$\left(\frac{V_2}{V_3}\right)^{\gamma-1} = \frac{T_3}{T_1}$$

When the gas is compressed isothermally from V_3 to V_4, the work required is

$$- W_{3-4} = RT_3 \ln\left(\frac{V_3}{V_4}\right) = -Q$$

The value of V_4 is such than an adiabatic compression will return the gas to its original state. The work required in this process is

$$- W_{4-1} = C_v(T_1 - T_3)$$

$$\left(\frac{V_4}{V_1}\right)^{\gamma-1} = \frac{T_1}{T_3}$$

Since this cyclic process restores the gas to its original condition, the net work done must equal the heat added minus the heat rejected. The efficiency η is then

$$\eta = \frac{Q_{1-2} + Q_{3-4}}{Q_{1-2}} = \frac{T_1 \ln\left(\dfrac{V_2}{V_1}\right) - T_3 \ln\left(\dfrac{V_3}{V_4}\right)}{T_1 \ln\left(\dfrac{V_2}{V_1}\right)}$$

Since

$$\left(\frac{V_2}{V_3}\right)^{\gamma-1} = \frac{T_3}{T_1} = \left(\frac{V_1}{V_4}\right)^{\gamma-1}$$

it can be seen that

$$\frac{V_2}{V_1} = \frac{V_3}{V_4}$$

$$\eta = \frac{T_1 - T_3}{T_1} = \frac{Q_{1-2} + Q_{3-4}}{Q_{1-2}}$$

Another important relation applying to reversible cyclic processes can be found by rearrangement

$$\frac{Q_{1-2}}{T_1} + \frac{Q_{3-4}}{T_3} = 0$$

ENTROPY

By dividing a cyclic process into a number of Carnot cycles as shown in Fig. 2-13, with a large number of such subdivisions, the entire process can be accurately represented; and for each quantity of heat, such as Q_{1-2}, added at a higher temperature, there is a corresponding quantity, $-Q_{3-4}$, rejected at a lower temperature. For the reversible Carnot cycle, it has been shown previously that

$$\frac{Q_{1-2}}{T_1} = -\frac{Q_{3-4}}{T_3}$$

For an infinite number of subdivisions of these reversible cycles, the heat added in each step becomes dQ and for the entire cycle

$$\sum \frac{dQ}{T} = 0$$

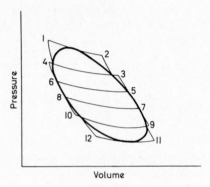

FIG. 2-13   Cyclic processes.

This function $\frac{dQ}{T}$ has been found so useful in thermodynamics that it has been given a name, entropy, designated by S. The entropy change is

$$\Delta S = S_2 - S_1 = \int_{1}^{2} \frac{dQ_{\text{rev}}}{T}$$

Note that heat flowing into a system (Q positive) increases the entropy of the system but decreases the entropy of the surroundings.

Since by definition Q is zero for an adiabatic process, the entropy change for a reversible adiabatic process is also zero. This fact is used in calculations related to the compression and expansion of gases. The use of tables of gas properties and charts is facilited since constant entropy processes can be easily identified, as will be described in a following section.

For a reversible constant temperature process, the change in entropy can be obtained directly

$$\Delta S = \frac{Q_{\text{rev}}}{T}$$

If an average or constant value of heat capacity can be assumed, the entropy change for a reversible process at constant pressure becomes

$$\Delta S = C_p \int_{T_1}^{T_2} \frac{dT}{T} = C_p \ln \frac{T_2}{T_1}$$

The entropy change produced by any reversible cyclic process has been shown to be zero. However, any irreversible process produces an increase in entropy and the sum of the entropy changes caused by the system and its surroundings must be greater than zero. Since actual processes are irreversible, they always produce a net entropy increase; and thus the total entropy of the earth is continuously increasing. However radiant energy from the sun can produce chemical reactions in photosynthesis with a decrease in entropy. Therefore this radiant energy has been considered by some to have special thermodynamic properties.

The continuous increase in entropy in actual processes is associated with increased disorder in molecular motion. The kinetic energy of a flowing fluid in theory can be transformed completely into other forms of energy since this kinetic energy is the result of ordered molecular motion. However fluid friction will convert part of this ordered motion into the random molecular motion of thermal energy with an associated increase in entropy. This random molecular motion of thermal energy can not be transformed completely into those forms of energy resulting from ordered molecular motions. This conversion of ordered into disorder molecular energy and the associated entropy increase results from any irreversible process.

The Carnot cycle can be described conveniently in terms of entropy changes. Referring to the temperature–entropy diagram, Fig. 2-14, it is seen that the constant temperature expansion is represented by the straight line 1–2. The reversible adiabatic expansion is isentropic (no entropy change) and this is represented

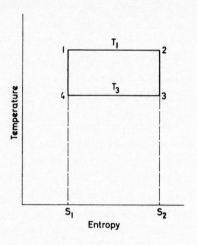

FIG. 2-14　Carnot cycle.

by the vertical line 2–3. Similarly the constant temperature compression and the isentropic compression are represented by the straight lines 3–4 and 4–1 respectively. Thus the Carnot cycle becomes a rectangle on a temperature–entropy diagram.

The heat added in the constant temperature expansion at T_1 is

$$Q_{1-2} = T_1 \Delta S = T_1(S_2 - S_1)$$

This quantity is represented by the area under the line 1–2. The heat rejected at the constant temperature T_3 is

$$-Q_{3-4} = \tfrac{1}{m}T_3 \Delta S = T_3(S_2 - S_1)$$

This is the area under the line 3–4. The work done is the difference between the heat added and rejected, or

$$W = Q_{1-2} + Q_{3-4} = (T_1 - T_3)(S_2 - S_1).$$

This work is represented by the area of the rectangle between lines 1–2 and 3–4. The efficiency of the cycle thus becomes

$$= \frac{(T_1 - T_3)(S_2 - S_1)}{T_1(S_2 - S_1)} = \frac{T_1 - T_3}{T_1}$$

Many thermodynamic processes can be described most simply in terms of entropy changes. Tables and charts showing entropy as a function of temperature and other variables are used for process calculations.

SECOND LAW OF THERMODYNAMICS

According to the first law of thermodynamics, the total energy in an isolated system remains constant and this energy can be accounted for in its various forms. However, this law provides no information as to whether a process is possible. The evolution of heat such as in a chemical reaction has been found to be an inadequate criterion for there are many spontaneous endothermic chemical reactions. Since the entropy of an isolated system increases or, at best, the entropy change approaches zero during any actual process, a positive change in entropy is an acceptable standard for determining that a process is possible. A statement of the second law is that heat cannot flow from a lower temperature body to a higher temperature body unless there are changes in the surroundings. This follows from the requirement for a positive entropy change in any possible actual process. The flow of heat from a lower to a higher temperature body would result in a decrease in entropy of an isolated system and therefore this process is not possible.

The expansion of a gas into a vacuum without any exchange of energy with the surroundings is certainly a spontaneous process. It is irreversible and the increase in entropy is

$$\Delta S = R \ln \left(\frac{V_2}{V_1} \right)$$

To restore the expanded gas to its original volume V_1 and temperature would require work from the surroundings and the removal of thermal energy from the compressed gas. The expansion of a gas into a vacuum is not a reversible process since permanent changes in the surroundings are required to return the gas to its original condition.

GAS TABLES

Tables and charts of the thermodynamic properties of fluids are used for accurate and convenient engineering calculations (Refs. 5 and 6). For example, the properties of air in Table 2-5 are suited particularly for power plant performance calculations. Also available are correction factors for adjusting the dry air data to account for the effects of atmospheric water vapor and combustion products in air.

In this table are values of the enthalpy, internal energy, relative pressure p_r, relative volume v_r and the integral $\phi = \int\limits_0^T C_p \dfrac{dT}{T}$ all as a function of temperature (according to the method developed by Keenan and Kays in Ref. 5). The enthalpy and internal energies above the base reference temperature, $T_0 = 0\,^\circ R$, were obtained by the integrations

$$h = \int\limits_0^T C_p\, dT$$

$$u = \int\limits_0^T C_v\, dT$$

where h and u are the enthalpy and internal energy respectively of a unit mass of material.

The useful concept of reduced pressure and reduced volume relating conditions during a reversible process can be derived starting with the definition of the change in entropy

$$dS = \frac{dQ_{\mathrm{rev}}}{T} = \frac{dH - V dp}{T}$$

Since the process is reversible

$$dS = 0 = \frac{dH - Vdp}{T} = \frac{C_p dT}{T} - \frac{Rdp}{p}$$

An entropy function ϕ is defined by the relation

$$\phi = \int_0^T \frac{C_p dT}{T}$$

Changes in entropy are then

$$S_2 - S_1 = \phi_2 - \phi_1 - R \ln \left(\frac{p_2}{p_1} \right)$$

The relative pressure p_r is defined with reference to atmospheric pressure, p_0, by the relation for a reversible process where $\Delta S = 0$, or

$$R \ln \left(\frac{p_2}{p_0} \right) = \phi = R \ln (p_r)$$

The relative pressure ratio along any isentropic process is related to the actual pressure by

$$\frac{p_2}{p_1} = \frac{p_{r2}}{p_{r1}}$$

Therefore by finding values for the relative pressure from the gas tables, the actual pressure ratios for a reversible process can be computed. The relative volume is obtained from

$$V_r = \frac{RT}{p_r}$$

The volume at any point in a reversible process can be found from the ratios

$$\frac{V_2}{V_1} = \frac{V_{r2}}{V_{r1}}$$

The following examples illustrate the use of gas tables. It should be noted that for air the values of h, u, p_r, v_r and ϕ are for 1 lb of air. Tables of these thermodynamic functions for other gases in Ref. 5 are for 1 lb-mole.

EXAMPLE 2-12. How much work is done by 1 lb of air in expanding through a turbine from inlet conditions of 2000 °R and 5 atm absolute pressure to an exit pressure of 1.0 atm? The turbine efficiency is 85 percent.

Solution: It will be assumed that the difference between the inlet and exit velocities and heat losses from the turbine can be neglected. From Table 2-5 the following values are found for the inlet conditions

$$h_1 = 504.71 \text{ Btu/lb}$$

$$p_{r1} = 174.00$$

For an isentropic expansion over the pressure ratio of 5/1, the relative pressure at the exit is

$$p'_{r2} = \frac{174.00}{5} = 34.80$$

The enthalpy of air corresponding to this value of the relative pressure is found in the gas table

$$h'_2 = 323.41 \text{ Btu/lb}$$

Therefore the work done by 1 lb of air in a reversible process is

$$W'_{\text{rev}} = -\Delta h' = 504.71 - 323.41 = 181.3 \text{ Btu/lb}$$

The actual work at an efficiency of 85 percent is

$$W_{\text{actual}} = 0.85 \times 181.3 = 154.1 \text{ Btu/lb}$$

The enthalpy of the exit air is therefore

$$h_2 = 504.7 - 154.1 = 350.6 \text{ Btu/lb}$$

The air temperature corresponding to this enthalpy is found from the tables to be

$$T_2 = 1429 \text{ °R}$$

EXAMPLE 2-13. Find the entropy change for Example 2-12.

Solution: Values of the entropy function ϕ are found from the tables for the inlet and exit conditions

$$\phi_1 = 0.93205 \text{ Btu/lb °R}$$

$$\phi_2 = 0.84140 \text{ Btu/lb °R}$$

The entropy change is

$$S_2 - S_1 = \phi_2 - \phi_1 - R \ln \left(\frac{p_2}{p_1} \right)$$

Using the value of 29 for the average molecular weight of air

$$R \ln \frac{p_2}{p_1} = \frac{1.987}{29} \ln \left(\frac{1}{5} \right) = -0.1103 \text{ Btu/lb °R}$$

The entropy change is then

$$\Delta S = 0.8414 - 0.9321 + 0.1103 = 0.0196 \text{ Btu/lb °R}$$

EXAMPLE 2-14. Calculate the work required to compress 1 lb of air at 520 °R and 0.1 atm absolute pressure to $\frac{1}{50}$ the inlet volume. The efficiency is 75 percent.

Solution: From the air tables the following values are found at he inlet conditions:

$$T_1 = 520 \text{ °R}$$
$$h_1 = 124.27$$
$$v_{r1} = 158.58$$

The value of the relative volume for an isotropic process is given by

$$\frac{v_{r1}}{v'_{r2}} = \frac{v_1}{v_2} = 50$$

and

$$v'_{r2} = \frac{158.58}{50} = 3.172$$

The enthalpy corresponding to this relative volume is

$$h'_2 = 560.9$$

The work required for a reversible compression is

$$w_{rev} = h_2 - h_1 = 560.9 - 124.27 = 436.6 \text{ Btu/lb}$$

The actual work at a compressor efficiency of 75 percent is then

$$W_{actual} = \frac{436.6}{0.75} = 582.1 \text{ Btu/lb}$$

ELEMENTS OF ENERGY CONVERSION

TABLE* 2-5   AIR AT LOW PRESSURES (FOR ONE POUND)

T °R	t °F	h Btu/lb	p_r	u Btu/lb	v_r	ϕ Btu/lb °R
400	−59.7	95.53	0.4858	68.11	305.0	0.52890
420	−39.7	100.32	0.5760	71.52	270.1	0.54058
440	−19.7	105.11	0.6776	74.93	240.6	0.55172
460	0.3	109.90	0.7913	78.36	215.33	0.56235
480	20.3	114.69	0.9182	81.77	193.65	0.57255
500	40.3	119.48	1.0590	85.20	174.90	0.58233
520	60.3	124.27	1.2147	88.62	158.58	0.59173
540	80.3	129.06	1.3860	92.04	144.32	0.60078
560	100.3	133.86	1.5742	95.47	131.78	0.60950
580	120.3	138.66	1.7800	98.90	120.70	0.61793
600	140.3	143.47	2.005	102.34	110.88	0.62607
620	160.3	148.28	2.249	105.78	102.12	0.63395
640	180.3	153.09	2.514	109.21	94.30	0.64159
660	200.3	157.92	2.801	112.67	87.27	0.64902
680	220.3	162.73	3.111	116.12	80.96	0.65621
700	240.3	167.56	3.446	119.58	75.25	0.66321
720	260.3	172.39	3.806	123.04	70.07	0.67002
740	280.3	177.23	4.193	126.51	65.38	0.67665
760	300.3	182.08	4.607	129.99	61.10	0.68312
780	320.3	186.94	5.051	133.47	57.20	0.68942
800	340.3	161.81	5.526	136.97	53.63	0.69558
820	360.3	196.69	6.033	140.47	50.35	0.70160
840	380.3	201.56	6.573	143.98	47.34	0.70747
860	400.3	206.46	7.149	147.50	44.57	0.71323
880	420.3	211.35	7.761	151.02	42.01	0.71886
900	440.3	216.26	8.411	154.57	39.64	0.72438
920	460.3	221.18	9.102	158.12	37.44	0.72979
940	480.3	226.11	9.834	161.68	35.41	0.73509
960	500.3	231.06	10.610	165.26	33.52	0.74030
980	520.3	236.02	11.430	168.83	31.76	0.74540
1000	540.3	240.98	12.298	172.43	30.12	0.75042
1020	560.3	245.97	13.215	176.04	28.59	0.75536
1040	580.3	250.95	14.182	179.66	27.17	0.76019
1060	600.3	255.96	15.203	183.29	25.82	0.76496
1080	620.3	260.97	16.278	186.93	24.58	0.76649
1100	640.3	265.99	17.413	190.58	23.40	0.77426
1120	660.3	271.03	18.604	194.25	22.30	0.77880
1140	680.3	276.08	19.858	197.94	21.27	0.78329
1160	700.3	281.14	21.18	201.63	20.293	0.78767
1180	720.3	286.21	22.56	205.33	19.377	0.79201
1200	740.3	291.30	24.01	209.05	18.514	0.79628
1220	760.3	296.41	25.53	212.78	17.700	0.80050
1240	780.3	301.52	27.13	216.53	16.932	0.80466
1260	800.3	306.65	28.80	220.28	16.205	0.80876

TABLE* 2-5 (cont.)   AIR AT LOW PRESSURES (FOR ONE POUND)

T °R	t °F	h Btu/lb	p_r	u Btu/lb	v	ϕ Btu/lb °R
1280	820.3	311.79	30.55	224.05	15.518	0.81280
1300	840.3	316.94	32.39	227.83	14.868	0.81680
1320	860.3	322.11	34.31	231.63	14.253	0.82075
1340	880.3	327.29	36.31	235.43	13.670	0.82464
1360	900.3	332.48	38.41	239.25	13.118	0.82848
1380	920.3	337.68	40.59	243.08	12.593	0.83229
1400	940.3	342.90	42.88	246.93	12.095	0.83604
1420	960.3	348.14	45.26	250.79	11.622	0.83975
1440	980.3	353.37	47.75	254.66	11.172	0.84341
1460	1000.3	358.63	50.34	258.54	10.743	0.84704
1480	1020.3	363.89	53.04	262.44	10.336	0.85062
1500	1040.3	369.17	55.86	266.34	9.948	0.85416
1520	1060.3	374.47	58.78	270.26	9.578	0.85767
1540	1080.3	379.77	61.83	274.20	9.226	0.86113
1560	1100.3	385.08	65.00	278.13	8.890	0.86456
1580	1120.3	390.40	68.30	282.09	8.569	0.86794
1600	1140.3	395.74	71.73	286.06	8.263	0.87130
1620	1160.3	401.09	75.29	290.04	7.971	0.87462
1640	1180.3	406.45	78.99	294.03	7.691	0.87791
1660	1200.3	411.82	82.83	298.02	7.424	0.88116
1680	1220.3	417.20	86.82	302.04	7.168	0.88439
1700	1240.3	422.59	90.95	306.06	6.924	0.88758
1720	1260.3	428.00	95.24	310.09	6.690	0.89074
1740	1280.3	433.41	99.69	314.13	6.465	0.89387
1760	1300.3	438.83	104.30	318.18	6.251	0.89697
1780	1320.3	444.26	109.08	322.24	6.045	0.90003
1800	1340.3	449.71	114.03	326.32	5.847	0.90308
1820	1360.3	455.17	119.16	330.40	5.658	0.90609
1840	1380.3	460.63	124.47	334.50	5.476	0.90908
1860	1400.3	466.12	129.95	338.61	5.302	0.91203
1880	1420.3	471.60	135.64	342.73	5.134	0.91497
1900	1440.3	477.09	141.51	346.85	4.974	0.91788
1920	1460.3	482.60	147.59	350.98	4.819	0.92076
1940	1480.3	488.12	153.87	355.12	4.670	0.92362
1960	1500.3	493.64	160.37	359.28	4.527	0.92645
1980	1520.3	499.17	167.07	363.43	4.390	0.92926
2000	1540.3	504.71	174.00	367.61	4.258	0.93205
2020	1560.3	510.26	181.16	371.79	4.130	0.93481
2040	1580.3	515.82	188.54	375.98	4.008	0.93756
2060	1600.3	521.39	196.16	380.18	3.890	0.94026
2080	1620.3	526.97	204.02	384.39	3.777	0.94296
2100	1640.3	532.55	212.1	388.60	3.667	0.94564
2120	1660.3	538.15	220.5	392.83	3.561	0.94829

continued

TABLE* 2-5 (cont) AIR AT LOW PRESSURES (FOR ONE POUND)

T °F	t °R	h Btu/lb	p_r	u Btu/lb	v_r	ϕ Btu/lb °R
2140	1680.3	543.74	229.1	397.05	3.460	0.95092
2160	1700.3	549.35	238.0	401.29	3.362	0.95352
2180	1720.3	554.97	247.2	405.53	3.267	0.95611
2200	1740.3	560.59	256.6	409.78	3.176	0.95868
2220	1760.3	566.23	266.3	414.05	3.088	0.96123
2240	1780.3	571.86	276.3	418.31	3.003	0.96376
2260	1800.3	577.51	286.6	422.59	2.921	0.96626
2280	1820.3	583.16	297.2	426.87	2.841	0.96876
2300	1840.3	588.82	308.1	431.16	2.765	0.97123
2320	1860.3	594.49	319.4	435.46	2.691	0.97369
2340	1880.3	600.16	330.9	439.76	2.619	0.97611
2360	1900.3	605.84	342.8	444.07	2.550	0.97853
2380	1920.3	611.53	355.0	448.38	2.483	0.98092
2400	1940.3	617.22	367.6	452.70	2.419	0.98331
2420	1960.3	622.92	380.5	457.02	2.356	0.98567
2440	1980.3	628.62	393.7	461.36	2.296	0.98802
2460	2000.3	634.34	407.3	465.70	2.237	0.99035
2480	2020.3	640.05	421.3	470.05	2.180	0.99266
2500	2040.3	645.78	435.7	474.40	2.125	0.99497
2520	2060.3	651.51	450.5	478.77	2.072	0.99725
2540	2080.3	657.25	465.6	483.13	2.021	0.99952
2560	2100.3	662.99	481.1	487.51	1.9709	1.00176
2580	2120.3	668.74	497.1	491.88	1.9225	1.00400
2600	2140.3	674.49	513.5	496.26	1.8756	1.00623
2620	2160.3	680.25	530.3	500.65	1.8302	1.00843
2640	2180.3	686.01	547.5	505.05	1.7861	1.01063
2660	2200.3	691.79	565.2	509.44	1.7434	1.01281
2680	2220.3	697.56	583.3	513.85	1.7019	1.01497
2700	2240.3	703.35	601.9	518.26	1.6617	1.01712
2720	2260.3	709.13	620.9	522.68	1.6226	1.01926
2740	2280.3	714.93	640.5	527.10	1.5847	1.02138
2760	2300.3	720.72	660.5	531.53	1.5480	1.02348
2780	2320.3	726.53	681.0	535.96	1.5122	1.02558
2800	2340.3	732.33	702.0	540.40	1.4775	1.02767
2820	2360.3	738.15	723.5	544.85	1.4439	1.02974
2840	2380.3	743.96	745.5	549.29	1.4112	1.03179
2860	2400.3	749.79	768.1	553.74	1.3794	1.03383
2880	2420.3	755.61	791.2	558.19	1.3485	1.03586
2900	2440.3	761.45	814.8	562.66	1.3184	1.03788
2920	2460.3	767.29	839.0	567.13	1.2892	1.03989
2940	2480.3	773.13	863.8	571.60	1.2608	1.04188
2960	2500.3	778.97	889.1	576.07	1.2332	1.04386
2980	2520.3	784.83	915.0	580.56	1.2064	1.04583
3000	2540.3	790.68	941.4	585.04	1.1803	1.04779

TABLE* 2-5 (cont)   AIR AT LOW PRESURESS (FOR ONE POUND)

T °R	t °F	h Btu/lb	p ,	u Btu/lb	v_r	φ Btu/lb °R
3050	2590.3	805.34	1010.5	596.28	1.1181	1.05264
3100	2640.3	820.03	1083.4	607.53	1.0600	1.05741
3150	2690.3	834.75	1160.5	618.82	1.0056	1.06212
3200	2740.3	849.48	1241.7	630.12	0.9546	1.06676
3250	2790.3	864.24	1327.5	641.46	0.9069	1.07134
3300	2840.3	879.02	1418.0	652.81	0.8621	1.07585
3350	2890.3	893.83	1513.0	664.20	0.8202	1.08031
3400	2940.3	908.66	1613.2	675.60	0.7807	1.08470
3450	2990.3	923.52	1718.7	687.04	0.7436	1.08904
3500	3040.3	938.40	1829.3	698.48	0.7087	1.09332
3550	3090.3	953.30	1945.8	709.95	0.6759	1.09755
3600	3140.3	968.21	2067.9	721.44	0.6449	1.10172
3650	3190.3	983.15	2196.0	732.95	0.6157	1.10584
3700	3240.3	998.11	2330.3	744.48	0.5882	1.10991
3750	3290.3	1013.09	2471.1	756.04	0.5621	1.11393
3800	3340.3	1028.09	2618.4	767.60	0.5376	1.11791
3850	3390.3	1043.11	2772.9	779.19	0.5143	1.12183
3900	3440.3	1058.14	2934.4	790.80	0.4923	1.12571
3950	3490.3	1073.19	3103.4	802.43	0.4715	1.12955
4000	3540.3	1088.26	3280	814.06	0.4518	1.13334
4050	3590.3	1103.36	3464	825.72	0.4331	1.13709
4100	3640.3	1118.46	3656	837.40	0.4154	1.14079
4150	3690.3	1133.59	3858	849.09	0.3985	1.14446
4200	3740.3	1148.72	4067	860.81	0.3826	1.14809
4250	3790.3	1163.87	4285	872.53	0.3674	1.15168
4300	3840.3	1179.04	4513	884.28	0.3529	1.15522
4350	3890.3	1194.23	4750	896.04	0.3392	1.15874
4400	3940.3	1209.42	4997	907.81	0.3262	1.16221
4450	3990.3	1224.64	5254	919.60	0.3137	1.16565
4500	4040.3	1239.86	5521	931.39	0.3019	1.16905
4550	4090.3	1255.10	5800	943.21	0.2906	1.17241
4600	4140.3	1270.36	6089	955.04	0.2799	1.17575
4650	4190.3	1285.63	6389	966.88	0.2696	1.17905
4700	4240.3	1300.92	6701	978.73	0.2598	1.18232
4750	4290.3	1316.21	7026	990.60	0.2505	1.18556
4800	4340.3	1331.51	7362	1002.48	0.2415	1.18876
4850	4390.3	1346.83	7711	1014.37	0.2330	1.19194
4900	4440.3	1362.17	8073	1026.28	0.2248	1.19508
4950	4490.3	1377.51	8448	1038.20	0.2170	1.19820
5000	4540.3	1392.87	8837	1050.12	0.20959	1.20129
5050	4590.3	1408.24	9241	1062.07	0.20245	1.20435
5100	4640.3	1423.62	9658	1074.02	0.19561	1.20738
5150	4690.3	1439.02	10091	1085.98	0.18906	1.21038

[continued

TABLE* 2-5 (cont)   AIR AT LOW PRESSURES (FOR ONE POUND)

T °R	°F	h Btu/lb	p_r	u Btu/lb	v_r	ϕ Btu/lb °R
5200	4740.3	1454.41	10539	1097.96	0.18279	1.21336
5250	4790.3	1469.83	11002	1109.95	0.17677	1.21631
5300	4840.3	1485.26	11481	1121.95	0.17101	1.21923
5350	4890.3	1500.70	11978	1133.96	0.16547	1.22213
5400	4940.3	1516.14	12490	1145.98	0.16015	1.22500
5450	4990.3	1531.60	13021	1158.01	0.15506	1.22785
5500	5040.3	1547.07	13568	1170.04	0.15016	1.23068
5550	5090.3	1562.55	14135	1182.10	0.14545	1.23348
5600	5140.3	1578.03	14719	1194.16	0.14093	1.23626
5650	5190.3	1593.53	15323	1206.24	0.13659	1.23902
5700	5240.3	1609.04	15946	1218.31	0.13242	1.24174
5750	5290.3	1624.57	16588	1230.41	0.12840	1.24445
5800	5340.3	1640.09	17252	1242.50	0.12454	1.24714
5850	5390.3	1655.63	17937	1254.62	0.12082	1.24981
5900	5440.3	1671.17	18643	1266.73	0.11723	1.25246
5950	5490.3	1686.73	19371	1278.86	0.11379	1.25508
6000	5540.3	1702.29	20120	1291.00	0.11047	1.25769
6050	5590.3	1717.88	20894	1303.15	0.10726	1.26028
6100	5640.3	1733.45	21691	1315.30	0.10418	1.26284
6150	5690.3	1749.05	22512	1327.47	0.10120	1.26539
6200	5740.3	1764.65	23357	1339.64	0.09833	1.26791
6250	5790.3	1780.27	24228	1351.83	0.09556	1.27042
6300	5840.3	1795.88	25123	1364.02	0.09289	1.27291
6350	5890.3	1811.51	26046	1376.23	0.09031	1.27538
6400	5940.3	1827.14	26994	1388.43	0.08783	1.27783
6450	5990.3	1842.79	27970	1400.65	0.08542	1.28026
6500	6040.3	1858.44	28974	1412.87	0.08310	1.28268

* Abridged from *Gas Tables* by Joseph H. Keenan and Joseph Kaye, Copyright 1948, John Wiley, New York.

TEMPERATURE–ENTROPY DIAGRAM

The thermodynamic properties of a fluid can be presented graphically as diagrams convenient for many approximate engineering calculations and for visualizing a process and its variables. In the diagrams for hydrogen (Fig. 2-15) temperature is plotted as a function of entropy with lines included of constant pressure, enthalpy and relative density v_0/v, where v_0 refers to the specific volume at 0 °C and 1 atm.

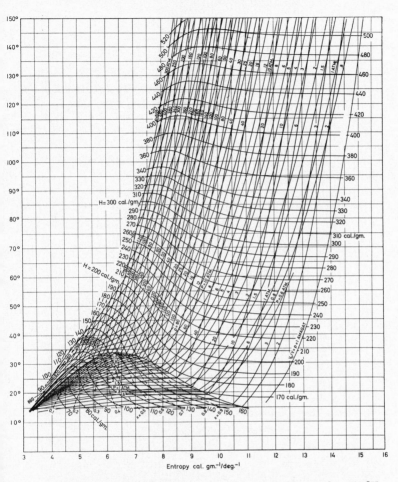

FIG. 2-15 Temperature–entropy diagram for H_2 in the region 0° to 150 °K. Reproduced from "Compilation of Thermal Properties of Hydrogen and its Various Isotopes and Ortho-Para Modifications", Wooley Scott and Brickwedde, *National Bureau of Standards J. of Research*, **41**, 470–2, 1948.

A major feature of this diagram is the area where liquid and vapor are in equilibrium under the dome-shaped saturation line. Below this line both phases may be present at the same temperature. The gaseous fraction X, of the mixed phase is called the quality of the vapor–liquid mixture. The liquid fraction is then $(1-X)$ and the total enthalpy of a unit mass of the mixture is

$$h = Xh_v + (1-X)h_1$$

Since reversible adiabatic processes are represented on these diagrams by vertical lines (constant entropy), the analysis of ideal engine cycles can be plotted, as discussed previously.

EXAMPLE 2-15. Hydrogen at 60 °K is expanded through a turbine from a pressure of 16 atm to 1.0 atm. Assuming that the process approaches constant entropy, determine the temperature change.

Solution: The initial entropy value is found at the intersection of the 60 °K line with the 16 atm pressure line on Fig. 2-15. Vertically below this point where this constant entropy line intersects the 1.0 atm pressure line, the temperature is found to be 21 °K.

SYMBOLS

A	area
C	compressibility factor
C_p or C_v	heat capacity per mole
E	energy
F	force
H	enthalpy
I	current
J	mechanical equivalent of heat
l	latent heat
m	mass $\left(\dfrac{w}{g}\right)$
M	mole fraction
MW	molecular weight
N	number of moles

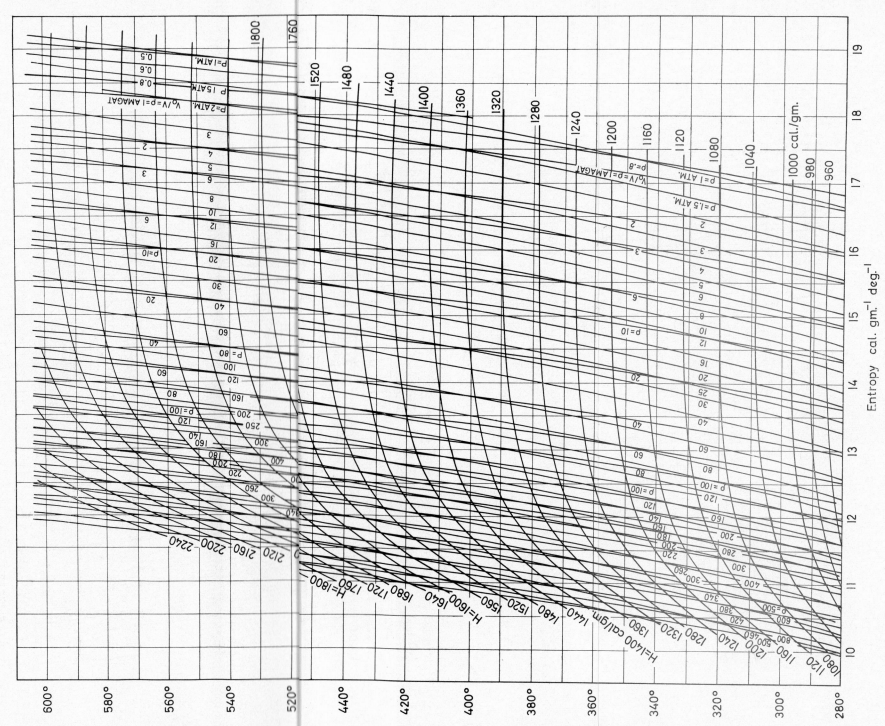

FIG. 2-16 *Temperature-entropy diagram for* H_2 *in the region 280° to 600 °K. Reproduced from "Compilation of Thermal Properties of Hydrogen and its Various Isotopes and Ortho-Para Modifications", Wooley, Scott and Brick wedde, National Bureau of Standards J of Research,* **41**, *470-2, 1948.*

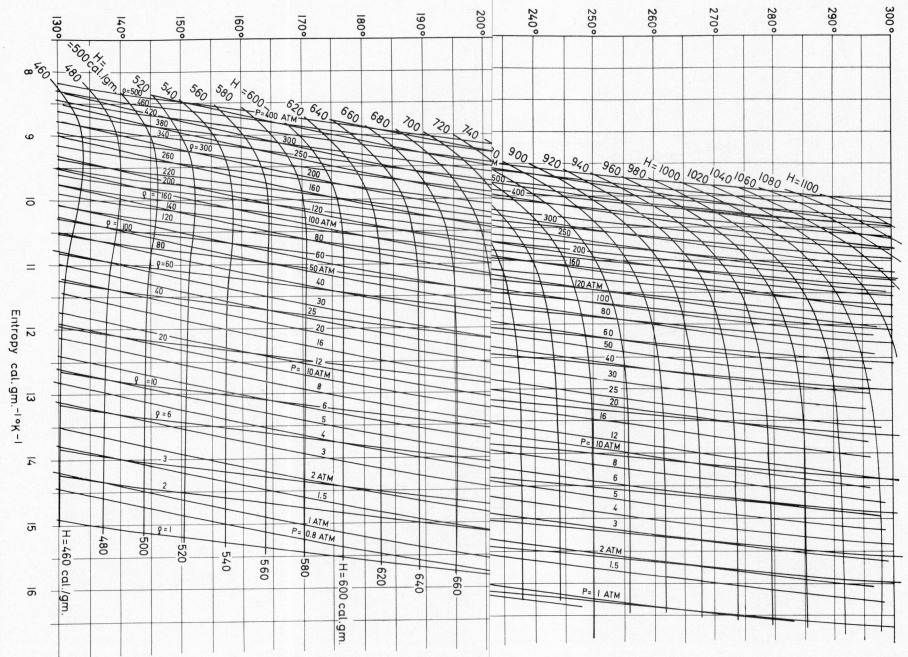

Fig. 2-17 *Temperature-entropy diagram for H₂ in the region 130° to 300 °K. Reproduced from "Compilation of Therma Properties of Hydrogen and its Various Isotopes and Ortho-Para Modifications", Wooley, Scott and Brickwedde, National Bureau of Standards J. of Research,* **41,** *470–2, 1948.*

Entropy cal. gm.⁻¹ °K⁻¹

n	polytropic exponent
p	pressure
Q	quantity of heat flowing into a system
R	gas constant per mole
R'	gas constant per gram or pound mass
S	entropy
t	temperature
T	absolute temperature
U	internal energy
v	velocity
w	quantity of material (grams or pounds mass)
W	work done by a system
x	distance
η	efficiency
γ	C_P/C_V
ϱ	density

Note: Lower case symbols h, u and s refer to a unit amount of material.

REFERENCES

1. C. D. Hodgman, ed., *Handbook of Chemistry and Physics*, Cleveland, The Chemical Rubber Publishing Co., 1962.
2. O. A. Hougen and K. M. Watson, *Chemical Process Principles*, New York, John Wiley, 1950.
3. G. P. Sutton, *Rocket Propulsion Elements*, New York, John Wiley, 1949.
4. H. C. Weber, *Thermodynamics for Chemical Engineers*, New York, John Wiley, 1939.
5. J. H. Keenan and J. Kaye, *Gas Tables*, John Wiley, 1948.
6. J. H. Keenan and F. G. Keyes, *Thermodynamic Properties of Steam*, New York, John Wiley, 1937.

CHAPTER 3

HEAT ENGINES

THERMAL energy released in combustion is converted into mechanical energy by an appropriate heat engine for the generation of electricity or the propulsion of vehicles. For example, the steam turbine is used in large steam electric generator stations, the reciprocating internal combustion engine in vehicles, and the gas turbine in aircraft. Thermodynamic descriptions of their operation are provided by power cycles such as the Rankine, Otto and Brayton cycles. These theoretical cycles serve as a basis for analyzing the operation of heat engines.

RANKINE CYCLE

The power cycle for the steam power plant and other vapor engines consists of evaporating a fluid in a boiler, adiabatically expanding the vapor through an engine to do work, condensing the vapor, and pumping the liquid back into the boiler. The ideal reversible Rankine cycle is illustrated in Fig. 3-1. Here the curve

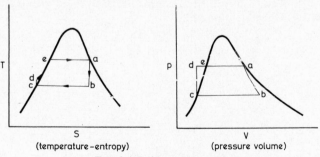

FIG. 3-1 Rakine power cycle.

is the saturation line (vapor dome) between vapor above the curve and the liquid–vapor mixture below. This cycle is similar to the Carnot cycle with the exception of the process of heating the liquid being fed to the boiler (line d–e in Fig. 3-1); this exception reduces the theoretical efficiency of the Rankine cycle to a value less than the maximum established by the Carnot cycle for the same temperature limits. The Rankine cycle with modifications for superheat, reheat and regeneration approximates the operation of the practical steam plant. The line a–b in Fig. 3-1 represents a reversible adiabatic expansion in an engine producing work. The vapor–liquid mixture (wet vapor) from this expansion is completely condensed at constant temperature (line b–c). When the condensate is pumped directly into the boiler, heat is added to this liquid in a process that is highly irreversible because of the large temperature difference between the boiler and this liquid stream. However, to approximate a reversible process, heat can be added to the feed stream in a number of steps as will be discussed later. After the liquid is heated to the temperature of the boiler, vaporization of the liquid takes place at constant temperature (line e–a).

Since the volume of the condensate does not change greatly with pressure, the boiler feed pumping process usually takes place at nearly constant volume. Due to the small volume of the liquid as compared to the volume of the steam, the pump work required to feed the boiler is relatively small. It is equal to

$$ - W_{cd} = -(H_d - H_c) = -(\Delta p V) $$

The work done in the adiabatic expansion of the vapor through the turbine is equal to the enthalpy change

$$ W_{ab} = H_a - H_b $$

The net work, then, is

$$ W_{\text{net}} = (H_a - H_b) - (H_d - H_c) $$

This net work must also equal the difference between the heat added and rejected

$$ W_{\text{net}} = Q_{da} - Q_{bc} = (H_a - H_d) - (H_b - H_c) $$

The cycle efficiency becomes

$$\eta = \frac{Q_{da}-Q_{bc}}{Q_{da}} = \frac{(H_a-H_b)-(H_d-H_c)}{(H_a-H_d)}$$

A mixture of liquid and vapor resulting from the expansion of a vapor through a turbine can cause serious erosion. This can be avoided and, at the same time, the efficiency of the cycle can be increased by superheating the steam. The amount of superheat is limited by the allowable operating temperatures of the super-heater and turbine. However, these limits have been raised by the development of high-temperature alloys. The Rankine cycle with

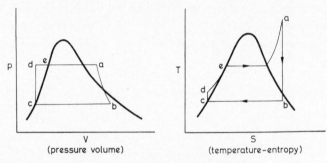

FIG. 3-2   Rankine cycle with superheat.

superheat (Fig. 3-2) illustrates the expansion extending into the wet steam area until the maximum allowable liquid content of about 10 percent is reached. The efficiency of the cycle can be increased further by reheating the vapor after partial expansion (Fig. 3-3). In addition, the reheat cycle permits a greater pressure ratio between the boiler and the condenser. The condenser temperature and corresponding pressure are established by the cooling water or other heat rejection system.

As mentioned previously, the process of mixing cold conden-sate with the high-temperature liquid in the boiler is thermo-dynamically inefficient. Heating of the boiler feed can be made more nearly reversible by the use of regenerative stages—that is, by withdrawing vapor from the turbine at several intermediate temperatures to heat the boiler feed (Figs. 3-4 and 3-5). As many as eight stages of regenerative heating may be justified in a large steam power plant to increase efficiency. As the number of regenerative stages is increased, the efficiency of the cycle approaches that of the Carnot cycle.

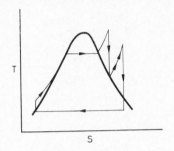

FIG. 3-3 Rankine cycle with reheat.   FIG. 3-4   Rankine cycle with superheat and regenerative heaters.

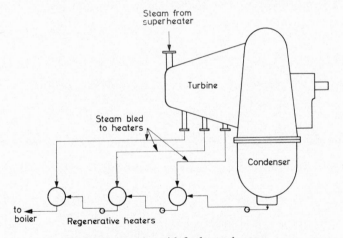

FIG. 3-5   Turbine with feedwater heaters.

Nuclear power stations have been built without superheat in order to avoid complexities in the reactor. The problems associated with very wet steam in the low-pressure regions of the turbine have been reduced by moisture separators between stages of the turbine and by erosion-resistant materials. The return of the water from the moisture separators can increase the efficiency of the boiler feed heating since this water is at intermediate temperatures depending upon the points of separation.

EXAMPLE 3-1. Compute the efficiency of a theoretical Rankine cycle, where the steam conditions at the turbine throttle are 1000 °F and 800 psia. The steam is expanded isentropically through the turbine to the condenser pressure of 0.49 psia (79 °F). Compare the efficiency of this cycle with that of a Carnot cycle having the same temperature limits.

Solution: From the properties of steam in Ref. 3, the following values for the turbine inlet are found:

$$t_a = 1000 \ ^\circ F$$
$$h_a = 1511.0 \ \text{Btu/lb}$$
$$s_a = 1.6801 \ \text{Btu/lb} \ ^\circ F$$

At point *b*, the turbine outlet, the entropy per pound of wet steam remains at the same value

$$s_b = 1.6801$$

At 79 °F the entropies of pure liquid and vapor are

$$s_1 = 0.0914 \ \text{Btu/lb} \ ^\circ F$$
$$s_v = 2.0387 \ \text{Btu/lb} \ ^\circ F$$

Then the quality *X*, or the fraction of vapor in the mixture is found

$$2.0387 \ X + (1-X) \ (0.0914) = 1.6801$$
$$X = 0.816 \ \text{vapor fraction}$$
$$1-X = 0.184 \ \text{liquid fraction}$$

From values of the enthalpy of the pure liquid and vapor at 79 °F, the enthalpy of the wet steam is

$$h_{bv} = 0.816 \times 1096.3 \ = 894.6 \ \text{Btu/lb}$$
$$h_{b1} = 0.184 \times \quad 47.05 = \quad \underline{8.7}$$
$$h_b \qquad\qquad\qquad\qquad = 903.3 \ \text{Btu/lb}$$

The work done in the isentropic expansion through the turbine is

$$W = h_a - h_b = 1511.0 - 903.3 = 607.7 \text{ Btu/lb}$$

The pump work is found from the specific volume and the pressure change

$$-W = V(p_d - p_c) = \frac{(0.01608)(800 - 0.49)(144)}{778.3} = 2.4 \text{ Btu/lb}$$

The net work is

$$W_{\text{net}} = 607.7 - 2.4 = 605.3 \text{ Btu/lb}$$

The enthalpy of the saturated liquid at point c (from the steam tables) is

$$h_c = 47.05 \text{ Btu/lb}$$

The enthalpy at 800 psia and 79 °F, point d, is then

$$h_d = h_c + h_{cd} = 47.05 + 2.38 = 49.43 \text{ Btu/lb}$$

The heat added to the process in the boiler is

$$Q = 1511.0 - 49.4 = 1461.6 \text{ Btu/lb}$$

The cycle efficiency can be found

$$\eta = W_{\text{net}}/Q = \frac{605.3}{1461.6} = 0.41 \text{ or 41 percent}$$

The efficiency of a Carnot cycle between the same temperature limits is

$$\eta = \frac{(1000 - 79)}{(1000 + 460)} = 0.63 \text{ or 63 percent}$$

WORKING FLUID

The fluid for a high-temperature Rankine cycle power plant is selected according to the maximum temperature and the requirement that the material remain liquid and condense under reasonable pressure at the radiator–condenser temperature. Several fluids that have been considered are listed in Table 3-1.

TABLE 3-1   FLUIDS FOR RANKINE CYCLE

Material	Melting point	Boiling point
Water	32 °F	212 °F
Diphenyl	158	489
Aluminium bromide	208	507
Mercury	−38	674
Sulfur	235	832
Rubidium	101	1292
Sodium	208	1618

The actual cycle efficiency is a function of the properties of the working fluid and the operating conditions as shown in Fig. 3-6. These values are the efficiencies of converting thermal energy into electrical energy from an alternator with an efficiency of 90 percent driven by a turbine with an efficiency of 80 percent and allowing 5 percent mechanical losses. With a low vapor pressure fluid such as rubidium, high cycle temperatures can be obtained without high pressures in lightweight equipment.

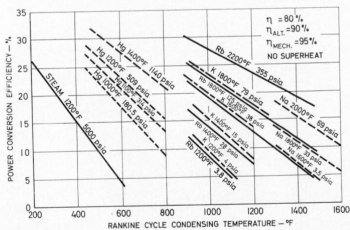

FIG. 3-6 Comparison of Rankine cycle working fluids. Reproduced with permission from WADD TR 60-699, R. Spies "Dynamic Thermal Converters", *Energy Conversion Reference Handbook*, W. R. Menetry, ed. Electro-Optical Systems, 1960.

It can be seen in Fig. 3-2 that a fluid having the vapor dome line vertical or with a positive slope would be desirable. Then expansion from the saturated state would not produce a wet vapor, thereby eliminating erosion. In some cases, however, a superheated vapor might result with resulting losses. Also the fluid should be noncorrosive, easily handled, and without decomposition. For use with nuclear heat sources, the fluid should be resistant to radiation damage. Aromatic hydrocarbons such as diphenyl are much more resistant to radiation damage than many other types of organic material. However, some decomposition does occur even with the aromatic hydrocarbons, and a purification system is required.

EXAMPLE 3-2. System Nuclear Auxiliary Power (SNAP) II has an alternator driven by a mercury turbine to convert heat from a nuclear reactor into electrical energy. The heat from the reactor will be carried to the mercury boiler and superheater by liquid sodium–potassium alloy (NaK). The specifications for the turbine and alternator are

Net electrical output	3 kW
Superheater temperature	1150 °F
Boiler pressure	110 psia
Turbine exhaust	7 psia
Parasitic load	0.3 kWe
Control requirements	0.10 kWe
NaK pump power	0.44 kW
Mercury pump efficiency	10 percent
Mechanical losses	0.6 kW
Alternator efficiency	0.80
Turbine efficiency	0.55
Mercury subcooling	200 °F

Using these values, compute the system efficiency and the mercury flow rate as pounds of mercury per minute. Also plot the power cycle on Fig. 3-7 (page 91).

TABLE 3-2 PRESSURE TABLE OF ENTHALPY AND ENTROPY FOR MERCURY

(General Electric Company Report GET-1879A by L. A. Sheldon, reprinted from ASME paper 49-A-30)

Press. psia	Temp. °F	Enthalpy, Btu/lb			Entropy, Btu/lb/°F			Sp. vol. Sat. vapor ft³/lb	Press. psia
		Sat. liquid	Evap.	Sat. vapor	Sat. liquid	Evap.	Sat. vapor		
0.010	233.57	6.668	127.732	134.400	0.01137	0.18428	0.19565	3637	0.010
0.020	259.88	7.532	127.614	135.146	0.01259	0.17735	0.18994	1893	0.020
0.030	276.22	8.068	127.540	135.608	0.01332	0.17332	0.18664	1292	0.030
0.040	288.32	8.463	127.486	135.949	0.01386	0.17044	0.18430	986.0	0.040
0.050	297.97	8.778	127.442	136.220	0.01427	0.16821	0.18248	799.0	0.050
0.075	316.19	9.373	127.361	136.734	0.01504	0.16415	0.17919	545	0.075
0.100	329.73	9.814	127.300	137.114	0.01561	0.16126	0.17687	416	0.100
0.200	364.25	10.936	127.144	138.080	0.01699	0.15432	0.17131	217.3	0.200
0.300	385.92	11.639	127.047	138.686	0.01783	0.15024	0.16807	148.6	0.300
0.400	401.98	12.159	126.975	139.134	0.01844	0.14736	0.16580	113.7	0.400
0.500	415.00	12.568	126.916	139.484	0.01892	0.14511	0.16403	92.18	0.500
0.600	425.82	12.929	126.868	139.797	0.01932	0.14328	0.16260	77.84	0.600
0.700	435.23	13.233	126.825	140.058	0.01965	0.14172	0.16137	67.45	0.700
0.800	443.50	13.500	126.788	140.288	0.01994	0.14038	0.16032	59.58	0.800
0.900	451.00	13.740	126.755	140.495	0.02021	0.13919	0.15940	53.40	0.900
1.00	457.72	13.959	126.724	140.683	0.02045	0.13814	0.15859	48.42	1.00
2.00	504.93	15.476	126.512	141.988	0.02205	0.13116	0.15321	25.39	2.00
3.00	535.25	16.439	126.377	142.816	0.02302	0.12706	0.15008	17.50	3.00
4.00	557.85	17.161	126.275	143.436	0.02373	0.12434	0.14787	13.38	4.00

5.00	575.7	17.741	126.193	143.934	0.02430	0.12188	0.14618	10.90	5.00
6.00	591.2	18.233	126.124	144.357	0.02477	0.12002	0.14479	9.26	6.00
7.00	604.7	18.657	126.065	144.722	0.02516	0.11846	0.14362	8.04	7.00
8.00	616.5	19.035	126.011	145.046	0.02551	0.11712	0.14262	7.12	8.00
9.00	627.3	19.381	125.962	145.343	0.02583	0.11588	0.14171	6.39	9.00
10	637.0	19.685	125.919	145.604	0.02610	0.11483	0.14093	5.81	10
20	706.0	21.864	125.609	147.473	0.02800	0.10779	0.13579	3.09	20
30	750.6	23.277	125.407	148.684	0.02918	0.10361	0.13279	2.14	30
40	784.4	24.345	125.255	149.600	0.03004	0.10068	0.13072	1.648	40
50	812.1	25.203	125.131	150.334	0.03070	0.09839	0.12909	1.348	50
60	835.7	25.940	125.024	150.964	0.03127	0.09652	0.12779	1.144	60
70	856.4	25.585	124.931	151.516	0.03175	0.09493	0.12668	0.998	70
80	874.8	27.159	124.849	152.008	0.03218	0.09356	0.12574	0.885	80
90	891.5	27.680	124.774	152.454	0.03255	0.09234	0.12489	0.797	90
100	906.8	28.152	124.706	152.858	0.03290	0.09127	0.12417	0.725	100
110	921.0	28.596	124.641	153.237	0.03321	0.09027	0.12348	0.667	110
120	934.3	29.005	124.582	153.587	0.03350	0.08938	0.12288	0.617	120
130	946.6	29.390	124.526	153.916	0.03377	0.08855	0.12232	0.575	130
140	958.3	29.748	124.474	154.222	0.03401	0.08778	0.12179	0.538	140
150	969.4	30.090	124.424	154.514	0.03425	0.08707	0.12132	0.507	150
160	979.9	30.415	124.376	154.791	0.03447	0.08640	0.12087	0.478	160
170	989.9	30.724	124.331	155.055	0.03468	0.08577	0.12045	0.453	170
180	999.5	31.018	124.288	155.306	0.03488	0.08518	0.12006	0.431	180
190	1008.8	31.290	124.249	155.539	0.03506	0.08464	0.11970	0.410	190

[continued

Press. psia	Temp. °F	Enthalpy, Btu/lb			Entropy, Btu/lb/°F			Sp. vol. Sat. vapor ft³/lb	Press. psia
		Sat. liquid	Evap.	Sat. vapor	Sat. liquid	Evap.	Sat. vapor		
200	1017.2	31.560	124.209	155.769	0.03523	0.08411	0.11934	0.392	200
225	1038.0	32.204	124.115	156.319	0.03565	0.08287	0.11852	0.354	225
250	1057.2	32.784	124.029	156.813	0.03603	0.08178	0.11781	0.322	250
275	1074.8	33.322	123.950	157.272	0.03637	0.08079	0.11716	0.297	275
300	1091.2	33.824	123.876	157.700	0.03669	0.07989	0.11658	0.276	300
350	1121.4	34.747	123.740	158.487	0.03725	0.07828	0.11553	0.241	350
400	1148.4	35.565	123.620	159.185	0.03775	0.07688	0.11463	0.215	400
450	1173.2	36.315	123.509	159.824	0.03820	0.07566	0.11386	0.194	450
500	1196.0	37.006	123.406	160.412	0.03861	0.07455	0.11316	0.177	500
600	1236.8	38.245	123.221	161.466	0.03932	0.07264	0.11196	0.151	600
700	1273.3	39.339	123.058	162.397	0.03993	0.07102	0.11095	0.132	700
800	1306.1	40.324	122.910	163.234	0.04047	0.06961	0.11008	0.118	800
900	1336.2	41.226	122.775	164.001	0.04095	0.06837	0.10932	0.106	900
1000	1364.0	42.056	122.649	164.705	0.04139	0.06726	0.10865	0.098	1000
1100	1390.0	42.828	122.533	165.361	0.04179	0.06625	0.10804	0.090	1100

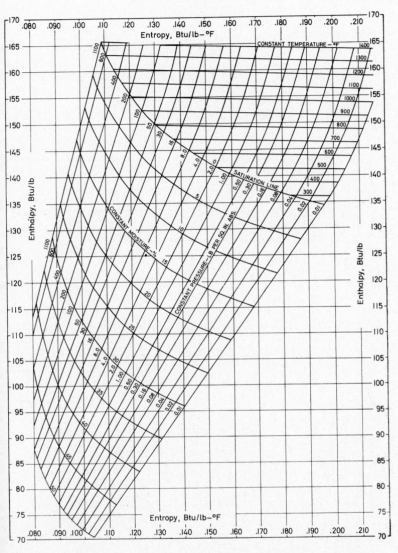

FIG. 3-7   Enthalpy-entropy diagram for mercury (General Electric Company Report GET-1879A by L. A. Sheldon, reprinted from ASME paper 49-A-30).

TABLE 3-5 TEMPERATURE TABLE OF ENTHALPY AND ENTROPY FOR MERCURY

(General Electric Company Report GET-1879A by L. A. Sheldon, reprinted from ASME paper 49-A-30)

Temp. °F	Press. psia	Enthalpy, Btu/lb			Entropy, Btu/lb/°F			Sp. vol. Sat. vapor ft³/lb	Temp. °F
		Sat. liquid	Evap.	Sat. vapor	Sat. liquid	Evap.	Sat. vapor		
225	0.00790	6.390	127.770	134.160	0.01094	0.18661	0.19755	4558.63	225
250	0.01551	7.210	127.658	134.868	0.01214	0.17988	0.19202	2406.00	250
275	0.02909	8.028	127.546	135.574	0.01327	0.17361	0.18688	1328.88	275
300	0.05230	8.845	127.433	136.278	0.01436	0.16774	0.18210	764.66	300
325	0.09049	9.660	127.321	136.981	0.01541	0.16226	0.17767	456.58	325
350	0.15129	10.473	127.209	137.682	0.01643	0.15711	0.17354	281.90	350
375	0.24511	11.285	127.096	138.381	0.01741	0.15227	0.16968	179.43	375
400	0.38591	12.095	126.984	139.079	0.01836	0.14771	0.16607	117.42	400
425	0.59188	12.903	126.871	139.774	0.01929	0.14341	0.16270	78.81	425
450	0.88625	13.710	126.759	140.469	0.02018	0.13934	0.15952	54.10	450
475	1.2981	14.515	126.647	141.162	0.02105	0.13550	0.15655	38.00	475
500	1.8629	15.318	126.534	141.852	0.02189	0.13185	0.15374	27.19	500
550	3.6319	16.919	126.309	143.228	0.02350	0.12510	0.14860	14.69	550
600	6.6385	18.513	126.085	144.598	0.02503	0.11898	0.14401	8.439	600
650	11.476	20.101	125.860	145.961	0.02648	0.11342	0.13990	5.116	650

700	18.900	21.680	125.635	147.315	0.02785	0.10833	0.13618	3.249	700
750	29.836	23.257	125.410	148.667	0.02916	0.10367	0.13283	2.148	750
800	45.372	24.825	125.185	150.010	0.03041	0.09938	0.12979	1.472	800
850	66.759	26.387	124.960	151.347	0.03160	0.09541	0.12701	1.041	850
900	95.390	27.943	124.736	152.679	0.03274	0.09174	0.12448	0.7570	900
950	132.78	29.492	124.511	154.003	0.03384	0.08833	0.12217	0.5643	950
1000	180.54	31.043	124.286	155.320	0.03489	0.08515	0.12004	0.4300	1000
1100	313.96	34.097	123.836	157.933	0.03686	0.07940	0.11626	0.2647	1100
1200	509.47	37.135	123.387	160.522	0.03868	0.07434	0.11302	0.1738	1200
1300	780.73	40.145	122.937	163.082	0.04037	0.06986	0.11023	0.1204	1300
1400	1140.19	43.129	122.487	165.616	0.04194	0.06586	0.10780	0.0873	1400

Solution: The properties of saturated mercury vapor at 110 psia are found from Table 3-2.

$$t = 921.0 \,°F$$
$$h_v = 153.237 \text{ Btu/lb}$$
$$s = 0.12348 \text{ Btu/lb °F}$$

Since mercury vapor is a monatomic gas, the heat capacity at constant pressure will be taken to be 5 Btu/lb-mole °F. The heat capacity per pound of mercury (molecular weight 200.6) is

$$C_p = 5/200.6 = 0.0249 \text{ Btu/lb °F}$$

The entropy change between 921.0 °F and 1150 °F is found from the relation

$$\Delta s = \int_{T_1}^{T_2} C_p \frac{dT}{T} = C_p \ln\left(\frac{T_2}{T_1}\right)$$

$$\Delta s = 0.0249 \ln\left(\frac{1610}{1381}\right) = 0.00375 \text{ Btu/lb °F}$$

Thus the entropy of the superheated mercury vapor is

$$s_a = 0.00375 + 0.12348 = 0.12723 \text{ Btu/lb °F}$$

The enthalpy of the superheated vapor is found by extrapolating from the value at 921 °F in Table 3-2

$$h_a = h_{921} + C_p \Delta T$$
$$h_a = 153.237 + 0.0249 (1150 - 921) = 158.95 \text{ Btu/lb}$$

After an isentropic expansion to 7.0 psia to form wet vapor, the entropies of saturated liquid and vapor at this condition are

$$s_1 = 0.02516 \text{ Btu/lb}$$
$$s_v = 0.14362 \text{ Btu/lb}$$

The quality X, of the wet vapor is found from the relation

$$0.14362 \, X + (1 - X) (0.02516) = 0.12723 \text{ Btu/lb °F}$$
$$X = 0.862$$
$$1 - X = 0.138$$

From these values and the enthalpies of the saturated liquid and vapor from Table 3-2, the enthalpy of the mixture is

$$h_b' = 0.861 \times 144.722 + 0.138 \times 18.657 = 127.18 \text{ Btu/lb}$$

Then the enthalpy change for an isentropic expansion is

$$h_a - h_b' = 158.946 - 127.18 = 31.77 \text{ Btu/lb}$$

The work is found from the enthalpy change for the actual turbine at 55 percent engine efficiency to be

$$W = \Delta h_{ab} = 0.55 \times 31.77 = 17.47 \text{ Btu/lb}$$

The mercury is subcooled to 405 °F, and the enthalpy h_c of the liquid at this temperature (by interpolation from Table 3-2) is

$$h_c = 12.25 \text{ Btu/lb}$$

The pump work $-W_p$ for a constant volume process is $-V\Delta p$. The volume of 1 lb of liquid mercury with a specific gravity of 13.1 is 0.0012 ft^3. The pump work is then

$$-W_p' = \frac{0.0012 \times (110-7) \times 144}{778.3} = 0.023 \text{ Btu/lb}$$

At 10 percent efficiency this pump work becomes

$$-W_p = 0.023/0.1 = 0.23 \text{ Btu/lb}$$

The enthalpy of the mercury entering the boiler can then be found to be

$$h_d = 12.25 + 0.23 = 12.48 \text{ Btu/lb}$$

and the heat added to the mercury in the boiler and superheater is

$$Q = 158.95 - 12.48 = 146.47 \text{ Btu/lb}$$

The cycle efficiency is found from the net work and the heat added

$$\eta = \frac{17.47 - 0.23}{146.47} = 0.118 \text{ or } 11.8 \text{ percent}$$

The total electrical power to be generated is

Net output	3.0 kWe
Parasitic load	0.3
Controls	0.1
	3.4 kWe

At 80 percent alternator efficiency, the shaft power to the alternator is

$$\text{Shaft power} = \frac{3.4}{0.8} = 4.25 \text{ kW}$$

In addition there are power requirements for the NaK pump and for bearing losses so that the total shaft power becomes

Alternator	4.25
NaK pump	0.44
Bearings, etc.	0.60
Total	5.29 kW

The heat delivered from the reactor to the mercury is

$$\text{Thermal power} = \frac{5.29}{0.118} = 45 \text{ kW thermal}$$

The system efficiency for a net output of 3.0 kW becomes

$$\eta = \frac{3.0}{45} = 0.067 \text{ or } 6.7 \text{ percent}$$

Since 5.29 kW or 301 Btu/min must be delivered and the net work per pound of mercury has been found to be 17.24 Btu, the mercury flow rate is found to be

$$\text{Flow rate} = \frac{301}{17.24} = 17.5 \text{ lb/min}$$

Values for the enthalpies at point a and b' can also be found from Fig. 3-7. These values and lines for the processes over the range covered by this diagram are shown in Fig. 3-8. Such diagrams permit the rapid solution of power cycle problems.

BRAYTON CYCLE

Several power cycles using gases for the working fluid were devised in the nineteenth century. Since the engines based upon these power cycles used piston expanders and compressors with heat exchangers for heating and cooling the gases, the temperatures were limited to about 800 °F and the engines were large,

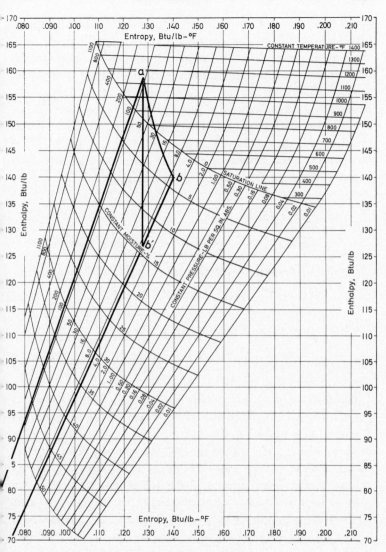

FIG. 3-8 SNAP II power cycle.

heavy and expensive. With the development of the high temperature gas turbine and efficient axial and centrifugal compressors,
the Brayton cycle engine has become a practical and advantageous
power plant for many applications including aircraft propulsion.
Direct combustion of fuel in the compressed air avoids the
temperature limitations of a heat exchanger. New materials of
construction make possible turbine inlet temperatures over 1800°F
resulting in light weight, efficient power plants. A schematic of
an open-cycle gas turbine is shown in Fig. 3-9. The turboshaft
engine with an axial and centrifugal compressor delivering air to

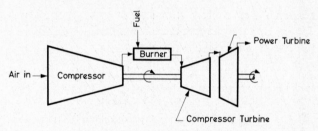

FIG. 3-9   Open cycle gas turbine.

the combustion chamber in Fig. 3-10 has separate turbines driving
the compressor and power shafts.

The Brayton gas cycle is illustrated in Fig. 3-11. Starting at
point *a*, the gas is compressed isentropically before being heated
at constant pressure to the turbine inlet temperature *c*. The
compressed hot gas expands through the engine to deliver shaft
energy and the exhaust gases discharges at the same pressure as
the compressor inlet but at a higher temperature. Cooling the
gases from the exhaust temperature *d* to the compressor inlet
temperature *a* completes the cycle. The gases can be heated and
cooled in heat exchangers for a closed cycle or for the open
Brayton cycle, air is drawn from the atmosphere at point *a* and
the turbine is exhausted to the atmosphere at point *d* so that the
atmosphere serves as the heat sink for the constant pressure
process *d–a*. The theoretical Brayton gas cycle, either open or
closed, then consists of two isentropic processes, *a–b* and *c–d*, and
two constant pressure processes *b–c* and *d–a*. By modifications of

AXIAL-FLOW
COMPRESSOR

CENTRIFUGAL
COMPRESSOR

EXHAUST

TURBINE WHEELS FOR
DRIVE SHAFT

TURBINE WHEELS FOR
COMPRESSOR DRIVE

COMBUSTION
CHAMBER

FUEL
INLET

DUCT

GEAR BOX

FIG. 3-10   Turboshaft engine (Allison).

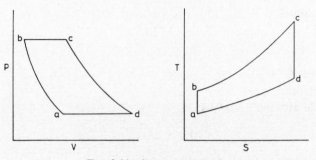

FIG. 3-11 Brayton gas cycle.

this theoretical cycle to account for losses and inefficiencies, the operation of gas turbine power plants can be described for design and analytical studies.

The net work done in the cycle is the difference of the work in the expansion and compression processes. This is also the difference between the heat added in combustion and the heat rejected in the turbine exhaust, or

$$W_{net} = (H_c - H_d) - (H_b - H_a) = (H_c - H_b) - (H_d - H_a)$$

Thus the efficiency becomes

$$\eta = \frac{W_{net}}{Q_{added}} = \frac{Q_{added} - Q_{rejected}}{Q_{added}}$$

Calculation using tabulated enthalpy values are preferred for accuracy and facility in solving most power cycle problems. However, the derivation of the efficiency of the Brayton cycle in terms of temperatures is of interest for comparing the Brayton with the Carnot and other power cycles. A constant average heat capacity $\bar{C}_p$ will be assumed. Then the heat added and rejected become

$$Q_{added} = \bar{C}_p(T_c - T_b)$$
$$Q_{rejected} = \bar{C}_p(T_d - T_a)$$

In these terms the efficiency is

$$\eta = \frac{\bar{C}_p(T_c - T_b) - \bar{C}_p(T_d - T_a)}{\bar{C}_p(T_c - T_b)} = \frac{(T_c - T_b) - (T_d - T_a)}{T_c - T_b}$$

The pressure ratios p_a/p_b and p_d/p_c are identical, so that

$$\frac{p_a}{p_b} = \frac{p_d}{p_c}$$

From the relations between temperature and pressure ratios for isentropic processes of a perfect gas, the following temperature ratios also are equal

$$\frac{T_a}{T_d} = \frac{T_b}{T_c}.$$

The relation for the cycle efficiency can be rearranged in terms of these temperature ratios

$$\eta = \frac{T_c\left(1-\dfrac{T_b}{T_c}\right)-T_d\left(1-\dfrac{T_a}{T_d}\right)}{T_c\left(1-\dfrac{T_b}{T_c}\right)} = \frac{T_c-T_d}{T_c}.$$

Thus operating over the same temperature range, the efficiency of the Brayton cycle is less than the Carnot cycle.

EXAMPLE 3-3. For a Brayton gas cycle with a pressure ratio of 5/1 and a maximum temperature of 1500 °F, calculate the efficiency using the above relations and assuming $\gamma = 1.4$. Compare the efficiency with that of a Carnot cycle having the temperature limits of 70 °F and 1500 °F.

Solution: The temperature ratio T_c/T_d is obtained from the pressure ratio

$$\frac{T_c}{T_d} = \left(\frac{p_c}{p_d}\right)^{\frac{\gamma-1}{\gamma}} = \left(\frac{5}{1}\right)^{\frac{1.4-1}{1.4}} = 1.584$$

$$T_d = \frac{1500+460}{1.584} = 1237 \ ^\circ R$$

$$\eta = \frac{(1960-1237)}{1960} = 0.37 \text{ or } 37 \text{ percent Brayton cycle efficiency}$$

$$\eta = \frac{(1500-70)}{1960} = 0.73 \text{ or } 73 \text{ percent Carnot cycle efficiency}$$

EXAMPLE 3-4. Calculate the efficiency for the Brayton cycle described in Example 3-3, but using valu esfrom Table 2-5 for the thermodynamic properties of air.

Solution: The conditions at the compressor inlet temperature of 70 °F are (basis 1 lb of air)

$$T_a = 70+460 = 530 \text{ °F}$$
$$p_{ra} = 1.2983$$
$$h_a = 126.66 \text{ Btu/lb}$$

Following an isentropic compression over the 5/1 pressure ratio, the relative pressure can be found. Then the corresponding values of enthalpy and temperature are determined

$$p_{rb} = 5 \times p_{ra} = 5 \times 1.2983 = 6.4915$$
$$T_b = 837 \text{ °R}$$
$$h_b = 200.85 \text{ Btu/lb}$$

The isentropic compressor work is

$$W_{ab} = h_b - h_a = 200.85 - 126.66 = 74.19 \text{ Btu/lb}$$

The conditions at the turbine inlet temperature of 1500 °F are

$$T_c = 1500+460 = 1960 \text{ °R}$$
$$p_{rc} = 160.37$$
$$h_c = 493.64 \text{ Btu/lb}$$

For an isentropic expansion over a pressure ratio of 5/1 the relative pressure, enthalpy and temperature at the turbine exhaust are found

$$p_{rd} = \frac{160.37}{5} = 32.07$$

$$h_d = 316.05 \text{ Btu/lb}$$
$$T_d = 1297 \text{ °R}$$

The work done in the expansion is

$$W_{cd} = h_c - h_d = 493.64 - 316.05 = 177.59 \text{ Btu/lb}$$

The heat added by combustion is determined from the change in enthalpy

$$Q_{bc} = h_c - h_b = 493.64 - 200.85 = 292.79 \text{ Btu/lb}$$

The cycle efficiency is thus

$$\eta = \frac{W_{cd} - W_{ab}}{Q_{bc}} = \frac{177.59 - 74.19}{292.79} = 0.35 \text{ or 35 percent,}$$

The difference between this more accurate calculation using the gas tables and the approximation of constant heat capacity and an average value of the specific heat ratio γ of 1.4 is some 2 percent. It should be noted that this efficiency applies only to a theoretical cycle without allowances for (1) mass of the fuel burned in the combustion chamber, (2) pressure and heat losses, and (3) inefficiencies in the compressor and turbine.

TURBOJET ENGINE

The Brayton gas cycle can be used as a basis for analysis of operation of the turbojet engine. In this engine, only part of the available energy in the hot gas is removed in the compressor drive turbine. The exhaust from this turbine at intermediate pressure and temperature is further expanded through a nozzle to produce a high velocity jet. Thermodynamically the expansion through the

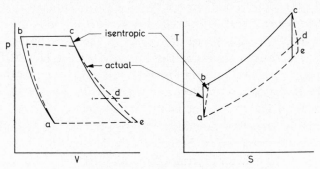

Fig. 3-12 Turbojet power cycle.

turbine to do work and the expansion through the nozzle to convert thermal energy into kinetic energy are similar. The turbojet power cycle, including inefficiencies in the compression and expansion processes, is illustrated in Fig. 3-12. This open cycle is completed along the dashed line e–a with the atmosphere serving as the constant pressure heat sink. The work produced by the gas in the turbine must equal that required to compress the air

$$W_{cd} = W_{ba}$$

By expansion from the intermediate pressure at d to atmospheric pressure e, the kinetic energy of the gas is increased.

Additional fuel burned in the turbine exhaust at pressure d will reheat the gas and increase the exhaust velocity. This process of afterburning is used to augment thrust for short periods. However, the relative inefficiency of the process results in high fuel consumption.

In flight, the velocity of the air entering the engine is reduced in a diffuser to match the compressor inlet requirements. The increase in pressure and temperature can be computed for an isentropic compression using the relations already discussed. The difference between an actual and an isentropic diffuser compression can be expressed as a thermodynamic efficiency or as a pressure efficiency (the ratio of the actual pressure to that from a reversible process). For low subsonic flight velocities, the diffuser is quite efficient; however, at supersonic velocities, the highly irreversible processes in the shock wave at the diffuser inlet considerably reduce the pressure and increase the temperature of the gas at the diffuser outlet. These diffuser effects are not involved in the computation of the static thrust of the engine. Therefore, for simplicity, the diffuser compression has not been included in the turbojet power cycle illustrated in Fig. 3-12.

The thrust of a turbojet engine results from the difference in momentum between the incoming air and the outgoing jet. The increase in mass flow rate due to the fuel burned is a secondary effect, but a correction can be included easily in the thrust calculations by using a factor in terms of the air–fuel ratio. The differ-

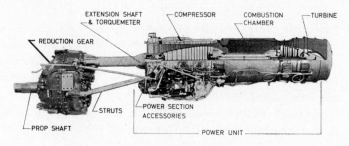

FIG. 3-13   Aircraft turbo-prop engine (Allison).

ences between the thermal properties of the combustion products and of air are small when the air to fuel ratio is large. This large excess of air is necessary to limit the temperature of the gases entering the turbine. Correction factors for the actual combustion products are available from Ref. 2-1. However, problems can be solved with reasonable accuracy using the values of the thermodynamic properties of air given in Table 2-5 and Ref. 2-1.

EXAMPLE 3-5. Calculate the static thrust of a turbojet engine compressing 100 lb/sec of air at 60 °F and 14.7 psia with a compression ratio of 5/1 and a compressor efficiency of 80 percent. The turbine efficiency is 85 percent. After a 3 psi pressure drop in the combustion chamber, the gases at 1500 °F enter the turbine. The expansion of the turbine exhaust is completed in the nozzle with 96 percent efficiency.

Solution: From Table 2-5, the thermodynamic properties of air at the engine inlet, point *a* in Fig. 3-12, are:

$$T_a = 520 \text{ °R}$$
$$h_a = 124.27 \text{ Btu/lb}$$
$$p_{ra} = 1.2147$$

Using this value of the relative pressure, the conditions following an isentropic compression can be found

$$p'_{rb} = 5 \times 1.2147 = 6.0735$$
$$h'_b = 197.08 \text{ Btu/lb}$$

The isentropic enthalpy change is

$$\Delta h' = 197.08 - 124.27 = 72.81 \text{ Btu/lb}$$

The actual enthalpy change at 80 percent efficiency is then

$$\Delta h_{ab} = \frac{72.81}{0.80} = 91.01 \text{ Btu/lb}$$

$$h_b = 91.01 + 124.27 = 215.28 \text{ Btu/lb}$$

The conditions at the compressor outlet, point b, corresponding to this pressure ratio and enthalpy are

$$p_b = 5.0 \times 14.7 = 73.5 \text{ psia}$$
$$T_b = 896 \text{ °R}$$

At the entrance to the turbine, point c, following combustion of fuel in the compressed air with a pressure drop of 3 psi, the conditions are

$$p_c = 73.5 - 3 = 70.5 \text{ psia}$$
$$T_c = 1500 + 460 = 1960 \text{ °R}$$
$$h_c = 493.64 \text{ Btu/lb}$$
$$p_{rc} = 160.37$$

The work that must be done by the gas in the turbine to drive the compressor has been found to be 91.01 Btu/lb of inlet air. The amount of fuel burned is about 0.02 lb per pound of air; thus, there are 1.02 lb of combustion products per pound of inlet air. Therefore, neglecting the small energy losses from mechanical friction and other losses, the work done in the turbine per pound of gas must be

$$\Delta h_{cd} = 91.0 / 1.02 = 89.23 \text{ Btu/lb}$$
$$h'_d = 493.64 - 89.23 = 404.41 \text{ Btu/lb}$$
$$p'_{rd} = 77.57$$

This amount of work is done in an adiabatic process of 85 percent efficiency that corresponds to an isentropic process with an enthalpy change of

$$\Delta h_{cd} = \frac{89.23}{0.85} = 104.98 \text{ Btu/lb}$$

$$h_d = 493.64 - 104.98 = 388.66 \text{ Btu/lb}$$

$$p_{rd} = 67.20$$

The turbine exhaust pressure then can be found from this relative pressure

$$p_d = \frac{p_{rd}}{p_{rc}} \times p_c = \frac{67.20}{160.37} \times 70.5 = 29.5 \text{ psia}$$

The turbine exhaust at this pressure is expanded in the nozzle to atmospheric pressure. For an isentropic expansion (neglecting the velocity of the gas leaving the turbine) the relative pressure and the enthalpy at the nozzle exit are

$$p'_{re} = \frac{14.7}{29.5} \times 77.57 = 38.65$$

$$h'_e = 333.07 \text{ Btu/lb}$$

The actual enthalpy change in the nozzle is then

$$\Delta h_{de} = (h_d - h_e) = 0.96(404.41 - 333.07) = 68.49 \text{ Btu/lb}$$

The jet velocity can be obtained from the relation

$$\frac{v^2}{2g} = -\Delta h$$

$$\Delta v = (2 \times 32.2 \times 68.49 \times 778.3)^{\frac{1}{2}} = 1852 \text{ ft/sec}$$

The impulse per pound of exhaust gas is found from the change in momentum. When $v_1 = 0$, the specific impulse is

$$I = \frac{\Delta v}{g} = \frac{1852}{32.2} = 57.5 \text{ sec}$$

The specific impulse per pound of inlet air is

$$I_{\text{inlet}} = 57.5 \times 1.02 = 58.6 \text{ sec}$$

Therefore the static thrust of the engine for 100 lb/sec air flow becomes

$$\text{Thrust} = 100 \times 58.6 = 5860 \text{ lb}$$

GAS TURBINE WITH REGENERATOR

The temperature of the exhaust from the power turbine T_d (Fig. 3-14) is well above that of the compressed air from the compressor T_b. Therefore, the cycle efficiency can be improved (and fuel consumption decreased) by a heat exchanger transferring

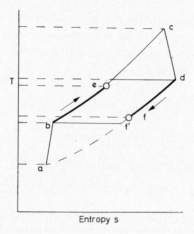

FIG. 3-14   Gas turbine with regenerator.

heat from the turbine exhaust to the compressed air before it
enters the combustion chamber. This is shown schematically in
Fig. 3-15. A counterflow heat exchanger makes it possible for the
temperature of the compressed air, T_e, to approach the temperature of the turbine exhaust, T_d. However, a lightweight rotary
basket type of heat exchanger (Fig. 3-16), although less effective,
may be preferred for gas turbine power plants for use where
reducing weight is more important than obtaining the highest
possible efficiency. Rotary disc heat exchangers have been used
for many years in steam power plants to recover waste boiler
heat for preheating combustion air.

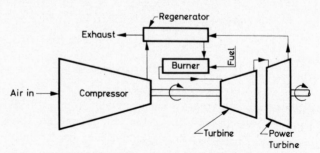

FIG. 3-15   Gas turbine with regenerator.

The effectiveness of a regenerator η_r, is the ratio of the actual heat transferred to the amount that could be transferred, if the turbine exhaust were cooled to the compressor outlet temperature. Since the mass flow rate of turbine exhaust is greater than the

FIG. 3-16 Basket type rotary heat exchanger for gas turbine power plant (Allison).

compressed air flow rate by the factor $1 + r_f$ where r_f is the fuel to air ratio, the regenerator effectiveness is

$$\eta_r = \frac{(h_e - h_b)}{(h_d - h_{f'})(1 + r_f)}$$

The value of the regenerator effectiveness is always less than unity and depends upon the size and type of heat exchanger selected. In addition to weight and effectiveness, the pressure drop in the regenerator is important. By the use of compact efficient regenerators, it has been possible to increase the efficiency of gas turbine power plants so that they are competitive with reciprocating engines for some applications.

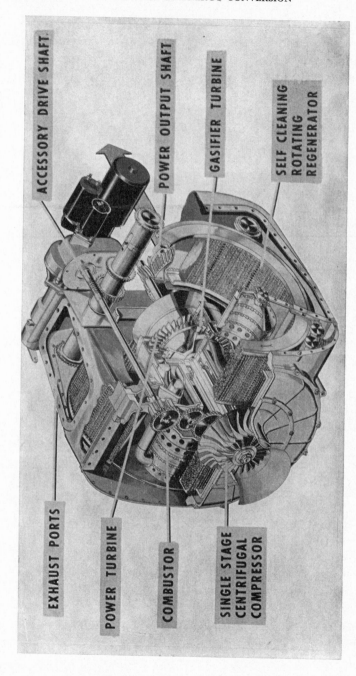

Fig. 3-17 Gas turbine power plant with rotating regenerators (Allison).

EXAMPLE 3-6. What is the theoretical efficiency of the Brayton gas cycle described in Example 3-3 with 100 percent effective regeneration?

Solution: In this theoretical problem, the mass flow rate from the turbine equals that entering the combustion chamber. Also, the compressed air is regeneratively heated to the turbine exhaust temperature so that (Fig. 3-14)

$$T_e = T_d$$

The heat required to raise the temperature of the gas from T_e to T_c is

$$Q = h_c - h_e = h_c - h_a$$

Using values for these enthalpies from Example 3-4

$$Q = 493.64 - 316.05 = 177.59 \text{ Btu/lb}$$

The work required in compressing the gas W_{ab} and the work done in the turbine W_{cd} remain unchanged from Example 3-4, so the efficiency becomes

$$\eta = \frac{W_{cd} - W_{ab}}{Q} = \frac{(177.59 - 74.19)}{177.59} = 0.58 \text{ or } 58 \text{ percent}$$

This value is intermediate to the efficiencies of the simple Brayton cycle (37 percent) and the Carnot cycle (73 percent).

INTERCOOLING

The work required to compress a gas can be reduced by compressing in stages and cooling the gas between each stage (Figs. 3-18 and 3-19). Intercooling is used in industrial high-pressure compressors where the weight of the additional heat exchangers is not objectionable. Also there may be applications for intercooling in mobile and stationary gas turbine power plants where weight is not critical and water would be available for cooling. In general the use of intercooling favors higher pressure power cycles.

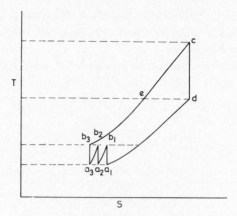

FIG. 3-18   Brayton cycle with intercooling.

Usually the work of compression with intercooling is a minimum when the pressure ratio across each compressor stage is the same, as shown in Fig. 3-18

$$\frac{p_{b1}}{p_{a1}} = \frac{p_{b2}}{p_{a2}} = \frac{p_{b3}}{p_{a3}}$$

In the limit of an infinite number of intercooling stages the compression would approach a constant temperature process with minimum work.

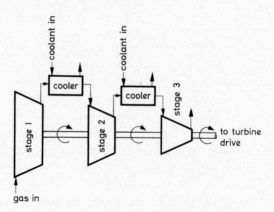

FIG. 3-19   Compressor with intercooling.

EXAMPLE 3-7. What is the efficiency of the power cycle described in Example 3-6 with three compression stages of equal pressure ratios and intercooling to 70 °F between each stage?

Solution: For a total pressure ratio of 5/1, each of the three equal stages has a ratio of

$$\frac{p_{b1}}{p_{a1}} = \frac{p_{b2}}{p_{a2}} = \frac{p_{b3}}{p_{a3}} = \left(\frac{5}{1}\right)^{1/3} = 1.710$$

The compressor inlet conditions are

$$T_{a1} = 530 \ ^{\circ}\text{R}$$
$$p_{ra1} = 1.2983$$
$$h_{a1} = 126.66 \ \text{Btu/lb}$$

The outlet conditions for an isentropic compression over the pressure ratio of 1.710 are found from the relative pressure

$$p'_{rb1} = 1.710 \times 1.2983 = 2.2200$$
$$h'_{b1} = 147.73 \ \text{Btu/lb}$$

The work required for an isentropic compression stage is

$$-W_{ab1} = 147.73 - 126.66 = 21.07 \ \text{Btu/lb}$$

After cooling at constant pressure in the intercooler to 70 °F, the inlet conditions to the second compressor stage are, again

$$T_{a2} = 530 \ ^{\circ}\text{R}$$
$$p_{ra2} = 1.2983$$
$$h_{a2} = 126.66 \ \text{Btu/lb}$$

Since the compression ratio is the same in each stage,

$$p_{rb2} = 1.710 \times 1.2983 = 2.220$$
$$h_{b2} = 147.73 \ \text{Btu/lb}$$
$$-W_{a2b2} = 21.07$$

The third stage compressor work is identical to that for the first and second stages, and therefore the total compressor work is

$$-W_{ab3} = 3 \times 21.07 = 63.21 \ \text{Btu/lb}$$

A regenerator of 100 percent effectiveness will remove heat from the turbine exhaust and raise the temperature of the compressed air to $T_e = T_d$, so that the heat required in the combustion chamber to increase the gas temperature from T_e to T_c remains the same as in Example 3-6, or

$$Q = 177.59 \text{ Btu/lb}$$

The work done by the gas in the turbine also remains

$$W_{cd} = h_c - h_d = 177.59 \text{ Btu/lb}$$

The cycle efficiency is then

$$\eta = \frac{W_{cd} - W_{ab}}{Q} = \frac{177.59 - 63.21}{177.59} = 0.64 \text{ or } 64 \text{ percent}$$

GAS TURBINE WITH REHEAT

The average temperature at which heat is added to the gas turbine power cycle can be increased by reheating the gas between turbine stages. This is similar to the Rankine reheat cycle. The increases in capacity or efficiency obtained by reheating are offset by the added weight and complexity of equipment. In the future reheating should be attractive for large closed-cycle gas turbine power plants such as those to be operated with liquid metal cooled nuclear reactors. Reheating between turbine stages may or may not be used with compressor intercooling; however by using both in several stages, the Carnot cycle efficiency can be approached.

CLOSED-CYCLE GAS TURBINE

As its name implies, the closed cycle does not communicate with the atmosphere as a source of working fluid. Attractive features may include (1) greater power by increased density of gas at a higher base (compressor inlet) pressure, (2) use of an inert gas to permit higher temperatures without oxidation of container materials, (3) prevention of contamination of the atmosphere from radioactive materials and (4) use in space where oxygen is not available. To obtain these advantages, a heat exchanger for cooling the turbine exhaust to the compressor inlet temperature and another for heating the compressed gas to the turbine inlet temperature (Fig. 3-20) are necessary. A semiclosed power cycle has been proposed eliminating one of the heat exchangers by using air for internal combustion and bleeding the equivalent amount of gas from the system.

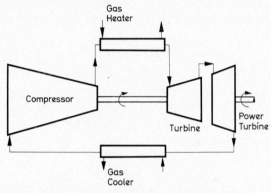

FIG. 3-20 Closed-cycle gas turbine.

The first closed-cycle gas turbine power plant to be operated in the United States was an experimental unit for the Army's gas-cooled nuclear power plant program. This initial unit used an oil-fired furnace to heat the gas. Based upon the performance data obtained, a successful power system has been constructed and operated using a gas-cooled nuclear reactor as the gas heater. With this system, a lightweight mobile power plant permitting rapid assembly and dismantling was being developed.

GAS PROPERTIES

In the closed-cycle gas turbine, a working fluid other than air may be preferred. Studies have been made of several gases that might be suitable for use with closed-cycle nuclear power plants where there are the additional problems of materials for reactor construction and radiation damage. Theoretically, the efficiency of a cycle operating between fixed temperature limits is independent of the properties of the working fluid; and from the studies that have been made, it has been found that there is little advantage in efficiency to be obtained with any particular gas. However the work done in an expansion process between fixed temperatures is proportional to the average heat capacity of the gas. Thus carbon dioxide with its high molal heat capacity can produce more work per mole than air or helium. Since the molal volumes of gases are very nearly equal at the same conditions, carbon dioxide can produce more work per unit volume. Turbine and compressor sizes therefore are smaller for carbon dioxide. However much of the cost and size of a closed-cycle power plant is associated with the heat exchangers. As shown in Table 3-4, both hydrogen and helium provide exceptional heat transfer properties and the size of heat exchangers for these gases would be smaller than for carbon dioxide or nitrogen.

TABLE 3-4   PROPERTIES OF GASES

	Mol. wt.	Molal heat capacity*	Thermal conductivity Btu/hr ft °F at 600 °F
Hydrogen	2	7.1	0.18
Helium	4	5.0	0.16
Steam	18	9.0	0.026
Nitrogen	28	7.3	0.027
Air	29	7.4	0.027
Carbon dioxide	44	11.5	0.023

* Average value 70 °F to 1500 °F.

The chemical properties of the gas must be compatible with the materials in the power system at the operating temperature. Since helium is inert chemically, high surface temperatures are permitted without corrosion. Nitrogen is reasonably inert at moderate temperatures, however at 1500 °F nitriding reactions will occur unless special precautions are taken. Hydrogen has advantageous chemical properties particularly with metal hydride moderated nuclear reactors. Carbon dioxide will react with graphite at elevated temperatures although claddings can provide protection.

The selection of the gas for a power system represents a compromise between many desired characteristics including logistics, heat transfer and chemical properties. It is probable that the use of hydrogen would lead to a minimum weight nuclear gas turbine power plant.

OTTO CYCLE

The operation of spark-ignition (gasoline) engines and compression-ignition (Diesel) engines can be approximated by the theoretical Otto and Diesel cycles respectively. These cycles are useful for analytical studies, and the relations between the results of such studies and actual engine performance have become known through experience. In the air standard cycle it is assumed that the gas undergoes no chemical or mass changes in the combustion process and this cycle therefore serves as a simplified convenient basis for approximate studies. Factors for the actual changes in mass and composition can be applied to the results to provide a more accurate description of engine operation. The following elementary derivations of efficiency will be made on the basis of the air standard cycles.

In the Otto cycle (Fig. 3-21), as the piston moves up, the air–fuel mixture is compressed along the path a–b, and in the theoretical cycle this compression is assumed to be isentropic. When the piston is near the top of its stroke, the fuel is ignited by a spark and combustion heats the gas from T_b to T_c. This is assumed to be a constant volume process. The gas expansion (c–d) produces work as the piston moves down. In the four-cycle engine, the upward motion of the piston next forces the gas out to the atmosphere, and during the fourth stroke of the piston (downward), air and fuel are drawn into the cylinder to complete the cycle. In the two-cycle engine, the combustion products are released (d–a) when the piston nears the bottom of its second stroke (the power stroke) and a fresh charge of air and fuel is injected into the cylinder to complete the cycle in two strokes.

The cycle efficiency will be derived in terms of the compression ratio r_c. This is determined by the cylinder volume V_a and clearance volume V_b, or

$$r_c = \frac{V_a}{V_b}$$

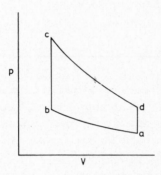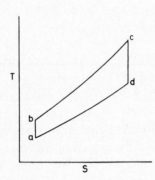

FIG. 3-21   Otto cycle.

The heat added in the constant-volume combustion is given by

$$Q_{bc} = C_v(T_c - T_b)$$

The heat rejected to the atmosphere $(-Q_{da})$ in process d–a at constant volume is also

$$\tfrac{1}{m} Q_{da} = C_v(T_d - T_a)$$

Then the net work and the efficiency become

$$W = Q_{bc} + Q_{da}$$

$$\eta = \frac{Q_{bc} + Q_{da}}{Q_{bc}} = \frac{C_v(T_c - T_b) - C_v(T_d - T_a)}{C_v(T_c - T_b)}$$

If it is assumed that the heat capacity remains constant, the term C_v can be eliminated, and

$$\eta = 1 - \frac{T_d - T_a}{T_c - T_b}$$

The relations between temperatures and volumes for isentropic processes are

$$\frac{T_c}{T_d} = \left(\frac{V_d}{V_c}\right)^{\gamma-1} = \frac{T_b}{T_a} = \left(\frac{V_a}{V_b}\right)^{\gamma-1}$$

The temperatures T_c and T_b can be expressed then in terms of the compression ratio, γ, and the temperatures T_d and T_a

$$\eta = 1 - \frac{T_d - T_a}{T_a\left(\frac{V_a}{V_b}\right)^{\gamma-1} - T_a\left(\frac{V_a}{V_b}\right)^{\gamma-1}} = 1 - \frac{1}{(r_c)^{\gamma-1}}$$

Thus the efficiency of the Otto cycle is a function of the compression ratio r_c and the heat capacity ratio γ. The cycle efficiency increases with the compression ratio. For the air standard cycle based on the properties of cold air the average value of γ is 1.4. A hot-air standard cycle is defined in terms of the average air properties over the engine operating conditions and the value of the heat capacity ratio is then 1.3. Also procedures are described in Ref. 3-1 for engine calculations using the properties of the actual combustion products to more accurately described the processes in a real engine.

EXAMPLE 3-8. Compute the theoretical Otto cold-air standard cycle efficiencies for compression ratios of 4, 6, 8 and 10.

Solution: Substituting values of r_c and γ in the efficiency formula gives

$$\eta_4 = 1 - \frac{1}{(4)^{1.4-1}} = 0.43$$

$$\eta_6 = 1 - \frac{1}{(6)^{1.4-1}} = 0.51$$

$$\eta_8 = 1 - \frac{1}{(8)^{1.4-1}} = 0.56$$

$$\eta_{10} = 1 - \frac{1}{(10)^{1.4-1}} = 0.60$$

EXAMPLE 3-9. What would the theoretical Otto cycle efficiency be on the basis of the hot-air standard cycle at a compression ratio of 8?

Solution: Using the value $\gamma = 1.3$, the cycle efficiency is found to be

$$\eta_8 = 1 - \frac{1}{(8)^{1.3-1}} = 0.46$$

The clearance with the piston at top dead center and the piston displacement (*PD*) determine the compression ratio, or

$$PD = V_a - V_b$$

$$c = \frac{V_b}{PD} = \frac{V_b}{V_a - V_b}$$

The relations between compression ratio, clearance and efficiency are then

$$r_c = \frac{V_a}{V_b} = \frac{1+c}{c}$$

$$\eta = 1 - \left(\frac{c}{1+c}\right)^{\gamma-1}$$

The maximum value of the compression ratio for a spark-ignition engine is limited by the combustion characteristics of the fuel–air mixture. The increase in temperature of the air–fuel mixture during the compression process may cause pre-ignition or promote detonation of the mixture after ignition with resulting "spark knock". The octane number of fuel for a spark ignition engine is measured in a standard test engine by comparison with a reference fuel. A fuel with an octane number of 95 would require the same compression ratio to produce knocking as a mixture of 95 percent isooctane and 5 percent heptane. Tetraethyl lead and certain other additives retard detonation and thereby improve the octane number of a fuel. However, the amount of energy in the fuel is not increased. A compression ratio of 7.5 is the maximum that will accommodate the lower octane gasolines whereas the higher octane gasolines will permit a compression ratio of 10.

DIESEL CYCLE

The Diesel cycle differs from the Otto cycle in that a much higher compression ratio is used and the fuel is injected near top dead center. Burning of the fuel proceeds during the downward stoke of the piston. The air is above the fuel ignition temperature when compressed so that ignition occurs as soon as the fuel is injected. Burning of the fuel is controlled by the rate of injection to approximate a constant pressure process as shown in Fig. 3-22.

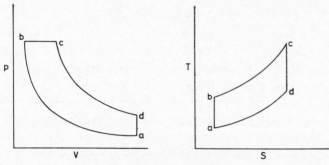

FIG. 3-22   Diesel cycle.

The theoretical Diesel cycle then consists of an isentropic compression a–b followed by a constant pressure addition of heat along b–c. Expansion of the gas along c–d produces work and the cycle is completed by discharge of the combustion products to the atmosphere in a constant volume process d–a.

The efficiency of the air-standard Diesel cycle can be derived in terms of a compression ratio r_c and cut off ratio r_i (the ratio of the volume V_c at the end of fuel injection to the clearance volume V_b) so that

$$r_i = \frac{V_c}{V_b}$$

$$\eta = 1 - \frac{1}{r_c^{\gamma-1}} \left[\frac{r_i^{\gamma}-1}{\gamma(r_i-1)} \right]$$

The efficiency therefore increases with the compression ratio and decreases with the cut off ratio, r_i. However, the compression ratio of the Diesel cycle is not limited as severely by the combustion characteristics (cetane rating) of the fuel. Much higher compression ratios can be used with corresponding higher efficiencies. Compression ignition engines usually have lower specific fuel consumptions than similar spark ignition engines, and the efficiency of a large Diesel engine may exceed that of a modern steam power plant. In some applications, the heat rejected from the engine to the coolant and exhaust can be used for space or process heating.

CLOSED CYCLE

The operation of an Otto or Diesel cycle engine can be made independent of the atmosphere by circulating the exhaust to an absorber for removal of the carbon dioxide and water formed in combustion. The remaining gas, usually nitrogen, is returned to the engine inlet where oxygen is added. An engine of this type can be operated efficiently at constant load, but changing the rate of oxygen feed rapidly to follow changes in engine speed and load has been found to be difficult. An oxygen deficiency will cause ignition failure, while too much oxygen can cause violent and destructive pressure surges from the burning of oil that may have accumulated in the engine. Thus engine operation is critically dependent upon oxygen control. In general the system is heavy and complex.

WALTER CYCLE

A power system based on the combustion of petroleum fuel in the hot oxygen-rich decomposition products from hydrogen peroxide was developed for submarine propulsion. It is of interest for other applications isolated from atmospheric oxygen. The combustion products can be used to drive a turbine or piston engine or to generate steam. Since the exhaust is mostly carbon dioxide and water vapor, it can be discharged directly without recycling.

STIRLING CYCLE

A practical power cycle with a theoretical efficiency equal to that of the Carnot cycle was described by the Reverend Robert Stirling in a patent of 1816 and a successful engine was built in 1843. Small power plants of this type were used until about 1920 for pumping water on farms and generating power in small communities. Wood, coal or cobs were burned in the firebox of this engine which fulfilled many requirements for power during

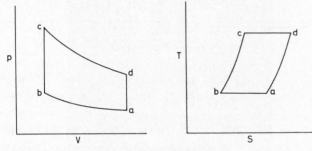

Fig. 3-23   Stirling cycle.

the development of this country. About 1940 in Holland there was a revival of interest in the Stirling engine and extensive development effort has produced efficient, compact silent engines which may now find applications in many places. The gaseous working fluid in the Stirling engine is heated by external combustion and a regenerator is used to store thermal energy during the cycle.

The basic Stirling cycle (Fig. 3-23) consists of an isothermal compression $a-b$, followed by heat addition at constant volume along $b-c$. Then the gas is expanded at constant temperature from c to d, and a constant volume step d to a completes the cycle. These operations are accomplished by the displacement of gas in a cylinder with two pistons driven up and down by linkages that approximate the required sequence of motion. The top piston is moved by a rod that passes through the bottom piston and its connecting rod (Fig. 3-24). The displacer piston at the top is simply a hollow shell fitting loosely inside the cylinder since there is little pressure difference between the top and bottom of this

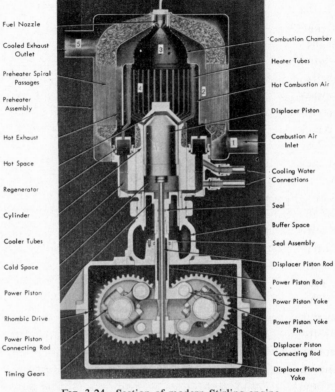

Fuel Nozzle

Cooled Exhaust Outlet

Preheater Spiral Passages

Preheater Assembly

Hot Exhaust

Hot Space

Regenerator

Cylinder

Cooler Tubes

Cold Space

Power Piston

Rhombic Drive

Power Piston Connecting Rod

Timing Gears

Combustion Chamber

Heater Tubes

Hot Combustion Air

Displacer Piston

Combustion Air Inlet

Cooling Water Connections

Seal

Buffer Space

Seal Assembly

Displacer Piston Rod

Power Piston Rod

Power Piston Yoke

Power Piston Yoke Pin

Displacer Piston Connecting Rod

Displacer Piston Yoke

FIG. 3-24 Section of modern Stirling engine.

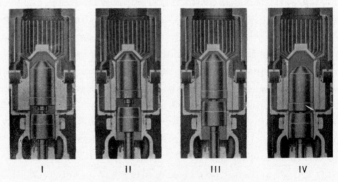

I   II   III   IV

FIG. 3-25 Piston position sequence.

piston and some leakage of gas can be tolerated. It is the bottom
piston that provides the compression and delivers work from the
gas expansion. Its location in the cooler part of the engine away
from the combustion zone permits lubrication and a close fit in
the cylinder.

The sequence of operation in Fig. 3-25 starts at position I as
the displacer piston moves up to displace the gas out of the top
of the cylinder at temperature T_d. The gas flows down through
the regenerator where thermal energy of the gas is absorbed by
the filler material (a packing of fine wires or ceramic shapes).
Next the gas passes through the heat exchanger where the gas is
cooled to temperature T_a before entering the space between the
pistons. An isothermal compression takes place when the power
piston moves up from position II to III with heat rejected to the
cold walls to maintain constant temperature. Clearance around
the top part of the power piston then allows the gas to flow back
through the heat exchanger and into the regenerator where the
heat previously absorbed now is returned to the gas. Finally the
gas is heated to the maximum cycle temperature in the heater
tubes during flow into the top of the cylinder. The pistons move
down from position III to IV in a constant volume process to
complete the cycle.

The heat added to the gas in the constant volume process b–c
must equal the heat removed from the gas in the similar process
d–a since the temperature limits of these processes are the same.
If the regenerator is 100 percent effective, all this heat is recovered
from the gas in process d–a and returned in process b–c. These
quantities of thermal energy are exchanged within the engine and
need not be considered in the overall exchange of energy with the
environment. In the constant temperature expansion c–d the heat
added is

$$Q_{c-d} = RT_c \ln\left(\frac{V_d}{V_c}\right)$$

Similarly, the heat rejected in the constant temperature compression a–b is

$$-Q_{ab} = RT_a \ln\left(\frac{V_a}{V_b}\right)$$

Since $\dfrac{V_d}{V_c} = \dfrac{V_a}{V_b}$ the efficiency can then be found

$$\eta = \frac{Q_{c-d} + Q_{a-b}}{Q_{c-d}} = \frac{RT_c \ln\left(\dfrac{V_d}{V_c}\right) - RT_a \ln\left(\dfrac{V_a}{V_b}\right)}{RT_c \ln\left(\dfrac{V_d}{V_c}\right)} = \frac{T_c - T_a}{T_c}$$

The theoretical efficiency of the Stirling cycle with 100 percent effective regeneration is identical to that for the Carnot cycle having the same operating limits. The Stirling cycle can be approximated in a compact mechanical system operating over a reasonable pressure ratio, whereas no simple and practical machine for the Carnot cycle has ever been devised.

CRYOGENIC POWER CYCLE

The use of liquid hydrogen offers some unusual advantages for space power generation. Since nearly all the electrical energy generated in a spacecraft appears ultimately as thermal energy, some means for cooling electrical components must be provided. This thermal energy can be used to evaporate the liquid hydrogen and warm the gas thereby contributing to the generation of power in the power cycle illustrated in Fig. 3-26. Here liquid hydrogen is delivered from a cryogenic container at a pressure of 200 psia. Warm hydrogen is passed through a heat exchanger immersed in the liquid hydrogen to evaporate sufficient liquid and maintain this pressure in the container. The liquid hydrogen then flows into a regenerator where evaporation and preheating takes place along line a–b. The heat for this process is supplied by the turbine exhaust which is cooled along line i–j in the regenerator. After the pressure is reduced by expansion through a regulating valve (b–c), the gas is circulated over electrical equipment. Also part of the hydrogen is passed through the heat exchanger in the cryogenic container. At point e in the cycle, the hydrogen temperature may be some 130 °F. Then a fraction of the hydrogen is catalytically oxidized to supply heat to a heat exchanger for raising the temperature of the remaining hydrogen to 300 °F. The water vapor produced in the catalytic combustion is discharged into space from the heat exchanger. The hydrogen can be expanded through a turbine to an intermediate pressure at point *g*. There may be

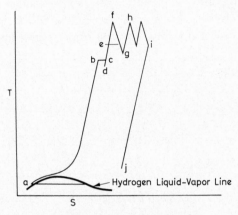

Fig. 3-26   Cryogenic power cycle.

several stages of reheating by catalytic combustion of additional hydrogen and expansion through turbines until the final stage exhaust pressure as low as 0.15 psia may be reached. Then as already discussed, the exhaust from the final turbine stage passes to the regenerator where the gas temperature is reduced to *j* before discharge overboard.

TABLE 3-5   DESIGN OBJECTIVES FOR SUNDSTRAND CRYOGENIC POWER CYCLE

Power	8 hp (shaft)
Specific fuel rate	1.5 lb/hp-hr
Design life	1000 hr
Environment	zero gravity in space
Maximum cycle temperature	300 °F
Turbine staging	four-stage, single-disc re-entry turbine

A power system based upon this cryogenic power cycle has been studied by the Sundstrand Corporation and the design objectives are listed in Table 3-5. Although the theoretical efficiency of this cycle is high, the equipment is complicated and the control problem is difficult.

HYDROGEN RECIPROCATING ENGINE

Positive displacement engines for auxiliary power units have the desirable characteristic of efficient operation even in small engines and at part-load conditions. An internal combustion engine burning hydrogen and oxygen (hydrox) is shown in Fig. 3-27. This engine developed by Vickers Incorporated operates on a

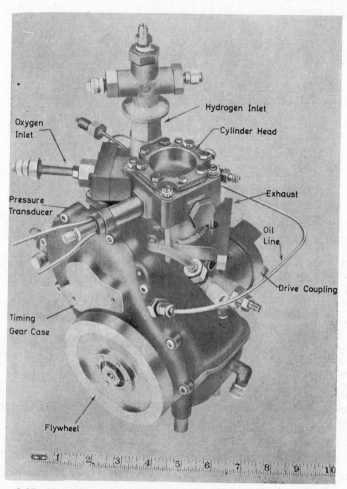

FIG. 3-27 Hydrogen-oxygen internal-combustion engine with oxygen injection (Vickers Incorporated).

regenerative cycle in which cryogenic hydrogen and oxygen are heated by the exhaust prior to admission to the engine to improve thermal efficiency. The propellants are supplied to the engine with a hydrogen pressure of 300 psia and an oxygen pressure of 800 psia. The hydrogen is admitted to the cylinder while the piston is at top dead center and during the first few degrees of the down stroke. Oxygen is injected into the cylinder near the end of the hydrogen admission with combustion and some thermal

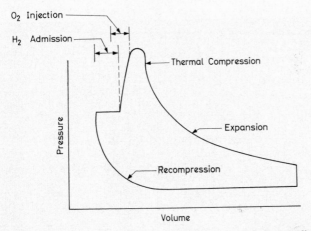

FIG. 3-28   Hydrogen–oxygen internal-combustion engine indicator diagram (Vickers Incorporated).

compression occurring when the oxygen is injected. This is followed by expansion as the piston completes its downward stroke. When the piston nears bottom dead center, the exhaust ports are uncovered by the piston and exhaust blowdown occurs. Any residual gas is recompressed when the piston moves upward as shown in the indicator diagram (Fig. 3-28). Combustion can be initiated by a spark or catalytic ignition system. The engine is cooled by circulating a glycol-type fluid through a closed system consisting of the engine cooling jacket, a heat exchanger and the engine driven coolant pump. Other equipment also can be cooled by this fluid and the heat transferred to the incoming hydrogen in a heat exchanger.

TURBINES

Steam turbines and aircraft gas turbines are highly developed, reliable, efficient devices for converting thermal energy into the mechanical energy of a high-speed rotating shaft. These are axial-flow turbines; however, other turbine types for which applications have never been found are being restudied and appear advantageous for the unusual operating conditions in some auxiliary power units. Turbines are classified according to the principal direction

FIG. 3-29 Aircraft turbine wheel with hollow air-cooled blades (Allison).

of fluid flow: axial, radial, and tangential. The first two correspond to axial-flow and centrifugal compressors with the direction
of flow reversed. The tangential-flow turbine is of possible interest
at very low pressures.

The working fluid enters an axial-flow turbine through nozzles
for expansion to a high velocity. The gas jets impinge on the
turbine blades attached to the rotor. In flowing through the
channels between the blades, the change in direction of flow
produces an impulse force on the blades. Also the channels
between the blades may be shaped to form nozzles for further
expansion of the gas to add a reaction force on the blades from

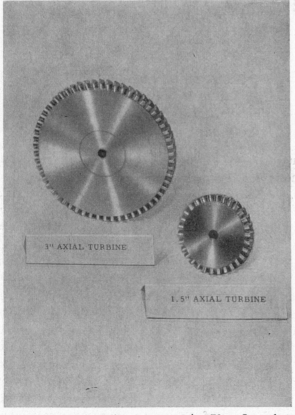

FIG. 3-30   Turbines for auxiliary power units (Varo Inc. photograph).

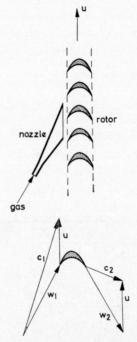

FIG. 3-31   Turbine velocity diagram.

this increase in gas velocity. There may be several sets of stationary and rotating blades for expanding and redirecting the gas in
stages. Turbines are classified as impulse or reaction according
to the amount of expansion taking place in the stator or rotor
blades; however, many turbine designs utilize both principles.
Figure 3-31 is the flow-vector diagram for a single-stage impulse
turbine. Here the gas is expanded through the stationary nozzle
to the velocity c_1 and strikes the rotor blade that is moving with a
velocity u. To minimize losses, the vector sum of these two
velocities, w_1, is tangential to the edge of the rotor blade at the
design operating conditions. In passing through the curved channel between the blades, the gas stream is changed in direction,
leaving the rotor with a velocity w_2 relative to the blade. The
vector difference between the velocity w_2 and the rotor velocity u
is the velocity c_2 relative to the stator. The force on the blades is
the rate of change of momentum of the gas stream along the

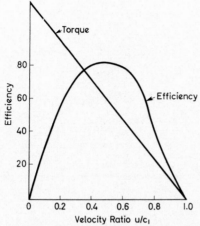

Fig. 3-32   Efficiency and torque as a function of velocity ratio.

direction of rotor motion; this is the product of the mass flow rate and the tangential velocity change.

The efficiency of a turbine is a function of the ratio of the blade velocity u to the spouting velocity c_1; the efficiency is at a maximum when the blade velocity is about half the spouting velocity (Fig. 3-32). However, the torque of a turbine is maximum when the rotor is stationary. The torque decreases about linearly with this velocity ratio and approaches zero as the velocity of the rotor approaches the spouting velocity. When the available energy per unit mass of working fluid is large, the spouting velocity is high. Then the turbine speed may be limited by stress factors to a region ($u/c_1 < 0.2$) where the efficiency is low. To avoid the losses at this low velocity ratio, multiple stage turbines can be used. In velocity staging (Fig. 3-33) all the enthalpy drop is taken in the first stage stator nozzles; but using two or more wheels will allow the tip speed to be reduced, since some of the energy that would have been lost at the exit of a single-stage turbine will be recovered in the other stages. When pressure staging is used, the enthalpy drop in each stage is a fraction of the overall enthalpy drop for the turbine. Then the velocity ratio can be maintained near the point of maximum efficiency. However, there are additional losses from fluid friction in gas flowing through more than

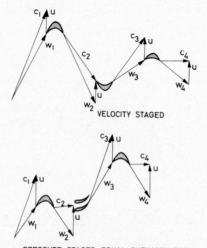

VELOCITY STAGED

PRESSURE STAGED—EQUAL ENTHALPY DROP

FIG. 3-33   Velocity diagrams for staged turbines. Reproduced from WADD TR 60-699, Vol. III, "Dynamic Thermal Converters", by C. W. Stephens, R. Spies and W. R. Menetrey, Electro-Optical Systems.

one row of blades. As a result, the peak efficiency of multiple-stage turbines may be less than that of single-stage units.

Radial-flow turbines have the gas introduced at the rim of the impeller and ducted radially inward to the center where the gas leaves the wheel along the axis of rotation. Inward flow is used to prevent flow separation from the blades. Because the radial flow turbine operates efficiently over a wide range of flow rates, this type of machine may be preferred where efficient operation is required at part load.

The tangential-flow turbine (Fig. 3-34) is of interest for low flow rates where the available energy is large. It also operates well at low pressures. None of the other types of turbines are efficient under these conditions. In the simplest design of the tangential-flow turbine, the fluid moves around the periphery of the turbine case to emerge from a port approximately 300 degrees from the inlet. A block seal separates the inlet and outlet. In flowing around the periphery of the case, the gas exerts a drag on the turbine wheel and the torque is determined by the velocity of the gas relative to the rotor. A particle of gas exchanges momentum with the wheel many times so that the turbine is, in effect, pressure staged. This type of turbine has been proposed for use with wet vapor since the droplets would be centrifuged out to the case for removal.

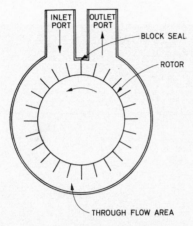

FIG. 3-34   Schematic of tangential-flow turbine. Reproduced from WADD TR 60–699, Vol. III, "Dynamic Thermal Converters", by C. W. Stephens, R. Spies and W. R. Menetrey, Electro-Optical Systems.

TURBINE COMPONENTS

The development of a new type of turbine has been found to be a long and difficult task even though the theory of turbine operation is reasonably well understood. Many of the problems come from components such as seals and bearing required to operate under unusual conditions. For example in space applications of long duration it is essential that leakage through seals on shafts be eliminated completely. This can be done by placing the electrical generator within the engine housing with only wires passing through the walls of the power unit. However within the housing, seals may be required to separate the lubricant from the working fluid. These seals may include labrinth seals for high speed shafts where the allowable speed of rubbing surfaces does not permit the use of face or packed shaft seals.

Fig. 3-35 Gauging the seal diameter of a compressor rotor (Allison).

In reaction turbine staging there is a pressure difference across the rotor and some fluid will leak over the blade tips. This leakage will be small, if the ratio of the tip clearance to the blade height is less than 0.02. Thus, if the blade height for a small turbine is 0.25 in., the tip clearance must be limited to 0.005 in. This radial clearance is difficult both to predict and to maintain, because the turbine wheel expands as its temperature rises during startup, and because the diameter gradually increases as a result of creep. This problem of tip clearance is sometimes handled by shrouding the blade tips; another method is to use a honeycomb material around the periphery of the wheel so that the blades cut their own channel without damage. Axial clearances are usually not a major problem since there is less wheel growth in that direction.

Precision ball bearings are customarily used in high-speed auxiliary power units. These bearings require some lubrication primarily for cooling since heat is produced by deformation energy being converted to heat as each ball in the bearing picks up and releases the load. The reliability of the bearing depends upon the care exercised in selection and inspection of the balls and retainers. Journal bearings are not subject to this type of fatigue; and, if the bearing operates in the hydrodynamic regime

FIG. 3-36   Solid propellant auxiliary power unit (Varo Inc. photograph).

wear is prevented by a thin film of lubricant that separates the shaft from the journal. Journal bearings may encounter trouble on startup and as loads are changed during the acceleration periods of a spacecraft. Journal bearings may be lubricated with the working fluid and mercury-lubricated bearings with long operating life have been developed for nuclear space power systems.

GAS TURBINE AUXILIARY POWER UNITS

The pressurized hot gases produced by the burning of a solid or liquid propellant in a confined space can be used to drive a turbine. Auxiliary power units of this type are used in missiles requiring large amounts of power for guidance and control but only for a short duration. Generators and hydraulic pumps can be driven by the turbine to power electronic equipment and control actuators. Solid propellent gas generators have mechanical simplicity since no pumps or flow controls are required. However, for long durations, the weight of the combustion chamber makes these units heavier than the more complicated liquid propellent systems.

High energy propellants (such as double base powder or nitric acid with hydrocarbon fuel) produce combustion products at temperatures far above those allowable for uncooled turbines operating for more than a few seconds. Special formulations of solid propellants and lower energy liquid propellants have been developed for auxiliary power units with maximum combustion temperatures below 1800 °F. Liquid monopropellants including hydrazine, ethylene oxide, propyl nitrate and hydrogen peroxide have been used successfully in gas generators. With some bipropellants, the combustion temperature can be reduced to the required level by operating with a fuel-rich mixture. Hydrogen and oxygen can be used in this manner for power generation and several stages of partial combustion can be used before the gas is discharged overboard.

The specific fuel consumption of auxiliary power units with two-stage turbines operating on hydrazine as a monopropellant and on hydrogen–oxygen with combustion products at 1800 °F is shown in Table 3-6. The pressure ratio across the turbines was 150 : 1, and their efficiencies varied from 30 percent for the hydrogen–oxygen units to 55 percent for those using hydrazine. (Note that the specific fuel consumption decreases for the larger units.)

TABLE 3-6   APU SPECIFIC FUEL CONSUMPTION

Horsepower	Hydrogen–Oxygen	Hydrazine
5	3.0 lb/hp-hr	6.4 lb/hp-hr
10	2.6	5.7
20	2.0	4.8
40	2.0	4.6

The major components of a liquid-propellant auxiliary power unit (APU) may include propellent storage tanks with helium pressurization, control valves, combustion chamber, turbine, governor, alternator and hydraulic pump. If the liquid propellant is used also as a heat sink for thermal control of other equipment such as electronic devices, a secondary coolant, usually nitrogen, may be circulated by a blower and cooled in a heat exchanger by the liquid propellant. Although the system may have many components, experience has shown that liquid-propellant auxiliary power units can be reliable.

REFERENCES

1. J. H. KEENAN and J. KAYE, *Gas Tables*, John Wiley, 1948.
2. W. N. BARNARD, F. O. ELLENWOOD and C. F. HIRSHFELD, *Elements of Heat-Power Power Engineering*, New York, John Wiley, 1926.
3. J. H. KEENAN and F. G. KEYES, *Thermodynamic Properties of Steam*, New York, John Wiley, 1937.
4. E. T. VINCENT, *The Theory and Design of Gas Turbines and Jet Engines*, New York, McGraw-Hill, 1950.
5. G. P. SUTTON, *Rocket Propulsion Elements*, New York, John Wiley, 1949.
6. M. J. ZUCROW, *Principles of Jet Propulsion and Gas Turbines*, New York, John Wiley, 1948.
7. J. F. LEE and F. W. SEARS, *Thermodynamics*, Reading, Mass., Addison-Wesley, 1955.
8. V. M. FAIRES, *Thermodynamics*, New York, Macmillan, 1957.

CHAPTER 4

CHEMICAL ENERGY

INTRODUCTION

Sufficient fuel has been stored by natural processes in coal, oil and gas reserves to meet most energy requirements at present. In addition, other chemical fuels such as hydrogen can be made to store energy for special purposes such as for rapid release of energy in a rocket motor. The chemical energy stored in a battery can be released in electrochemical reactions. Similar processes are utilized in fuel cells for direct energy conversion with high efficiency at moderate temperatures. Thus the chemical energy stored in fuels can be released by combustion to produce thermal energy for power generation or the chemical energy can be released by electrochemical processes directly yielding electrical energy.

Chemical energy is a part of the potential internal energy of molecules, and is associated with molecular and atomic structure. Thermochemistry describes the energy changes accompanying chemical reactions. This science provides a systematic procedure for writing chemical equations including the changes in enthalpy and free energy. The thermochemistry of combustion and electrochemical processes will be considered in this chapter.

HEAT OF REACTION

Chemical processes are accompanied by the release (exothermic reaction) or absorption (endothermic reaction) of energy usually as thermal energy. However, in electrochemical processes, electrical energy may be released or absorbed with only small thermal effects.

Thermochemical equations include the chemical reaction and resulting changes in enthalpy or free energy for the reactants and products in their indicated states, as

$$H_2(g) + \tfrac{1}{2}O_2(g) = H_2O \text{ (l)} \quad \Delta H° = -68.317 \text{ kg-cal/g-mole}$$

Unless otherwise indicated, the reactants and products are at a pressure of one atmosphere and some standard temperature, $T°$, such as 298 °K. In the thermochemical equation above, energy has been released (exothermic) since the enthalpy of the product is less than that of the reactants.

When the heat of reaction is measured in an open calorimeter at constant pressure and otherwise at standard conditions, the standard enthalpy change is

$$\Delta H_p = \Delta H°$$

When the heat of reaction is measured in a closed vessel such as a combustion bomb calorimeter at constant volume, the change in internal energy, $\Delta U°$, is determined since

$$\Delta H_v = \Delta U°$$

These values are related by

$$\Delta H° = \Delta U° + p\Delta V$$

Where only condensed phases (liquids and solids) are involved, the difference between the values of the enthalpy and internal energy changes is very small and may be neglected. For gaseous reactants and products, the values of $p\Delta V$, assuming an ideal gas, is

$$p\Delta V = \Delta n R T°$$

The value of Δn is the net increase in the number of moles of gaseous products.

Nearly two centuries ago studies of heats of reactions led to the conclusion that the energy required to decompose a compound into its elements exactly equals the negative of the energy required in forming the compound from its elements. Later it was established that the amount of energy associated with the formation of a compound from its elements is the same whether the reaction takes place in a single step or in a series of steps. By writing the chemical equations with notations for the state of each material (s—solid; l—liquid; g—gas) and giving the corresponding standard heats of reactions, a systematic procedure of adding and subtracting reactions has been established. For example, the combustion of carbon to produce carbon dioxide can be written in steps, and these can be added as follows:

$$C(s) \ + \tfrac{1}{2}O_2(g) = CO(g) \qquad \Delta H° = -26.416 \text{ kg-cal/g-mole}$$
$$\underline{CO(g) + \tfrac{1}{2}O_2(g) = CO_2(g) \qquad \Delta H° = -67.636 \hspace{3.8cm}}$$
$$C(s) \ + \ O_2(g) = CO_2(g) \qquad \Delta H° = -94.052 \text{ kg-cal/g-mole}$$

Most of the thermochemical data that are available in the literature are in units of kg-cal/g-mole. These units can be converted to Btu/lb-mole by multiplication by 1800. Care must be used in selecting consistent values preferably from only one table, since the heat of reaction may be the small difference between large numbers. Also values are given sometimes at different reference temperatures. In most thermochemical calculations it is not necessary to know the absolute values of the enthalpy, since only the change from some standard reference state is required.

The standard heats of formation of selected compounds are given in Tables 4-1 and 4-2. (Additional data can be found in Ref. 4-1.) In these tables, the standard state is the pure substance in its thermodynamically stable form at a temperature of 25 °C and a pressure of 1 atm. The values of zero are assigned to the elements in their standard state. Although in forming compounds, these elements may not react at a rate suitable for calorimetric measurements, the heat of formation can be obtained by adding and subtracting the reactions that lead to the end product. In this way, consistent tables of heats of formation have been built up.

These values of the heat of formation are particularly useful for calculating the energy change associated with other chemical reactions. A convenient procedure for determining the heat fo reaction can be established by first writing the chemical equation for the reaction including a designation for the state of each material. Below each reactant and each product is entered the value of its heat of formation multiplied by the number of moles that are indicated in the balanced chemical equation (elements in their standard state are assigned the value of zero, as noted previously). Since the enthalpy change is defined as heat added to the system, an energy balance relative to the elements from which all the reactants and products were formed can be made by adding the enthalpy change $\Delta H°$ to the reactant side of the equation. This value can then be found by simple arithmetic.

EXAMPLE 4-1. Calculate the heat of reaction of methyl alcohol with oxygen at 25 °C and 1 atm of pressure.

Solution: The standard heats of formation are found in the tables and values for the reactants and products and are entered below the chemical equation with the values of the enthalpy change $\Delta H°$ treated as a heat addition on the reactant side.

$$CH_3OH(l) + \frac{3}{2} O_2(g) = CO_2(g) + 2H_2O(l)$$

$$\Delta H° + (-57.02) + 0 = (-94.05) + 2(-68.32)$$
$$\Delta H° = -173.67 \text{ kg-cal/g-mole of methyl alcohol}$$

$$\frac{-173.67 \times 1800}{32} = -9769 \text{ Btu/lb}$$

Therefore the combustion of methyl alcohol releases 9769 Btu per pound of fue under standard conditions.

Many chemical reactions take place in solution, or one or more reactants or products may be in the form of a solution. Therefore, values are given of the heats of formation of materials either dissolved in water at infinite dilution or at some specified concentration. Since the solution and dilution of such materials as the strong acids involve the exchange of considerable thermal energy, the values of their heats of formation may differ appreciably from values for the undissolved materials. The energy associated with dilution usually increases with the amount of solvent until additional dilution produces no further effect. For this reason, the

TABLE 4-1 CHEMICAL THERMODYNAMIC PROPERTIES OF
INORGANIC COMPOUNDS*

(Standard state 1 atm at 25 °C)

Compound	Formula	State	ΔH_f° kg-cal/ g-mole	ΔG_f° kg-cal/ g-mole	C_p° cal/°C g-mole
Aluminium	Al	c	0.000	0.000	5.817
Aluminium oxide	Al_2O_3,	c	−399.09	−376.77	18.88
Ammonia	NH_3	g	−11.04	−3.976	8.523
Ammonium nitrate	NH_4NO_3	c	−87.27		43.5
Ammonium perchlorate	NH_4ClO_4	c	−69.42		
Argon	A	g	0.000	0.000	4.968
Beryllium	Be	c	0.000	0.000	4.26
Beryllium oxide	BeO	c	−146.0	−139.0	6.07
Boron	B	c	0.000	0.000	2.86
Boron oxide	B_2O_3	c	−302.0	−283.0	14.88
Cadmium	Cd	c	0.000	0.000	6.19
Cadmium hydroxide	$Cd(OH)_2$	c	−133.26	−122.46	
Cadmium oxide	CdO	c	−60.86	−53.79	10.38
Calcium carbide	CaC_2	c	−15.0	−16.2	14.90
Calcium carbonate	$CaCO_3$	c	−288.45	−269.78	19.57
Calcium hydroxide	$Ca(OH)_2$	c	−235.80	−214.33	20.2
Calcium oxide	CaO	c	−151.9	−144.4	10.23
Carbon (graphite)	C	c	0.000	0.000	2.066
Carbonate ion	CO_3	aq	−161.63	−126.22	
Carbon dioxide	CO_2	g	−94.0518	−94.2598	8.874
Carbon disulfide	CS_2	liq	21.0	15.2	18.1
Carbon monoxide	CO	g	−26.4157	−32.8075	6.965
Carbonic acid	H_2CO_3	aq	−167.0	−149.00	
Chlorine	Cl_2	g	0.000	0.000	8.11
Chlorine trifluoride	ClF_3	g	−37.0	−27.2	15.33
Chromic oxide	CrO_3	c	−138.4		
Copper	Cu	c	0.000	0.000	5.848
Copper chloride	CuCl	c	−32.2	−28.4	
Copper chloride	$CuCl_2$	c	−49.2		
Fluorine	F_2	g	0.000	0.000	7.52
Helium	He	g	0.000	0.000	4.9680
Hydrogen	H_2	g	0.000	0.000	6.892
Hydrogen (atom)	H	g	52.089	48.575	4.968
Hydrogen bromide	HBr	g	−8.66	−12.72	6.96

* National Bureau of Standards, *Selected Values of Chemical Thermo-dynamic Properties*, by F. D. Rossini, D. D. Wagman, W. H. Evans, S. Levine and I. Jaffe, NBS Circular 500, Washington, D.C., 1 Feb., 1952.

TABLE 4-1 (cont.)

Compound	Formula	State	ΔH_f° kg-cal/ g-mole	ΔG_f° kg-cal/ g-mole	C_p° cal/°C g-mole
Hydrogen chloride	HCl	g	−22.063	−22.769	6.96
Hydrogen fluoride	HF	g	−64.2	−64.7	6.95
Hydrogen cyanide	HCN	liq	31.2	28.7	8.58
Hydrogen oxide	H_2O	g	−57.7979	−54.6357	8.025
		liq	−68.3174	−56.6902	17.996
Hydrogen peroxide	H_2O_2	liq	−44.84		
		in 1 H_2O	−45.43		
Hydroxyl	OH	g	10.06	8.93	7.141
Hydrazine	N_2H_4	liq	12.05		
Hydrazine hydrate	N_2H_4 · H_2O	liq	−57.95		
Iodine	I_2	c	0.000	0.000	13.14
Iron	Fe	c	0.000	0.000	6.13
Iron oxide	Fe_2O_3	c	−196.5	−177.1	25
Iron oxide	Fe_3O_4	c	−267.0	−242.4	
Lead	Pb	c	0.000	0.000	4.968
Lead oxide	PbO_2	c	−66.12	−52.34	15.4
Lead sulfate	$PbSO_4$	c	−219.50	−193.89	24.9
Lithium	Li	c	0.000	0.000	5.65
Lithium oxide	Li_2O	c	−142.4		
Lithium chloride	LiCl	c	−97.70		
Lithium hydride	LiH	c	−21.6	−16.7	7.06
Lithium fluoride	LiF	c	−146.3	−139.6	10.04
Lithium nitride	Li_3N	c	−47.2		
Magnesium	Mg	c	0.000	0.000	5.71
Magnesium chloride	$MgCl_2$	c	−153.40	−141.57	17.04
Magnesium oxide	MgO	c	−143.84	−136.13	8.94
Manganese oxide	MnO	c	−92.0	−86.8	10.27
Manganese dioxide	MnO_2	c	−124.5	−111.4	12.91
Mercury	Hg	liq	0.000	0.000	6.65
Mercuric oxide	HgO (red)	c	−21.68	−13.990	10.93
Mercurous oxide	Hg_2O	c	−21.8		
Neon	Ne	g	0.000	0.000	4.9680
Nickel	Ni	c	0.000	0.000	6.21
Nickel hydroxide	$Ni(OH)_2$	c	−128.6	−108.3	
Nickel hydroxide	$Ni(OH)_3$	c	−162.1		
Nickel oxide	NiO	c	−58.4	−51.7	10.60
Nitric acid	HNO_3	liq	−41.404	−19.100	26.26
Nitric oxide	NO	g	21.600	20.719	7.137
Nitrogen dioxide	NO_2	g	8.091	12.390	9.06
Nitrogen tetroxide	N_2O_4	g	2.309	23.491	18.90

TABLE 4-1 (cont.)

Compound	Formula	State	ΔH_f° kg-cal/ g-mole	ΔG_f° kg-cal/ g-mole	C_p° cal/°C g-mole
Nitrous oxide	N_2O	g	19.49	24.76	9.251
Oxygen	O_2	g	0.000	0.000	7.017
Ozone	O_3	g	34.0	39.06	9.12
Phosphorus	P_2	g	33.82	24.60	7.63
Phosphoric acid	H_3PO_4	c	−306.2		
Phosphoric oxide	P_4O_{10}	c	−720.0		
Potassium	K	c	0.000	0.000	6.97
Potassium bromide	KBr	c	−93.73	−90.63	12.82
Potassium chlorate	$KClO_3$	c	−93.50	−69.29	23.96
Potassium chloride	KCl	c	−104.175	−97.592	12.31
Potassium fluoride	KF	c	−134.46	−127.42	11.73
Potassium hydroxide	KOH	c	−101.78		
		in oc H_2O	−115.00		
Potassium oxide	K_2O	c	−86.4		
Potassium perchlorate	$KClO_4$	c	−103.6	−72.7	26.33
Silicon	Si	c	0.000	0.000	5.318
Silicon carbide	SiC	c	−26.7	−26.1	6.37
Silicon tetrafluoride	SiF_4	g	−370	−360	18.2
Silicon oxide	SiO_2 (quartz)	c	−205.4	−192.4	10.62
Silver chloride	AgCl	c	−30.362	−26.224	12.14
Silver oxide	Ag_2O	c	−7.306	−2.586	15.67
Silver oxide	Ag_2O_2	c	−6.3		
Sodium	Na	c	0.000	0.000	6.79
Sodium bromide	NaBr	c	−86.030		
Sodium chloride	NaCl	c	−98.232	−91.785	11.88
Sodium fluoride	NaF	c	−136.0	−129.3	11.0
Sodium hydroxide	NaOH	c	−101.99		
		in oc H_2O	−112.236		
Sodium hydride	NaH	c	−13.7		
Sodium nitrate	$NaNO_3$	c	−111.54	−87.45	22.24
Sodium oxide	Na_2O	c	−99.4	−90.0	16.3
Sodium sulfate	Na_2SO_4	c	−330.90	−302.78	30.50
		in oc H_2O	−331.46		
Sulfur dioxide	SO_2	g	−70.96	−71.79	9.51
Sulfur trioxide	SO_3	g	−94.45	−88.52	12.10
Sulfuric acid	H_2SO_4	liq	−193.91		32.88
		in oc H_2O	−216.90		
Tin oxide	SnO	c	−68.4	−61.5	10.6

TABLE 4-1 (cont.)

Compound	Formula	State	ΔH_f° kg-cal/ g-mole	ΔG_f° kg-cal/ g-mole	C_p° cal/°C g-mole
Tin oxide	SnO_2	c	−138.8	−124.2	12.57
Titanium	Ti	c	0.000	0.000	6.010
Titanium chloride	$TiCl_4$	liq	−179.3	−161.2	37.5
Titanium oxide	TiO_2	c	−218.0	−203.8	13.16
Uranium fluoride	UF_6	c	−517	−486	
Uranium oxide	UO_2	c	−270	−257	
Vanadium oxide	V_2O_5	c	−370.71	−373	31.00
Vanadium oxide	V_2O_4	c	−341.94	−344	28.30
Vanadium oxide	V_2O_3	c	−290	−271	24.83
Zinc	Zn	c	0.000	0.000	5.99
Zinc chloride	$ZnCl_2$	c	−99.40	−88.255	18.3
Zinc hydroxide	$Zn(OH)_2$	c	−153.5		
Zinc oxide	ZnO	c	−83.17	−76.05	9.62
Zirconium	Zr	c	0.000	0.000	6.3624
Zirconium oxide	ZrO_2	c	−258.2	−244.2	

standard state for solutions may be taken as an infinitely dilute solution.

EXAMPLE 4-2. Using the heat of formation data, determine the heat of solution of sodium hydroxide.

Solution: Following the outlined procedure, heat of formation values are inserted below the chemical equation

$$NaOH(s) \rightarrow NaOH(\infty \text{ sol})$$
$$\Delta H^\circ + (-101.99) = (-112.24)$$
$$\Delta H^\circ = -10.25 \text{ kg-cal/g-mole}$$

This quantity of thermal energy is released when a gram-mole of sodium hydroxide is dissolved in water to make a very dilute solution. Since this amount of thermal energy is large, there is some danger in the addition of water to sodium hydroxide.

Thermochemical data for organic materials may be expressed as the heat of combustion—the amount of heat evolved through combustion with pure oxygen resulting in completely oxidized

TABLE 4-2   CHEMICAL THERMODYNAMIC PROPERTIES OF ORGANIC
COMPOUNDS*

(Standard state 1 atm at 25 °C)

Compound	Formula	State	ΔH_f° kg-cal/ g-mole	ΔG_f° kg-cal/ g-mole	C_p° cal/°C g-mole
Acetaldehyde	C_2H_4O	g	−39.76	−31.96	15.0
		in 50 H_2O	−49.88		
Acetic acid	$C_2H_4O_2$	liq	−116.4	−93.8	29.5
		in oc H_2O	−116.743		
Acetamide	C_2H_5ON	c	−76.60		15.9
Acetylene	C_2H_2	g	54.194	50.000	10.499
Ethane	C_2H_6	g	−20.236	−7.860	12.585
Ethanol (Ethyl alcohol)	C_2H_6O	liq	−66.356	−41.77	26.64
Ethylene	C_2H_4	g	12.496	16.282	10.41
Ethylene oxide	C_2H_4O	g	−12.19	−2.79	11.5
Ethyl nitrate	$C_2H_5O_3N$	liq	−44.3		
Formaldehyde	CH_2O	g	−27.7	−26.3	8.45
Formic acid	CH_2O_2	liq	−97.8	−82.7	23.67
Methane	CH_4	g	−17.889	−12.140	8.536
Methanol (Methyl alcohol)	CH_3OH	liq	−57.02	−39.73	19.5
Nitromethane	CH_5O_2N	liq	−21.28	2.26	25.3
Oxalic acid	$C_2H_2O_4$	c	−197.6	−166.8	26
Urea	CH_4ON_2	c	−79.634	−47.120	22.26

* National Bureau of Standards, *Selected Values of Chemical Thermodynamic Properties*, by F. D. Rossini, D. D. Wagman, W. H. Evans, S. Levine, and I. Jaffe, NBS Circular 500, Washington, D.C., 1. Feb., 1952.

products including carbon dioxide and liquid water. The heat of combustion is defined as the heat evolved and, therefore, it is the negative of the enthalpy change or the value of ΔH°. This change in sign between various tables in the literature is unfortunate and special attention is required to avoid errors in using such data. Also, it should be noted that the standard heat of combustion is determined with liquid water as one of the products, although most combustion processes result in the discharge of water vapor without recovery of its latent heat of vaporization. Therefore, the *lower heat of combustion* is sometimes used and it is defined in terms of water vapor as one of the products. The heat of combustion, higher or lower, can be used directly in process calculations or to compute the heat of formation.

EXAMPLE 4-3. Calculate the power of an engine burning 2 pounds of methyl alcohol per hour. The thermal efficiency of the engine, based on the lower heat of combustion, is 20 percent.

Solution: Using values from Tables 4-1 and 4-2, the lower heat of combustion is found; and from this value, converted to horsepower hours per pound of fuel, the power output of a 20 percent efficient engine is found

$$CH_3OH(l) + \frac{3}{2}O_2(g) \rightarrow CO_2(g) + 2H_2O(g)$$

$$\Delta H^\circ + (-57.02) + O = (-94.05) + 2(-57.80)$$

$$\Delta H^\circ = -152.63 \text{ kg-cal/g-mole}$$

$$\frac{152.63 \times 0.7071}{32} = 3.37 \text{ hp-hr/lb}$$

$$3.37 \times 2 \times 0.20 = 1.35 \text{ hp}$$

HIGH TEMPERATURE REACTIONS

Most processes of interest to power production take place at elevated temperatures, usually far above the reference temperature for the standard heat of reaction data; therefore , it may be necessary to obtain values of the heat of reaction as a function of temperature. This problem is complicated by changes in the composition of the reaction products at elevated temperatures. First the methods for calculating the heat of reaction as a function of temperature from thermal data for known products will be illustrated. Later the changes in chemical equilibrium with temperature will be considered.

When the reactants and products each have a different temperature and state, with an enthalpy greater or less than for the standard conditions, a simple energy balance can be written with reference to the elements from which each material is formed.

The values of the standard heats of formation are used. The enthalpies of the reactants relative to the standard state are added to the standard heat of formation values and the enthalpy change ΔH°. This is by definition energy added to the system. The enthalpies of the products relative to the standard state are added to the values of the heat of formation on the product side of the equation. For the reaction

$$a\text{A} + b\text{B} = c\text{C} + d\text{D}$$

where $\Delta H^\circ_{f\text{A}}$ is the standard heat of formation of A, and ΔH_A is the enthalpy of this reactant above the standard state, the energy balance becomes

$$\Delta H_t + a\Delta H^\circ_{f\text{A}} + a\Delta H_\text{A} + b\Delta H^\circ_{f\text{B}} + b\Delta H_\text{B} =$$
$$= c\Delta H^\circ_{f\text{C}} + c\Delta H_\text{C} + d\Delta H^\circ_{f\text{D}} + d\Delta H_\text{D}$$

The standard heat of reaction ΔH° is given by

$$\Delta H^\circ = c\Delta H^\circ_{f\text{C}} + d\Delta H^\circ_{f\text{D}} - a\Delta H^\circ_{f\text{A}} - b\Delta H^\circ_{f\text{B}}$$

Designating the enthalpy of the reactants and products above the reference state by

$$\sum H_\text{R} = a\Delta H_\text{A} + b\Delta H_\text{B}$$
$$\sum H_\text{P} = c\Delta H_\text{C} + d\Delta H_\text{D}$$

then the energy balance can be written in the form

$$\Delta H_t = \Delta H^\circ + \sum H_\text{P} - \sum H_\text{R}$$

When other materials, such as nitrogen from the air for the combustion of a fuel, may be present during the reaction but do not enter into the chemical reaction, the heat of formation values for these inert materials need not be included; however their initial and final enthalpies above the reference state are essential in accounting for the total energy as a function of temperature.

EXAMPLE 4-4. Calculate the energy released by the combustion of methyl alcohol at 50 °C with oxygen at atmospheric pressure and 200 °C to produce carbon dioxide and water vapor with these products of combustion at 500 °C.

Solution: The heat of combustion of methyl alcohol at 25 °C with water vapor as a product, $\Delta H°$, was found in Example 4-3 to be -152.63 kg-cal/g-mole. The heat capacity of methyl alcohol is found in Table 4-2 to be 19.5 cal/g-mole. Then the enthalpy at 50 °C relative to 25 °C is

$$\Delta H = \frac{(50-25)}{1000} \times 19.5 = 0.487 \text{ kg-cal/g-mole}$$

The enthalpy of oxygen at 200 °C (392 °F) relative to 25 °C (77 °F) is found in Table 2-3 by interpolation to be

$$\Delta H = 5980.9 - 3723.0 = 2257.9 \text{ Btu/lb-mole}$$

$$\frac{2257.9}{1800} = 1.254 \text{ kg-cal/g-mole}$$

For the chemical reaction written in the form

$$CH_3OH(1) + \frac{3}{2}O_2(g) = CO_2(g) + 2H_2O(g)$$

the value of $\sum H_R$ is

$$\sum H_R = 0.49 + \frac{3}{2} \times 1.25 = 2.37 \text{ kg-cal/g-mole}$$

Similarly the enthalpies of the products at 500 °C (932 °F) are found from Table 2-3

$$\Delta H_{CO_2} = H_{932°} - H_{77°}$$

$$= 13,243.6 - 4027.7 = 9215.9 \text{ Btu/lb-mole}$$

$$= \frac{9215.9}{1800} = 5.12 \text{ kg-cal/g-mole}$$

$$\Delta H_{H_2O} = 11,548.7 - 4255.9 = 7292.8 \text{ Btu/lb-mole}$$

$$= \frac{7292.8}{1800} = 4.05 \text{ kg-cal/g-mole}$$

Thus the value of $\sum H_P$ becomes

$$\sum H_P = 5.12 + 2 \times 4.05 = 13.22 \text{ kg-cal}$$

The heat of reaction at the elevated temperature is found from the energy balance to be

$$\Delta H_t = \Delta H^\circ + \sum H_P - \sum H_R = -152.63 + 13.22 - 2.37 =$$
$$= -141.8 \text{ kg-cal/g-mole}$$

It is noted that the heat of reaction is reduced for these conditions. Where the reaction products are at a much higher temperature than the reactants, energy from the reaction is required to heat the products to their final temperature.

Usually the internal energy of perfect gases and of solids and liquids can be considered to be almost independent of pressure. Therefore the heat of reaction for most systems in nearly independent of pressure. However, as already mentioned, there is a difference between the heats of reaction at constant volume and constant pressure when a change takes place in the number of gaseous moles.

REACTION TEMPERATURE

The energy released by a chemical reaction either may be absorbed by the reaction products, or a part of this energy may be exchanged with the surroundings as work, electrical energy or thermal energy. Maximum reaction temperatures result for adiabatic processes when all the energy released in the reaction appears as thermal energy in the reaction products. This maximum temperature is the theoretical flame temperature for combustion. The relations just developed for the heat of reaction as a function of temperature permit the calculation of the reaction temperature provided that the necessary thermal data are available, either as enthalpy tables or as heat capacities as a function of temperature in the form

$$C_p = a + bT - cT^{-2} + \ldots$$

These coefficient (a, b and c) can be combined for the reaction products so that their enthalpy above the reference state can be found by the single integration

$$\sum H_P = \int (a' + b'T - c'T^{-2}) \, dT$$

A similar relation for the reactants can be found and combined with the coefficients of the products. A graphical procedure for finding the reaction temperature is usually more convenient than analytical or iteration methods. Values of the functions $\sum H_P - H_R$ and of $-\Delta H^\circ$ can be plotted as functions of temperature. These curves intersect at the reaction temperature since the heat of reaction at this temperature is zero

$$\Delta H_t = 0 = \Delta H^\circ + \sum H_P - \sum H_R$$

Computer programs have been prepared for routine thermo-chemical calculations that require more precision.

FREE ENERGY

The kinetic and potential energies of a mechanical system in theory can be transformed completely into useful work or into other forms of energy, as discussed in Chapter 1. Similarly, electrical energy and other ordered forms of energy are completely available to do useful work. Therefore the kinetic and potential energies of a mechanical system and electrical energy are classed as free energy. However, in a system involving thermal energy the free energy is

$$G = H - TS$$

The change in free energy for a process having the same initial and final temperatures is

$$\Delta G_T = \Delta H - T \Delta S$$

The total work done by a system is the sum of the expansion work, W_e, and others forms of work, W_f, such as electrical work, that the system may do, or

$$W_t = W_e + W_f$$

Expansion work done against the atmosphere is not available as useful work since this energy is expended in pushing back the atmosphere.

From the first law of thermodynamics it follows that for a constant pressure process

$$Q = \Delta U + p\Delta V + W_f = \Delta H + W_f$$

For a reversible process with the same initial and final temperatures

$$Q = T\Delta S = \Delta H + W_f$$

$$-W_f = \Delta H - T\Delta S = \Delta G$$

Thus the decrease in free energy is equal to the useful work done in a reversible process at constant temperature and pressure.

Chemical energy can be converted directly into electrical energy in constant temperature and pressure electrochemical reactions in a fuel cell. The free energy change then establishes the maximum amount of electrical energy that can be produced. The efficiency of an electrochemical process is the ratio of the actual electrical energy to that determined by the change in free energy for a reversible process. Also a criterion of equilibrium in a system at constant temperature and pressure is that the free energy change is zero for any small displacement of the system. Thus values of the chemical equilibrium constants can be obtained from free energy data. This thermodynamic function is useful in many thermochemical calculations.

EXAMPLE 4-5. Calculate the electrical energy produced by the reversible oxidation of 1 lb of hydrogen to liquid water at 25 °C in a fuel cell.

Solution: Following the procedure described previously for calculating the enthalpy changes, the chemical equation and the free energy balance using data from Table 4-1 are written

$$H_2(g) + \tfrac{1}{2}O_2(g) \rightarrow H_2O(l)$$

$$\Delta G + 0 + 0 = -56.69 \text{ kg-cal/g-mole}$$

The electrical energy per pound of hydrogen is

$$\frac{56.69}{2.016} \times 453.6 \times 0.001162 = 14.94 \text{ kWh/lb } H_2$$

EFFECT OF TEMPERATURE ON FREE ENERGY CHANGE

The change of free energy with temperature determines both the change of potential (voltage) with temperature of an electrochemical reaction and the change in composition of products of an equilibrium reaction such as combustion. Since the chemical reactions of interest take place without any temperature difference between the equilibrium materials, the free energy change and its partial derivative (constant pressure) can be written as

$$\Delta G = \Delta H - \Delta(TS) = \Delta H - T\Delta S$$

$$\frac{\Delta G}{T} = \frac{\Delta H}{T} - \Delta S$$

$$\left[\frac{\partial\left(\dfrac{\Delta G}{T}\right)}{\partial T}\right]_p = \left(\frac{1}{T}\frac{\partial \Delta H}{\partial T}\right)_p - \frac{\Delta H}{T^2} - \left(\frac{\partial \Delta S}{\partial T}\right)_p$$

From this and a relation for the enthalpy change at constant pressure

$$\left[\frac{\partial(\Delta H)}{\partial T}\right]_p = T\left[\frac{\partial(\Delta S)}{\partial T}\right]_p$$

the important Gibbs–Helmholz equation is found. Written in terms of the enthalpy change ΔH° and free energy change ΔG° for the standard state, this equation is

$$\left[\frac{\partial\left(\dfrac{\Delta G^\circ}{T}\right)}{\partial T}\right]_p = -\frac{\Delta H^\circ}{T^2}$$

The standard enthalpy change ΔH° is a function of heat capacity. For an individual component this can be written as

$$C_p = a + bT - \frac{c}{T^2}$$

These coefficient (a, b, c) can be combined for the products and reactants. Integration with respect to temperature then gives

$$\Delta H^\circ = C_p dT \int = H' + \Delta aT + \tfrac{1}{2}\Delta bT^2 + \Delta cT^{-1}$$

where H' is an integration constant that can be evaluated from $\Delta H°$ at some temperature where this value is known. Then integration of the function $\dfrac{\Delta H°}{T^2}$ gives

$$\frac{-\Delta G°}{T} = -\frac{H'}{T} + \Delta a \ln T + \tfrac{1}{2}\Delta bT - 2\Delta cT^{-2} + I$$

$$-\Delta G° = -H' + \Delta aT \ln T + \tfrac{1}{2}\Delta bT^2 - 2\Delta cT^{-1} + IT$$

$$\Delta G° = H' + a'T \ln T + b'T^2 + c'T^{-1} + I'T$$

where I is a second integration constant that is evaluated from standard free energy data. The constants (a', b', c') are determined from the heat capacities of the products and reactants. Numerical values for these coefficients are available in the literature for many chemical equilibrium reactions (Refs. 4-8 and 4-9).

EXAMPLE 4-6. Calculate the electrical energy produced by the reversible oxidation of one pound of hydrogen to water vapor in a fuel cell at 800 °K.

Solution: From the above references, the coefficients in the free energy equation as a function of temperature for this reaction are found to be

$$H_2(g) + \tfrac{1}{2}O_2(g) \rightleftharpoons H_2O(g)$$
$$\Delta G = -56,930 + 6.75T \log_{10} T - 0.64 \times 10^{-3}T^2$$
$$-0.08 \times 10^{-5}T^{-1} - 8.74\,T \text{ g-cal/g-mole}$$

At 800 °K the free energy change is then

$$\Delta G = -56,930 + 15,677 - 410 - 10 - 6992 =$$
$$= -48,665 \text{ g-cal/g-mole}$$

The maximum electrical energy per pound of hydrogen is

$$-\Delta G = \frac{48.665}{2.016} \times 453.6 \times 0.001162 = 12.83 \text{ kWh/lb H}_2$$

It is noted that the useful work from this reaction decreases with temperature and conversely the electrical energy required to decompose water and produce hydrogen and oxygen also must decrease with temperature.

FUGACITY

The change of free energy with pressure at constant temperature is

$$\left(\frac{\partial G}{\partial p}\right)_T = V$$

For one mole of a perfect gas compressed isothermally from $p_1 = 1$ atm to a final pressure, p, the free energy change is

$$\Delta G_T = \int_1^p \frac{RT\,dp}{p} = RT \ln p$$

Chemical equilibrium calculations are based upon equations derived from this relation. It is convenient to retain the same relation when the fluid does not behave ideally. Therefore the property called fugacity f, has been defined so that the free energy change at constant temperature for one mole of any gas is

$$\Delta G_T = RT \ln f$$

The fugacity of a gas approaches the pressure in value at reduced pressures and at elevated temperatures. For combustion products at pressures below a few hundred atmospheres and at temperatures above 1000 °C, the assumption of an ideal gas and the use of pressures instead of fugacity values does not produce an error greater than a few percent in equilibrium composition calculations. Methods for estimating fugacity values for actual gases based on the reduced temperature and pressure are presented in Ref. 4-2.

When a liquid and a vapor are in equilibrium (saturated vapor) the fugacity of the liquid equals that of its vapor. At equilibrium there is no free energy change for an incremental change of liquid into vapor or of vapor into liquid. Thus the fugacity of a pure liquid can be determined from the value for its equilibrium vapor.

CHEMICAL EQUILIBRIUM

The calculation of the heat of reaction as a function of temperature requires knowledge of the composition of the reaction products as a function of temperature. For many processes of importance to power generation, such as high temperature combustion, an equilibrium is established between various products. In the hot combustion products of carbon compounds, for example, the reversible water gas reaction establishes an equilibrium between carbon dioxide, hydrogen, carbon monoxide and water vapor. This equilibrium reaction can be written as

$$CO_2 + H_2 \rightleftharpoons CO + H_2O$$

If carbon monoxide and water vapor are present initially with no carbon dioxide or no hydrogen, the reaction will proceed from right to left until the products form an equilibrium mixture. This equilibrium is established during the brief period that the materials are in the combustion zone.

The composition of the equilibrium mixture can be expressed in terms of the partial pressures (the product of the total pressure and mole fraction of each reactant). For the water gas reaction, an equilibrium constant K_p can be defined by the relation

$$K_p = \frac{p_{CO} \times p_{H_2O}}{p_{CO_2} \times p_{H_2}}$$

Here, for example, p_{CO_2} is the partial pressure of carbon dioxide in the equilibrium mixture. The value of the equilibrium constant K_p is independent of the initial composition of the mixture but this constant is a function of temperature. The relations between temperature and the equilibrium constant in terms of the thermodynamic properties of the system will be derived in the following section.

The equilibrium constant is accurately expressed in terms of the fugacities of the reactants and products

$$K_f = \frac{(f_{CO})(f_{H_2O})}{(f_{CO_2})(f_{H_2})}$$

However, for combustion at temperatures above 1000 °F, the assumption of a perfect gas and the use of partial pressures in the equilibrium constant equation do not produce a significant error.

The equilibrium constant applies to a specific chemical equation with the reaction products on the right side of the balanced equation appearing in the numerator. For reactions involving more than one mole of a substance, the partial pressure of each mole can be written as for a separate reactant. For example the reaction for the dissociation of a gas at very high temperatures

$$H_2 \rightleftharpoons 2H$$

may be written as

$$H_2 \rightleftharpoons H + H$$

so that the equilibrium constant becomes

$$K_p = \frac{p_H \times p_H}{p_{H_2}} = \frac{p_H^2}{p_{H_2}}$$

In the case of the general reaction

$$aA + bB \rightleftharpoons cC + dD$$

the equilibrium constant is

$$K_p = \frac{p_C^c \times p_D^d}{p_A^a \times p_B^b}$$

or the partial pressure of each component for the equilibrium constant appears in the equation with an exponent equal to the number of moles in the balanced chemical equation. Some equations may be written with fractions of moles such as

$$CO_2 \rightleftharpoons CO + \tfrac{1}{2}O_2$$

Then the equilibrium constant becomes

$$K_p = \frac{(p_{CO}) \times (p_{O_2})^{\frac{1}{2}}}{(p_{CO_2})}$$

This equation could be written as

$$2CO_2 \rightleftharpoons 2CO + O_2$$

However, the equilibrium constant for the equation written in this form would have a numerical value that is different from that in the previous example. Therefore before making computation it is necessary to note carefully the chemical equation defining the equilibrium constant. Values for the equilibrium constant as a function of temperature for several reactions that are of interest to power production are given in Figs. 4-1 and 4-2. Here the pressure unit is atmospheres.

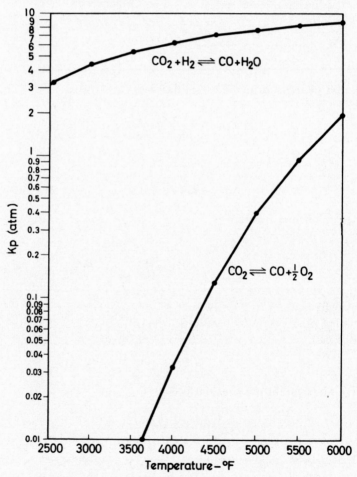

FIG. 4-1 Chemical equilibrium constants for carbon dioxide.

The equilibrium constant K_N for gaseous systems can be expressed in terms of the number of moles of each component

$$K_N = \frac{N_c^c \times N_d^d}{N_a^a \times N_b^b}$$

For a perfect gas, the partial pressure p_i of the ith component present at a concentration of M_i mole fraction with a total pressure

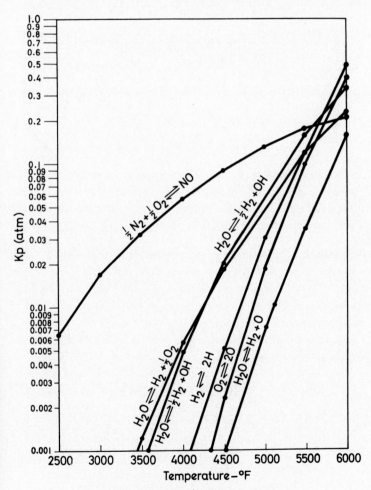

FIG. 4-2   Chemical equilibrium constants.

of p is

$$p_i = M_i p = \frac{N_i p}{\sum N}$$

where $\sum N$ is the total number of gaseous moles present. Substitution of this value for the partial pressure of each gaseous component in the equation for the equilibrium constant K_p gives

$$K_p = \frac{\left(\dfrac{N_c p}{N}\right)^c \times \left(\dfrac{N_d p}{N}\right)^d}{\left(\dfrac{N_a p}{N}\right)^a \times \left(\dfrac{N_b p}{N}\right)^b} = \frac{N_c^c \times N_d^d}{N_a^a \times N_b^b}\left(\frac{p}{\sum N}\right)^{\Delta N}$$

where ΔN is the increase in number of moles of gaseous products or

$$\Delta N = c + d - a - b$$

The equilibrium constant K_p is a function only of temperature, however the value of K_N is determined also by the pressure and $\sum N$ where $\Delta N \neq 0$. For the water gas reaction where the number of moles of products equals that of the reactants, the value of ΔN is zero and the two equilibrium constants have the same value.

EXAMPLE 4-7. Determine the composition that would result from mixing one mole of carbon monoxide and one mole of water vapor at 3000 °F and allowing these gases to react until an equilibrium mixture results. (Only the water gas reaction needs to be considered at this temperature.)

Solution: From Fig. 4-1 the value of K_p is found for the reaction written in the form

$$CO_2 + H_2 \rightleftharpoons CO + H_2O$$

Since $\Delta N = 0$, the two equilibrium constants are equal and

$$K_p = K_N = \frac{N_{CO} \times N_{H_2O}}{N_{CO_2} \times N_{H_2}} = 4.4 \text{ at } 3000 \text{ °F}$$

If y moles of carbon monoxide are oxidized to carbon dioxide, the moles of carbon monoxide remaining are

$$N_{CO} = 1 - y$$
$$N_{CO_2} = y$$
$$N_{H_2O} = 1 - y$$
$$N_{H_2} = y$$

Substitution of these values in the equilibrium relation gives

$$\frac{(1-y)^2}{y^2} = 4.4$$
$$y = 0.323$$

Since 0.323 mole of carbon dioxide and of hydrogen are formed, the remaining moles of carbon monoxide and of water are

$$N_{CO} = N_{H_2O} = 1 - y = 0.677$$

The total number of gaseous moles present is 2; therefore the composition of the equilibrium gas mixture is found as mole fractions (or volume fractions) of each component

$$M_{CO} = 0.34$$
$$M_{H_2O} = 0.34$$
$$M_{CO_2} = 0.16$$
$$M_{H_2} = 0.16$$

Certain dissociation reactions become significant at very high temperatures (see Fig. 4-2). These reactions include the dissociation of carbon dioxide into carbon monoxide and oxygen and the dissociation reactions involving hydrogen and oxygen listed in Table 4-3.

TABLE 4-3   DISSOCIATION REACTIONS

$$H_2 \rightleftharpoons 2H$$
$$O_2 \rightleftharpoons 2O$$
$$H_2O \rightleftharpoons \tfrac{1}{2}H_2 + OH$$
$$H_2O \rightleftharpoons H_2 + \tfrac{1}{2}O_2$$
$$H_2O \rightleftharpoons H_2 + O$$

At combustion temperatures either above about 4500 °F at atmospheric pressure or at lower temperatures in the very low pressures in space, the dissociation reactions can proceed to an extent that will be significant for thermochemical reactions. Large amounts of energy are absorbed in these highly endothermic reactions. The dissociation reactions tend to limit the combustion temperature since rapidly increasing amounts of energy are absorbed when the temperature approaches 5000 °F. This energy may be recovered, however, when the gas is cooled during expansion in an engine or through a nozzle. Then the recombination reactions will release this energy of dissociation as the temperature of the gas decreases.

EQUILIBRIUM CONSTANT

An isolated system at constant temperature and pressure is at equilibrium when there is no free energy change for any possible reaction. If a reversible reaction produces a negative free energy change, it is possible for this reaction to proceed, thereby increasing the concentration of the products and decreasing the amount of the reactants until the rate of the reverse reaction of the products just equals their rate of formation. At this condition the free energy change becomes zero

$$\Delta G = 0$$

For the equilibrium reaction of perfect gases at constant temperature and pressure

$$a\mathrm{A} + b\mathrm{B} \rightleftharpoons c\mathrm{C} + d\mathrm{D}$$

the component A will be at a partial pressure p_a. Where G_a° is the free energy at temperature T and at one atmosphere pressure, the free energy at partial pressure p_a is

$$G_a = G_a^\circ + RT \ln p_a$$

Using similar values of free energy for other components leads to the free energy change for the reaction

$$\Delta G = dG_d^\circ + dRT \ln p_d + cG_c^\circ + cRT \ln p_c - aG_a^\circ - aRT \ln p_a$$
$$- bG_b^\circ - bRT \ln p_b$$

Since at equilibrium $\Delta G = 0$, the following relation can be found by rearrangement

$$aG_a^\circ + bG_b^\circ - cG_c^\circ - dG_d^\circ = -\Delta G^\circ = RT \ln \left(\frac{p_d^d \times p_c^c}{p_a^a \times p_b^b} \right) = RT \ln K_p$$

$$\frac{-\Delta G^\circ}{RT} = \ln K_p$$

Here the value of ΔG° is the free energy change for the reaction materials each at 1 atm of pressure. For real gases that may not follow the perfect gas law, fugacities are used in the equilibrium constant as discussed previously.

The effect of temperature on the equilibrium constant can be found from the Gibbs–Helmholtz equation written in the form

$$R \left[\frac{\partial \ln K_p}{\partial T} \right]_p = - \left[\frac{\partial \left(\dfrac{\Delta G}{T} \right)}{\partial T} \right]_p = \frac{\Delta H^\circ}{T^2}$$

Also, since ΔG can be expressed as a function of temperature, the equilibrium constant can be calculated for any temperature range where adequate thermal data are available.

EXAMPLE 4-8. From free energy of formation data compute the equilibrium constant K_p at 298 °K for the ammonia synthesis reaction

$$\tfrac{1}{2} N_2(g) + \frac{3}{2} H_2(g) \rightleftharpoons NH_3(g)$$

Solution: Using values of the free energy of formation from Table 4-1 the standard free energy change for this reaction is found to be

$$\Delta G^\circ + 0 + 0 = -3.976 \text{ kg-cal/g-mole}$$

The logarithm of the equilibrium constant is then obtained

$$\log_{10} K_p = \frac{3.976 \times 1000}{1.987 \times 298 \times 2.303} = 2.92$$

COMBUSTION IN AIR

For combustion calculations the gases other than oxygen are included under "atmospheric nitrogen" and the composition of dry air is taken as 21 percent by volume oxygen and 79 percent atmospheric nitrogen. There are therefore $\frac{79}{21}$ or 3.76 moles of atmospheric nitrogen per mole of oxygen. The nitrogen and the other inert gases remain unchanged in the reaction except at very high temperatures; these diluents, however greatly reduce the flame temperature.

TABLE 4-4   COMPOSITION OF DRY AIR

Nitrogen	78.03 percent by volume
Oxygen	20.99 percent by volume
Argon	0.94 percent by volume
Carbon dioxide	0.03 percent by volume
Other gases	0.01 percent by volume

In addition to atmospheric nitrogen, air may contain varying amounts of moisture depending upon the temperature and the relative humidity. For example, saturated air at 70 °F will carry 0.025 mole of water vapor per mole of dry air at atmospheric pressure. Thus the chemical equation for the combustion of hydrogen in saturated air at these conditions can be written as

$$2H_2 + O_2 + 3.76\ N_2 + 0.12\ H_2O \rightarrow 2.12\ H_2O + 3.76\ N_2$$

Excess air is used to ensure complete combustion and to limit the flame temperature. Therefore free oxygen usually appears in the combustion products. The amount of excess air is expressed in terms of the amount of air required for complete combustion (for example, 100 percent excess air would be twice the theoretical requirement).

CHEMICAL SYSTEMS

The release of chemical energy by the combustion of a suitable fuel with an oxidizer may require a catalyst, diluents and other special additives depending upon the application. Fuels may include a wide variety of compounds of carbon, nitrogen and hydrogen. Metal additives such as aluminium may be used. Oxidizers may include atmospheric or liquid oxygen, liquid and solid oxygen compounds such as hydrogen peroxide, nitric acid or potassium perchlorate or the halogens (fluorine or chlorine). Water or an excess of fuel may be added to the combustion products to reduce the flame temperature or to lower the average molecular weight of the products.

Hydrogen peroxide may be used as a monopropellant. The addition of a solution of potassium permanganate to concentrated hydrogen peroxide produces a violent decomposition to steam and oxygen. Other monopropellants may have the fuel and oxidizer incorporated into the same mixture or even within the molecule (n-propyl nitrate or nitrocellulose). Solid propellants are mixtures of an oxidizer and fuel or they may be a solid monopropellant. Many chemical systems have been studied and several are used in various applications. The properties of some are listed in Table 4-5.

The hydrocarbon fuels provide the advantages of low cost and excellent handling and storage characteristics with high heat of combustion. Although liquid hydrogen has a greater heat of combustion per unit mass, the hydrocarbons are superior on a volume basis. Many grades of petroleum are available. Gasoline for use in spark-ignition engines is predominantly a mixture of aliphatic, branched-chain, low molecular weight hydrocarbons with a small amount of aromatic hydrocarbons. In a grade of gasoline that is typical for vehicles, the average molecular weight is about 90 and the heat of combustion (higher) is 20,000 Btu/lb. Aviation gasoline contains less light volatiles and less high boiling material. Aircraft turbojet fuel, JP-4 is a wide cut containing both gasoline and the higher boiling kerosene. The boiling range is 220 °F − 525 °F, and the average molecular weight is about 130. Diesel oil and the Army's "compression ignition fuel" (CIF) may be regarded as kerosenes with higher average molecular weights and densities.

Although the hydrocarbon fuels are now abundantly available from crude oil, they can be synthesized by coal hydrogenation and

ELEMENTS OF ENERGY CONVERSION

TABLE 4-5 PROPERTIES

Property	Ammonia (anhydrous)	Methyl alcohol	Ethyl alcohol	Ethylene oxide	Hydrazine (anhydrous)
Formula	NH_3	CH_3OH	C_2H_5OH	CH_2OCH_2	N_2H_4
Molecular weight	17	32	46	44	32
Boiling point	−28 °F	148 °F	173 °F	51 °F	236 °F
Freezing point	−108 °F	−144 °F	−174 °F	−168 °F	35 °F
Density of liquid at boiling point (lb/gal)	5.1 (70 °F)	6.6	6.6	7.1	8.48
Critical temp	270 °F	464 °F	470 °F	383 °F	714 °F
Critical pressure	1620 psig	1142 psig	913 psig	1028 psig	2120 psig
Vapor pressure	124.7 psia at 68 °F	1.8 psia at 68 °F	0.9 psia at 68 °F	27 spia at 80°F	0.31 psia at 80 °F
Autoignition temperature	1200 °F	800 °F	700 °F	804 °F to 1060 °F	518 °F
Flammability limits in air at 68 °F (% by volume)	16.1% to 26.8%	6% to 36%	3.3% to 19.0%	3.0% to 100%	4.7% to 100%
Solubility	Soluble in water, ether, alcohol	Soluble in water, ether, gasoline	Soluble in water, ether, gasoline	Reacts with water, alcohols	Soluble in water, alcohol
Stability	Stable to 900 °F	Stable at room temp	Stable at room temp	Catalytic decomposition	Thermal decomposition at 320 °F
Heat of combustion Btu/lb (higher)	9668 (gas)	9769	12,784		8346

* Unsymmetrical dimethylhydrazine.
† Bubble point.

OF CHEMICALS

UDMH*	Hydro-carbon JP-4	n-Propyl nitrate	Hydro-gen	Oxygen	Nitro-gen tetr-oxide	Nitric acid	Hydro-gen per-oxide
$(CH_3)_2$ N_2H_2	$(CH_2)_n$	$C_3H_3NO_3$	H_2	O_2	N_2O_4	HNO_3	H_2O_2 (80%)
60	130 ave.	105	2	32	92	63	(34)
146 °F	220 °F–525 °F	231 °F	−423 °F	−297 °F	70.1 °F	186 °F†	271 °F
−71 °F	−76 °F	−130.9 °F	−435 °F	−363 °F	11.84 °F	−45 °F	−13 °F
6.6	6.5	8.8	0.58	9.54	12.08	12.6	11.2
480 °F			−400 °F	−181.8 °F	316.8 °F		
865 psig			188 psia	716 psig	1455 °F		
3.1 psia at 80 °F	2.3 psia at 100 °F	1.6 psia at 122 °F	1.9 psia at −433 °F	495 psia at −200 °F	14.6 psia at 70 °F	0.28 psia at 32 °F	0.26 psia at 104 °F
454 °F	468 °F	379 °F	1075 °F				
2.0% to 100%		2% to 100%	4% to 74.2%				
Soluble in water, alcohol, gasoline	Soluble in alcohol & other hydro-carbons	Soluble in alcohol		Soluble in liquid, N_2, methane	Soluble in water	Soluble in water	Soluble in water
	Stable	Ther-mal decom-position	Chem-ically stable	Chem-ically stable	Stable at room temp		Ther-mal & catalytic decom-position
14,190	20,000		61,000 (gas)				

by the hydrogenation of carbon monoxide in the Fischer–Tropsch process. Both methods have been used industrially since before World War II in areas where crude oil is not available.

The alcohols are more reactive chemically but have lower heating values than the corresponding hydrocarbons since the alcohols are partially oxidized hydrocarbons. Ethyl alcohol is produced on a large scale from ethylene. Methyl alcohol can be made the primary product of the hydrogenation of carbon monoxide in a modification of the Fischer–Tropsch synthesis. Both are used industrially in large quantities. The alcohols are easily ignited and burn with a clean flame at a lower combustion temperature than the hydrocarbons. Although ethyl alcohol can be used in internal combustion engines, its performance and particularly its starting characteristics are greatly improved by adding some gasoline to the alcohol. Alcohols are added to gasoline to lower the freezing point (arctic fuel) and to improve the octane rating of the fuel. Now that catalysts have been found for the electrochemical oxidation of methyl alcohol, there is increasing interest in its use in a fuel cell.

Hydrogen is a most energetic fuel on a weight basis. It is used in high performance rockets, fuel cells and even in special internal combustion engines. Hydrogen can be produced in several ways, including the catalytic reaction between steam and natural gas and the electrolysis of water. Through this latter process, electrical energy can be converted to chemical energy for storage. For applications where weight and volume are of sufficient importance, hydrogen can be liquified at the very low temperature of $-423\,°F$ and stored in special cryogenic containers. These have been developed to insulate adequately the low temperature liquid so that it can be stored and transported with only a small loss from evaporation. Before hydrogen is liquified, it must first be purified carefully by removing air, oil, and water. Compressed hydrogen at liquid nitrogen temperatures, after passing over silica gel for final purification, is further cooled by an expansion process in which part of the gas is condensed. The gaseous hydrogen that is separated from the liquid is returned through heat exchangers for recompression and cooling.

Hydrogen can occur in two forms—the ortho state in which the nuclei of the two hydrogen atoms of the hydrogen molecule spin in the same direction, and the para state in which they spin in opposite directions. At room temperature, the molecular hydrogen in equilibrium contains 25 percent para-hydrogen and 75 percent ortho-hydrogen. At liquid hydrogen temperature, however, the equilibrium composition is 99.79 percent para-hydrogen. Since the transformation of ortho- to para-hydrogen evolves heat, this heat would cause a major loss of liquid by boiloff if hydrogen were liquified before conversion to the para state. Consequently, the conversion of ortho- to para-hydrogen is carried out catalytically at liquid nitrogen temperature prior to the hydrogen liquefaction step.

The production of liquid hydrogen is thus a complex process involving extensive equipment. However, much experience in this unusual material has been acquired in the large facilities that produce and use it. It has been learned that extreme care, such as avoiding any contact with air or moisture, must be taken with liquid hydrogen, and that there are some hazards associated with the production and use.

High purity liquid hydrogen is a transparent, colorless, odorless liquid. It is usually boiling vigorously when in an observable condition. The density of liquid hydrogen—only 0.59 lb/gal at −423 °F—is uncommonly low. The liquid and gas are noncorrosive. Combustible mixtures are formed with oxidizers. When mixed with air, the gas is highly combustible through the entire range from 4.0 to 74.2 percent hydrogen by volume.

Ammonia is also of interest as a fuel because it can be produced as a type of energy storage system by the expenditure of electrical energy. Hydrogen for ammonia production can be made by the electrolysis of water, as mentioned, and the necessary nitrogen comes from air through liquefaction and separation. A compressed mixture of hydrogen and nitrogen will react in the presence of catalysts to form ammonia according to the equation

$$N_2 + 3H_2 \rightarrow 2NH_3$$

The reaction must be carried out at an elevated temperature to obtain appreciable reaction rates, even though the conversion decreases with temperature. The reactants are compressed to a pressure of about 300 atm and, after final purification, are fed into the catalytic converter where they are heated to reaction temperature by the heat released in this exothermic reaction. The mixture of ammonia and unconverted synthesis gas then passes into an ammonia condenser where liquid ammonia is separated from the gas which is recirculated then to the converter.

At atmospheric temperatures and pressure, ammonia is a pungent, colorless vapor that is irritating to the skin, eyes, and respiratory tract. Its inhalation in large concentrations can be hazardous to life. Ammonia is highly reactive chemically, and it will burn in concentrations of 16 to 27 percent by volume in air.

Anhydrous ammonia can be transferred and stored as a liquified gas under pressure at ambient temperatures. Industrial experience has shown that liquified ammonia is comparatively easy to handle with properly designed equipment. Ammonia can be used directly as a fuel or it can be heated and catalytically decomposed to produce a mixture of hydrogen and nitrogen. This mixture can be fed to a fuel cell or burned in an engine.

Several other synthetic fuels, including aniline, hydrazine and unsymmetrical dimethylhydrazine (UDMH), are used in propellent systems. These fuels all ignite spontaneously upon contact with nitric acid and certain other oxidizers, thereby eliminating the need for an igniter system.

Oxygen is used where flame temperatures higher than would be obtained with air are necessary. For rocket propellent systems and other applications that require minimum storage weight and volume, liquid oxygen (specific gravity 1.14) is used. It is made from air by liquefaction after purification and distillation to separate nitrogen from the oxygen. This is a well-developed and efficient process and liquid oxygen is inexpensive and available in quantity. Excellent cryogenic containers have been developed permitting storage of liquid oxygen for long periods of time with only a slow rate of evaporation. Although extreme care must be exercised to prevent contamination of liquid oxygen by oil or other organic matter which could create an explosion hazard, this material can be handled in quantity without great difficulty. As a result of these favorable properties, liquid oxygen is used in many chemical systems where operation independent of the atmosphere is required.

Other liquid oxidizers include hydrogen peroxide, nitric acid and nitrogen tetroxide. The last is preferred for long-term storage because it is stable and does not corrode steel containers.

Extensive information is available on many materials that have been studied as propellants. Performance of these propellants over a wide range of mixture ratios and pressures has been obtained by using digital computers to calculate flame temperature and specific impulse. The literature on this subject has been collected and cataloged by the Solid Propellant Information Agency and the Liquid Propellant Information Agency of The Johns Hopkins University.

SOLID PROPELLANTS

Rockets and gas generators with solid propellants have inherent simplicity and reliability and many of the components of liquid propellent systems — pumps, nozzles, and controls — are not required. Regulation of the pressure and rate of burning is determined by the composition of the solid propellant and the design of the propellent grain. An igniter heats the surface of the propellant above its kindling temperature and burning proceeds to completion. Methods are available for terminating burning at any intermediate time by the sudden release of pressure. Many applications have been found for solid propellants in gas generators that operate auxiliary power units and actuators.

Solid propellants are of two basic types — organic derivatives of nitric acid (double base powder), and mixtures of inorganic oxidizers with a solid fuel (composite propellant). Both types are produced on a large scale for rocket propulsion. Double-base powder is preferred for gas generators because the gas is free of solid or corrosive combustion products. It is made from nitrocellulose by gelatinizing this hard, brittle material with a plasticizer. In a typical composition such as JPN, nitroglycerine is mixed with the nitrocellulose to produce a soft, tough colloidal product that can be extruded into grains when warmed slightly. These grains may be made with a diameter of several inches and a length of several feet for artillery rockets. Special casting processes for fabricating single grains for large rocket motors also have been developed. In the formulation of double-base powder, several minor ingredients are added — stabilizers to reduce the chemical decomposition, potassium sulfate to minimize burning of exhaust gas in the atmosphere (flash), and carbon black to make the produce opaque to thermal radiation. A typical composition of a double-base powder formulation is given in Table 4-6.

TABLE 4-6   JPN BALLISTITE

Nitrocellulose	51 percent
Nitroglycerine	43
Stabilizer	4.8
Potassium sulfate	1
Carbon black	0.2
Flame temperature	5300 °F
Specific impulse in typical application	220 sec

Composite propellants include the black powder of historic interest and the recently developed propellants for large booster rockets and other applications. Typical compositions are given in Table 4-7.

TABLE 4-7   TYPICAL COMPOSITE PROPELLANTS

	Type A	Type B
Organic binder	21 percent	19 percent
Ammonium perchlorate	74	
Ammonium nitrate		79
Additive	5	2

These propellants can be made by mixing the inorganic oxidizer with a plastic monomer that polymerizes during curing to a strong product of the desired shape.

The performance of solid propellants for rockets can be improved by adding a metal powder, such as aluminium, to the composition. This additive stabilizes the burning characteristics and increases the specific impulse of the composition.

The rate, r, of burning of a solid propellant is a function of pressure of the form

$$r = ap^n \text{ in./sec}$$

where n is a constant determined by the propellant composition and a is related to both the composition and the propellent temperature. The value of n should be small to avoid large changes in pressure during operation. The system will be unstable if this exponent has a value greater than unity. Also, many solid propellants require a minimum pressure for stable burning.

A solid propellant will burn on all exposed surfaces, and in the range of stable operating conditions, these surfaces will recede at the burning rate. Each surface layer is burned away with such precision that surface irregularities still remain after burning to some depth. Burning will penetrate even into small cracks and imperfections. It is therefore essential that the propellent grain be free from any surface or internal flaws. Since the rate of gas production and chamber pressure is determined by the exposed area and the burning rate, the exposed area of the propellant must remain nearly constant during burning to obtain constant pressure. Many grain shapes have been devised to provide constant burning areas, and these fall into two types as indicated in Fig. 4-3 — restricted "cigarette" grain and unrestricted grain. For the "cigarette" grain, the sides of the grain are wrapped with tape and one end is covered to limit burning to one end surface. This design is used for gas generators that require a long burning time. This burning time t_b is given by

$$t_b = \frac{l}{r}$$

where l is the grain length.

For the unrestricted grain, such as a tubular grain, the burning distance is half the propellent thickness. The surface is maintained nearly constant in the tubular grain since the increasing internal area partly compensates for the decreasing outer surface during

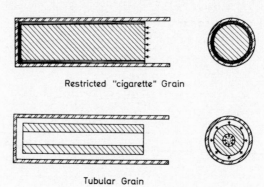

Restricted "cigarette" Grain

Tubular Grain

FIG. 4-3 Solid propellent grains.

burning. A serrated or star-shaped internal surface has also been used for this purpose. The great versatility possible with solid propellant grain design has led to applications ranging from microrockets to launch rockets weighing many tons.

REFERENCES

1. F. DANIELS, *Outlines of Physical Chemistry*, New York, John Wiley, 1955.
2. O. A. HOUGEN, K. A. WATSON and R. A. RAGATZ, *Chemical Process Principles, Part II*, New York, John Wiley, 1959.
3. J. H. PERRY, J. C. ELGIN and W. P. RYAN, *Physical and Chemical Principles*, Chemical Engineers Handbook, J. H. PERRY, ed., New York, McGraw-Hill, 1934.
4. J. F. LEE and F. W. SEARS, *Thermodynamics*, Reading, Mass., Addison-Wesley, 1955.
5. G. P. SUTTON, *Rocket Propulsion Elements*, New York, John Wiley, 1949.
6. F. R. BICHOWSKI and F. D. ROSSINI, *Thermochemistry of Chemical Substances*, New York, Reinhold, 1936.
7. F. D. ROSSINI, D. D. WAGMAN. W. S. EVANS, S. LEVINE snd I. JAFFE, *Selected Value of Chemical Thermodynamic Properties*, NBS Circular 500, Washington D.C., 1952.

8. U.S. Bureau of Mines Bulletin 542.
9. C. D. HODGMAN, ed., *Handbook of Chemistry and Physics*, Cleveland, Ohio, Chemical Rubber Publishing Co., 1961.
10. R. N. WIMPRESS, *Internal Ballistics of Solid-Fuel Rockets*, New York, McGraw-Hill, 1950.
11. F. C. WARREN, *Rocket Propellants*, New York, Reinhold, 1958.

CHAPTER 5

ELECTROCHEMICAL PROCESSES

INTRODUCTION

The direct production of electrical energy by electrochemical processes is an increasingly important power source because of its convenience and unusual efficiency. Batteries are electrochemical power sources that produce either primary or stored secondary electricity. They are highly developed and reliable devices. The closely related fuel cells provide power for space flight. Electrochemical reactions also are used for precisely measuring thermodynamic quantities.

Electrochemical effects have been studied since the observation by Galvani in 1786 that two dissimilar metals touching a frog's leg produce a muscular contraction. This led to investigations by Volta who in 1800 constructed batteries of two metals in contact with a salt solution. Volta's pile for producing higher potential was made of alternate plates of silver and zinc separated by cloth or paper soaked in salt solution. This new source of electricity made possible many other electrochemical discoveries including the electrolysis of water into hydrogen and oxygen. Davy in 1807 demonstrated the electrolysis of sodium hydroxide in contact with mercury producing sodium–mercury amalgam.

Such electrochemical experiments as the preparation of metals required heavy electrical currents and many types of batteries were developed for this purpose. The Daniell cell for example delivers a large current without much reduction in voltage. This cell, invented in 1836, is still used where nearly constant voltage under load is required. Here a zinc sulfate solution containing a zinc electrode is separated either by gravity or by a porous ceramic plate from a copper sulfate solution with a copper electrode. Excess copper sulfate is added to the bottom of the cell. As the cell discharges, zinc is dissolved and copper is deposited on the copper electrode. Thus chemical energy is converted directly into electrical energy in this primary battery.

The lead–acid secondary battery for storing electrical energy was developed in 1859 by Plante'. Reversible electrochemical

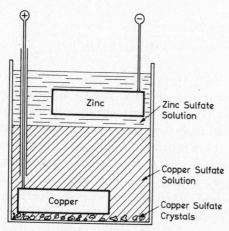

FIG. 5-1   Daniell cell.

reactions produce lead and lead oxide during the charging process and these react to release electricity during discharge. This battery has low internal resistance and will deliver a heavy current during discharge.

A battery devised by Sir William Grove in 1839 oxidizes hydrogen with oxygen on platinum electrodes at room temperature to generate electricity. The reactants are not contained within the battery but are fed continuously as required. Mond and Langer applied the term "fuel cell" to a similar device they studied near the end of the century. A major objective of electrochemical research was then the direct electrochemical oxidation of carbon or coal to supply the growing requirements for electricity. However, large generators driven by steam turbines or hydraulic power were developed to meet adequately these requirements, and interest in fuel cells dwindled for many years until about 1944. Then the needs of the military for efficient portable power supplies for electronic equipment started a new surge of fuel cell research that is still expanding. This effort has brought many discoveries such as the electrochemical oxidation of alcohol and hydrocarbons. By the use of such low cost fuels with high efficiency, the fuel cell may at last challenge many conventional power sources — more than a century after the first demonstration of the fuel cell.

TYPES OF BATTERIES

There are many types and combinations of systems that are useful for converting chemical energy directly into electricity. Some of these have been mentioned already. Their nomenclature is confused at times by terms having double meanings. For example, a battery is defined as a group of two or more electrochemical cells connected to provide an electrical current. Also by common usage, "battery" is used to designate the individual cell.

This cell is made up of an electrochemical fuel that can transfer electrons to the electrode which is therefore negative. This electron current then flows out of the cell, through an external circuit to the cathode. Here the electrons are absorbed by the oxidant. This may be oxygen, an oxide, a halogen or some reduceable material such as a nitrate. The transfer of ions through the electrolyte completes the electron circuit. In this process the electron-rich fuel is oxidized at the anode and the oxidant — the electron acceptor — is reduced at the cathode. A primary battery cannot be electrically recharged because the material in the electrodes are irreversibly consumed in the electrochemical process. A reversible electrochemical system can be electrically restored to its original condition after discharge and is designated a secondary battery. Actually most primary batteries can be recharged to a limited extent and the difference between some primary and secondary batteries is arbitrary.

A fuel cell is an electrochemical producer of electricity with the reactants fed to the cell and the reaction products removed for continuous operation. Inexpensive fuels such as hydrocarbons, alcohols, hydrogen or carbon are usually associated with fuel cells. Pure oxygen or oxygen from air may be used as the oxidant. Other fuel cell concepts are based upon the halogens. Electrolytes may be acid or alkaline aqueous solutions, ceramic or organic ion-exchange solid materials, fused salts, or other non-aqueous conductors. Thus there are many possible combinations. Only a few however have been selected for development. The oxidation of coal or carbon with nitric acid for example was studied many years ago but has since been abandoned. In the so-called redox (reduction-oxidation) fuel cell, the fuel and oxidant were made to react with other chemicals outside the cell to regenerate inter-mediate compounds for reactions within the cell to produce electricity. This indirect approach is of decreasing interest because the system becomes highly complex. However the direct electro-chemical oxidation of hydrocarbons, alcohols, hydrogen and other fuels is being vigorously developed to power space craft, electronic equipment and even commercial vehicles such as lift trucks and tractors.

FARADAY'S LAW

An electric current is carried through an electrolyte by ions that may be deposited on the electrodes. In a silver nitrate solu-tion, for example, a current strength of one ampere will deposit exactly 0.001118 g of silver per second on the negative electrode. A gram-mole of monovalent silver is thus equivalent to 96,493 coulombs (ampere-seconds) of electricity. A gram-mole of a divalent ion such as zinc (Zn^{++}) corresponds to 2 equivalents of electricity. By defining a gram-equivalent as the molecular weight in grams divided by the valence change, it follows that F coulombs of electricity produce a chemical change of one gram-equivalent. This quantity of electricity is the Faraday, and Faraday's law is followed precisely in electrochemical reactions over a wide range of conditions.

The quantity of electricity that a reactant can produce in a battery or fuel cell can be found in terms of the valence change n, and the molecular weight

$$\text{Capacity} = \frac{n \times F \times 453.6}{MW \times 3600} = \frac{n \times 12,158}{MW} \text{ Ah/lb}$$

Values of electrochemical capacities are listed in Tables 5-1 and 5-2 for various anode (negative electrode) and cathode (positive electrode) materials.

EXAMPLE 5-1. Determine the maximum quantity of electricity that can be produced by 1 lb of the reactants in a mercuric oxide–zinc battery.

Solution: This electrochemical reaction can be written as

$$\text{Zn} + \text{HgO} \rightarrow \text{ZnO} + \text{Hg}$$

A basis of 1000 Ah of electricity will be used. Then the amounts of reactants are

$$\text{Zinc} = \frac{1000}{372} = 2.69 \text{ lb}$$

$$\text{HgO} = \frac{1000}{112} = 8.93 \text{ lb}$$

TABLE 5-1   CAPACITY OF ANODE
MATERIALS

	Ah/lb
Hydrogen	12,100
Hydrocarbon	5200
Beryllium	2700
Lithium	1750
Aluminium	1350
Titanium	1015
Magnesium	1000
Calcium	607
Sodium	530
Iron (+++)	653
Iron (++)	435
Zinc	372
Cadmium	216
Lead (++)	117

TABLE 5-2   CAPACITY OF CATHODE
MATERIALS

	Ah/lb
Oxygen	1520
m-Dinitrobenzene	850
Fluorine	640
Chlorine	343
Cupric oxide	305
Cupric fluoride	240
Silver oxide (AgO)	196
Nickel fluoride	190
Bromine	152
Manganese dioxide (1 e)	141
Mercuric oxide	112
Lead dioxide	100
Mercuric chloride	89
Silver chloride	84

the total weight of material is

$$\text{wt.} = 2.69 + 8.93 = 11.6 \text{ lb}$$

The electricity per pound is

$$\frac{1000}{11.6} = 86 \text{ Ah/lb}$$

ELECTRICAL ENERGY AND POTENTIAL

The electrical energy released in an electrochemical process is identical with the decrease in free energy $-\Delta G$

$$W_t = nFE = -\Delta G$$

where

E = electromotive force

F = Faraday constant

n = number of gram-equivalents of material reacting.

EXAMPLE 5-2. Determine the maximum potential of a hydrogen–oxygen fuel cell operating at 25 °C and 1 atm pressure.

Solution: This reaction can be written in the form

$$H_2 + \tfrac{1}{2}O_2 \rightarrow H_2O$$

Here two gram-equivalents of hydrogen react with two gram-equivalents of oxygen. From Faraday's law, the maximum electricity that can be produced is 2 faradays. Also from the free energy change for this reaction, the maximum electrical energy is obtained

$$-\Delta G = 56.69 \text{ kg-cal/g-mole}$$

$$56.69 \times 4184 = 237,100 \text{ joules/g-mole}$$

Since a joule is a watt-second of energy, the voltage of a reversible hydrogen–oxygen cell is

$$E = \frac{-\Delta G}{2F} = \frac{237,100}{2 \times 96,493} = 1.229 \text{ V}$$

The coulombic efficiency − that is, the quantity of electricity compared to that predicted by Faraday's law − is usually high even though the efficiency on an energy basis of an electrochemical process such as that in a fuel cell, may be much less than 100 percent. The electrical energy is the product of the quantity of electricity times the voltage. Therefore the lower energy efficiency results from potential losses from the theoretical values. These losses are due to several sources including internal resistance and the irreversibility of the processes. Such losses are discussed as polarization losses in a later section.

TEMPERATURE EFFECTS

The temperature coefficient of potential of an electrochemical reaction at constant pressure is obtained from

$$E = \frac{-\Delta G}{nF}$$

$$\left(\frac{\partial E}{\partial T}\right)_p = \frac{-1}{nF}\left(\frac{\partial \Delta G}{\partial T}\right)_p$$

The rate of change of free energy with temperature at constant temperature is obtained from the Gibbs–Helmholtz equation written in the form

$$-\left(\frac{\partial \Delta G}{\partial T}\right)_p = \frac{\Delta H}{T} - \frac{\Delta G}{T} = \Delta S$$

This leads to an expression for the temperature coefficient in terms of the enthalphy or entropy change

$$T\left(\frac{\partial E}{\partial T}\right)_p = \frac{\Delta H}{nF} + E$$

From measured values of the reversible potential and its temperature coefficient, the enthalpy change can be found with some precision.

EXAMPLE 5-3. Find the temperature coefficient of the potential of a hydrogen–oxygen fuel cell operating at 25 °C at constant pressure.

Solution: The enthalpy change ΔH is found from the heat of formation data in Table 4-1 for the reaction

$$H_2(g) + \tfrac{1}{2}O_2(g) \rightarrow H_2O\,(1)$$
$$\Delta H = -68.32 \times 4184 \text{ joules}$$

Also from Example 5-2, the value of E at 25 °C is 1.229 V, so that

$$\left(\frac{\partial E}{\partial T}\right)_p = \frac{-68.32 \times 4184}{298 \times 2 \times 96,493} + \frac{1.229}{298}$$
$$= -0.00085 \text{ V/°C}$$

Thus the potential decreases with temperature. Also the voltage required to electrolyze water into hydrogen and oxygen decreases with temperature.

ELECTROMOTIVE FORCE

The potential difference between the electrodes of a cell is determined by the concentration of the materials, their chemical properties and the temperature. The convention is used of writing electrochemical equations to include the concentrations and other information in the form

$$Zn \mid ZnSO_4 \; (0.1m) \parallel CuSO_4 \; (0.1m) \mid Cu \qquad E = 1.1$$

In this equation for the Daniell cell, the single vertical lines indicate phase junctions where there are potential differences and the double vertical line symbolizes a junction where the difference is negligible. The concentration is expresses as molality (0.1 grammole of zinc sulfate per kilogram of water, for example). The equation is written for an electron flow within the cell from right to left, and a positive value of the potential difference E indicates a decrease in free energy and a spontaneous electrochemical reaction occurring when the electrodes are connected through an external circuit. This reaction can be described also by the chemical equation

$$Zn + Cu^{++} \rightarrow Zn^{++} + Cu \qquad E = 1.1$$

The total electromotive force is the algebraic sum of the potential difference across the phase juctions

$$Zn \rightarrow Zn^{++} + 2e \qquad E = 0.76$$
$$Cu^{++} + 2e \rightarrow Cu \qquad E + 0.35$$

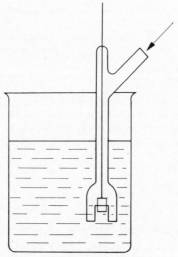

FIG. 5-2 Hydrogen electrode.

The standard for electrode potentials, with an assigned value of $E = 0$, is the standard hydrogen electrode. It consists of a platinum strip covered with platinum black and immersed in a dilute electrolyte with hydrogen gas at atmospheric pressure bubbling around it (Fig. 5-2). The electrochemical equation is

$$H_2 \rightarrow 2H^+ + 2e \qquad E = 0.00$$

The electromotive series, Table 5-3, was determined by using the standard hydrogen electrode as a reference in measuring the potential of various electrode materials.

TABLE 5-3   ELECTROMOTIVE FORCE AT 25 °C

$Li \rightarrow Li^+ \quad + e$	2.960
$K \rightarrow K^+ \quad + e$	2.924
$Ca \rightarrow Ca^{++} \quad +2e$	2.76
$Na \rightarrow Na^+ \quad + e$	2.713
$Mg \rightarrow Mg^{++} \quad +2e$	2.375
$Al \rightarrow Al^{+++} \quad +3e$	1.67
$Mn \rightarrow Mn^{++} \quad +2e$	1.18
$H_2 + OH^- \rightarrow 2H_2O + 2e$	0.828
$Zn \rightarrow Zn^{++} \quad +2e$	0.763
$Cr \rightarrow Cr^{++} \quad +2e$	0.577
$Fe \rightarrow Fe^{++} \quad +2e$	0.441
$Cd \rightarrow Cd^{++} \quad +2e$	0.402
$Co \rightarrow Co^{++} \quad +2e$	0.277
$Ni \rightarrow Ni^{++} \quad +2e$	0.23
$Sn \rightarrow Sn^{++} \quad +2e$	0.141
$Pb \rightarrow Pb^{++} \quad +2e$	0.126
$H_2 \rightarrow 2H^+ \quad +2e$	0.000
$Cu \rightarrow Cu^{++} \quad +2e$	−0.346
$2Ag + 2OH^- \rightarrow Ag_2O + H_2O + 2e$	−0.344
$Cu \rightarrow Cu^+ \quad + e$	−0.522
$2I^- \rightarrow I_2 \quad +2e$	−0.536
$H_2O_2 \rightarrow O_2 + 2H^+ + 2e$	−0.582
$Fe^{++} \rightarrow Fe^{+++} + e$	−0.770
$Ag \rightarrow Ag^+ \quad + e$	−0.800
$Hg \rightarrow Hg^{++} \quad +2e$	−0.852
$2Br^- \rightarrow Br_2 \quad +2e$	−1.065
$2H_2O \rightarrow O_2 + 4H^+ + 4e$	−1.229
$Sn^{++} \rightarrow Sn^{+++} + e$	−1.256
$2Cl^- \rightarrow Cl_2 \quad +2e$	−1.358
$MnO_2 + 4H_2O \rightarrow MnO_4^- + 8H^+ + 5e$	−1.50
$Ag^+ \rightarrow Ag^{++} \quad + e$	−1.987
$2F^- \rightarrow F_2 \quad +2e$	−2.85
$2H_2O \rightarrow H_2O_2 + 2H^+ + 2e$	−1.77

ACTIVITY

The concentrations of the solutions in contact with the electrodes in a cell influence the electromotive force. Thermodynamic relations for this can be derived on the basis that an electrochemical reaction is an equilibrium process. Then an equilibrium constant K can be determined in terms of concentrations (molality, m) instead of partial pressures or fugacities, and for the reaction

$$Zn + Cu^{++} \rightarrow Cu + Zn^{++}$$

$$K = \frac{m(Zn^{++})}{m(Cu^{++})}$$

The concentrations of the pure solid reactants, copper and zinc, are taken as unity. As discussed in Chapter 4, fugacities must be used instead of partial pressures to provide exact thermodynamic relations for nonideal systems. Similarly the "activity" of a solution was invented to accurately describe the behavior of solutions and other systems at concentrations where behavior is far from ideal. In very dilute solutions the activity a approaches the actual concentration. The activity of a pure solid phase is unity by definition, and in the above example

$$a_{Cu} = a_{Zn} = 1$$

Then as a function of activites the equilibrium constant is exactly

$$K = \frac{a_{Zn^{++}}}{a_{Cu^{++}}}$$

Concentration in terms of molality is related to the activity by the use of an activity coefficient γ, defined by

$$a = m\gamma$$

This activity coefficient γ approaches unity for very dilute solutions and there are various experimental methods for determining its value. The standard state for the electromotive force values in Table 5-3 is an effective concentration of one gram ion per kilogram of solvent. This is taken as unit activity.

Activity is more properly defined in terms of fugacity as the ratio of the fugacity f to the value f° at some standard condition

$$a = \frac{f}{f^\circ}$$

Thus the partial pressure of a perfect gas is equal to its activity. The value of the activity depends upon the standard state chosen — this may be the vapor pressure of the pure liquid, a gas at one atmosphere pressure, or a one-molal solution of an electrolyte, depending upon the intended use. The increase in free energy in a constant-temperature change of a substance from a partial pressure p_1 to p_2 or an activity a_1 to a_2 is

$$\Delta G = NRT \ln \left(\frac{p_2}{p_1} \right) = NRT \ln \left(\frac{a_2}{a_1} \right)$$

The relation for the equilibrium constant obtained in Chapter 4 was limited to the condition that each reactant is initially at the standard state of one atmosphere and each product leaving the reaction also is at this standard condition. The free energy change $-\Delta G^\circ$ is related to the equilibrium constant for these standard conditions by

$$-\Delta G^\circ = RT \ln K = nFE^\circ$$

For the electrochemical reaction

$$a\mathrm{A} + b\mathrm{B} \rightarrow c\mathrm{C} + d\mathrm{D}$$

where the reactants and products are at conditions other than unit activity, the free energy change is

$$-\Delta G = nFE = RT \ln K - RT \left(\frac{a_C^c \times a_D^d}{a_A^a \times a_B^b} \right)$$

$$E = E^\circ - \frac{RT}{nF} \ln \left(\frac{a_C^c \times a_D^d}{a_A^a \times a_B^b} \right)$$

Concentration cells can be made with $E^\circ = 0$ and the potential difference is produced entirely by the difference in ion concentration at otherwise identical electrodes. Hydrogen at different pressures on two hydrogen electrodes will produce a potential difference

$$H_2(p_1) \mid HCl \mid H_2(p_2)$$

The result of this electrochemical process is to transfer hydrogen at pressure p_1 to pressure p_2 with the production of electrical energy.

EXAMPLE 5-4. Determinine the reversible potential of a hydrogen concentration cell having a pressure ratio of 10. The temperature is 25 °C.

Solution: The electrochemical reaction of the hydrogen molecule, H_2, corresponds to 2 faradays ($n = 2$). Since hydrogen behaves as an ideal gas the following relation can be used

$$E = \frac{-RT}{2F} \ln \frac{p_2}{p_1} = \frac{1.987 \times 298 \times 4.184}{2 \times 96,493} \ln 10 = 0.029 \text{ V}$$

A hydrogen–oxygen fuel cell can be operated under conditions that will allow the potential to be determined by the oxygen partial pressure. The cell will then be a sensitive instrument for measuring oxygen concentrations.

POLARIZATION

The open-circuit potential E_t° is the difference between the potentials of the electrodes with respect to the standard hydrogen electrode, or

$$E_t^{\circ} = E_1^{\circ} - E_2^{\circ}$$

The thermodynamic relations that have been developed permit the open circuit voltage E_t° to be determined for reversible systems. Actual cells may be nearly reversible at very low currents. However, electrochemical processes taking place at useful rates have potentials that are different from theoretical; these differences are usually expressed as polarization voltages or overvoltages. The efficiency of an electrochemical process is determined largely by the potential since the coulombic efficiency is usually high, as discussed previously. The losses in potential represent energy losses that may come from several sources:

1. Concentration polarization, E_{conc}, from depletion of active material in the immediate electrode vicinity. As reactant molecules diffuse to the electrode surface, steady state concentrations of reactants and products limit the cell potential.

2. Reaction mechanism polarization, E_{rm}, losses from the reaction mechanism. For example, the oxygen potential of a hydrogen–oxygen fuel cell is limited to a voltage corresponding to hydrogen peroxide rather than to pure oxygen because the formation of the peroxide is an intermediate step in the reaction. The activation polarization (discussed in the following paragraph) may be included with the reaction mechanism polarization or it may be considered separately.

3. Activation polarization, E_{act}, or overvoltage, electrode losses in heterogeneous electrochemical reactions that involve a gas at a solid electrode with a liquid electrolyte. The voltage required to produce hydrogen by the electrolysis of an acidic solution depends on the material and condition of the electrode and the current density. For example, at 0.10 A/cm^2 in 1 molar sulfuric acid, the overvoltages of hydrogen on aluminium, shiny platinum and platinum black are 1.0 V, 0.29 V, and 0.04 V, respectively. The hydrogen overvoltage increases with current density and decreases with temperature at a rate of 0.02 to 0.03 V per 10 °C. The oxygen overvoltage is 0.64 V for electrolysis with platinum black electrodes in 1 molar potassium hydroxide solution and is even higher with other electrode materials.

Catalysts reduce the activation polarization. Experimentally determined reaction rates demonstrate that two active reaction sites are necessary for chemisorption by hydrogen in catalyzed porous carbon electrodes. This appears to be true also for oxygen electrodes. A catalyst poison can render a catalyst completely ineffective. This is possible even though the reaction sites make up only a fraction of the catalyst surface, and even when the amount of poison is too small to form a monomolecular layer. Thus, a catalyst such as platinum black may be highly sensitive to minute amounts of sulfides. Because of this, other catalysts that are insensitive to poisons, may be preferred in spite of the fact that they are less active at the start.

Promotors increase the activity of a catalyst, either by forming additional active centers, or by shortening the time that reaction products occupy them. Thus, a catalyst promotor added to the reactants in minute amounts will improve operation or counteract a catalyst poison.

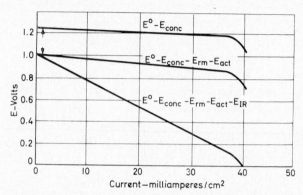

FIG. 5-3   Polarization curves for ion membrane fuel cell.

4. Ohmic polarization E_{IR} from internal resistance loss in the electrolyte. This is generally linear with current density, so that

$$E_{IR} = IR$$

High concentrations, thinness, and high temperatures usually reduce ohmic polarization. However, those cells that carry products away from the electrode must have enough electrode spacing to prevent precipitation or excessive dilution.

Thus the flow of a current causes each electrode to polarize (Fig. 5-3) decreasing the cell voltage according to the relation

$$E = E^\circ - (E_{conc} + E_{rm} + E_{act} + E_{IR})$$

HYDROGEN–OXYGEN FUEL CELL

The electrochemical reaction of hydrogen and oxygen at catalytic electrodes to produce water and electrical energy is more complex than indicated by the reaction

$$2H_2 + O_2 \rightarrow 2H_2O$$

The electrode processes depend upon the type of electrolyte (acidic or alkaline) and on the catalyst. As indicated in Fig. 5-3, the open-circuit potential of a hydrogen–oxygen fuel cell is less than the predicted value of 1.229 V at 25 °C because of intermediate reactions (reaction mechanism polarization). In an alkaline electrolyte such as a potassium hydroxide solution, oxygen is adsorbed onto the catalyst surface, there reacting with water to form perhydroxyl and hydroxyl ions

$$O_2(ads) + H_2O + 2e^- \rightarrow (HO_2)^- + (OH)^-$$

Since the perhydroxyl ion would reduce the cell potential to 0.9 V, catalysts that will decompose peroxide are added — cobalt, manganese and silver are effective. The amount of peroxide also depends upon the concentration of the alkaline electrolyts with a minimum occuring at some point. Heat also increases the peroxide decomposition rate. By the use of catalysts under favorable conditions the perhydroxyl ion concentration can be reduced until the four electron reaction predominates

$$O_2(ads) + 2H_2O + 4e^- \rightarrow 4(OH)^-$$

The cell potential is thereby increased to 1.10–1.13 V.

Hydroxyl $(OH)^-$ ions produced at the oxygen electrode diffuse through the electrolyte to the hydrogen electrode where they react with hydrogen on the catalyst surface. The adsorption of a hydrogen molecule on a pair of active catalyst sites produces active hydrogen atoms that are intermediate in this reaction

$$H_2 \text{ (gas)} \rightarrow H_2 \text{ (ads)} \rightarrow 2H$$

$$2H + 2(OH)^- \rightarrow 2H_2O + 2e^-$$

This chemisorption will control the reaction rate, if the number of active centers available on the hydrogen electrode catalyst is not adequate. This process also contributes a small amount to the polarization losses although the amount is small.

Catalysts for the hydrogen electrode include platinum black, rhodium, palladium, ruthenium and alloys of these metals. Less expensive catalysts are nickel, lithiated manganese oxide, and nickel boride. Since several functions must be performed — adsorption of the hydrogen molecule, splitting it into atoms, and then promoting the reaction of these with hydroxyl ions — it is not surprising that mixtures of several catalysts are more effective.

The oxygen electrode catalyst must adsorb the oxygen molecule and then promote its reaction with water. Also the perhydroxyl ion must be catalytically decomposed. Oxygen electrode catalysts used in alkaline electrolytes include copper, silver, nickel, cobalt on aluminium oxide, or mixtures of these or their alloys.

An acidic electrolyte, such as phosphoric acid, has the important advantage of rejecting carbon dioxide. Fuels of carbon compounds such as alcohols, hydrocarbons or carbon monoxide produce carbon dioxide upon oxidation and this reacts with an alkaline electrolyte to form the less soluble carbonates. Also the carbon dioxide in air will form carbonates in alkaline electrolytes. Thus the development of acidic fuel cell systems is an important step in the use of inexpensive fuels.

In an acidic electrolyte, hydrogen ions $(H)^+$ are available in abundance to transport electricity through the electrolyte. The chemical reaction is usually written

$$2H_2 \text{ (ads)} \rightarrow 4H^+ + 4e^-$$

These hydrogen ions diffuse through the electrolyte to the oxygen electrode where the reaction is

$$4H^+ + \frac{3}{2} O_2 \text{ (ads)} + 4e^- \rightarrow H_2O_2 + H_2O$$

Similar catalysts are effective for the acidic and alkaline hydrogen electrodes. However the acidic oxygen electrode presents a more difficult problem. Much effort has been spent on the development of effective catalysts that are resistant to acid corrosion. Most information about these is proprietary and is not available for publication, although reasonably effective oxygen electrodes are known to exist.

Water is formed at the oxygen electrode with an acidic electrolyte. This is an advantage when air is used as the source of oxygen, as an excess of air can be circulated through the oxygen electrode to remove water from the cell. With an alkaline electrolyte, water is formed at the fuel electrode, although some water can be removed from the oxygen electrode.

POROUS ELECTRODE

The three-phase reaction of a gas with a liquid on a solid catalyst presents a difficult engineering problem, because there is only a small reaction zone at the interface between the three phases. Therefore electrodes of a porous metal or of porous graphite impregnated with a catalyst are used to increase the

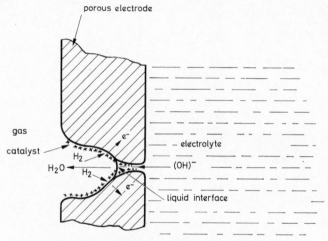

FIG. 5-4   Three-phase reaction in porous electrode.

reaction area. With fine pores on the liquid side and larger pores on the gas side (Fig. 5-4) the liquid will penetrate only part way into the electrode (depending upon the gas pressure and the treatment of the electrode surface with a nonwetting agent). In this way a greatly extended surface for chemical reaction is obtained. It is important that the pores on the liquid side be uniform in size since porous electrode can leak gas or flood with electrolyte if not properly constructed and operated. The catalyst can be added by soaking the porous matrix in a solution of the catalyst material followed by drying and heating.

Diffusion electrodes with multiple layers of materials having different pore sizes have been developed by Bacon in England and Justi in Germany. They found that an inactive sintered metal layer with very fine pores covering a catalytic layer with larger

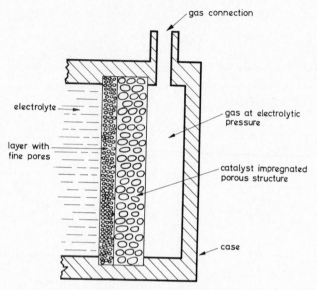

FIG. 5-5   Valve electrode.

pores (Fig. 5-5) will sustain excess gas pressure without leakage, because the liquid fills the small pores due to surface tension. Justi has demonstrated that electrodes of this construction, known as valve electrodes, can electrochemically generate and compress oxygen and hydrogen at high efficiency. When the valve electrode is used for the electrolysis of water, the gas is liberated within the catalytic layer where the pore sizes are much larger. Thus hydrogen can be generated at pressures up to 3 atm inside the electrode.

A gas electrode material of unusual effectiveness has been developed by Justi and Winsel. This is made by pressing and sintering a mixture of fine nickel powder and a pulverized alloy of nickel–aluminum or nickel–zinc. The aluminum or zinc is later removed by an electrochemical reaction with caustic leaving a strong porous structure that contains highly active particles of

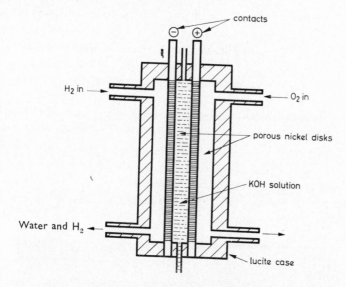

FIG. 5-6 Hydrogen–oxygen cell.

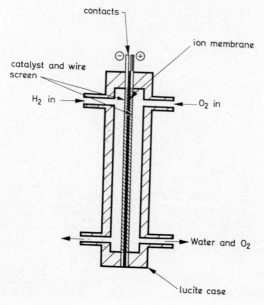

FIG. 5-7 Ion–membrane cell.

nickel (Raney nickel). The product known as double skeleton catalytic electrode (DSK) is effective at both the fuel and the oxygen
electrodes of fuel cells as well as for the electrolysis of water.

SOLID POLYMER ELECTROLYTE

Ion exchange resins can serve as solid electrolytes since these
materials have the ability to transfer ions. An acidic-type ion
exchange resin can be made by treating phenolic resin with
sulfuric acid. The product is molded into thin sheets (0.8 mm) for
the construction of cells. A layer of catalyst and perforated metal
(Fig. 5-7) provide chemically active areas and electrical contact
with the plastic membrane.

FIG. 5-8 Solid polymer membrane electrode with contacts (General Electric).

Hydrogen and oxygen, supplied on opposite sides of a sheet of solid polymer electrolyte, penetrate the porous electrodes to contact the surface of the polymer. At the anode, electrons are given up to the electrode in forming ions. These ions are conducted through the electrolyte to the cathode. Here oxygen reacts with the electrons that have travelled through the external circuit and the ions that have travelled through the electrolyte, forming water.

Fuel cells of this construction are rugged and inexpensive. The operation can be made independent of gravity by using a wick material (Fig. 5-9) to remove water from the cell. The solid electrolyte is unaffected by carbon dioxide. A simple fuel cell of this construction is shown in Fig. 5-7.

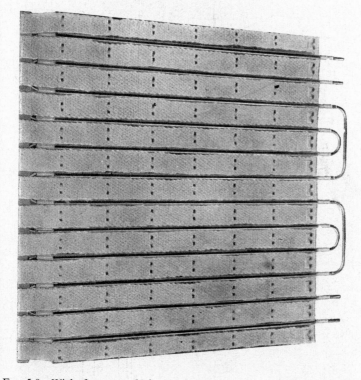

FIG. 5-9   Wicks for removal of water from solid polymer electrode (General Electric).

FIG. 5-10   Solid polymer fuel cell (General Electric).

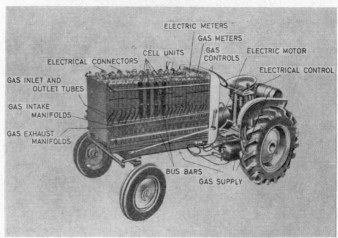

FIG. 5-11   Allis–Chalmers fuel cell tractor

FUEL CELL SYSTEMS

The Allis–Chalmers Research Division in October 1959 made a field demonstration of an experimental tractor with fuel cell power. It was silent, easily controlled and developed 3000 lb tractive force.

There were 1008 individual cells each 0.25 in. thick by 12 in. square (Fig. 5-12). The alkaline electrolyte was absorbed on asbestos sheet between catalytic metal electrodes. The general characteristics are given in Table 5-4. A mixture of propane and hydrogen was fed to the cells. The hydrogen was oxidized to

FIG. 5-12   Individual cell from Allis–Chalmers tractor.

TABLE 5-4   ALLIS–CHALMERS TRACTOR FUEL CELL

Output	15 kW
Fuel cell weight	1800 lb
Volume	20 ft^3
Efficiency	60 percent (about)
Current density	20 A/ft^2

water and the propane flushed this water out of the cells. Oxygen also was fed from pressure cylinders.

This tractor after many demonstrations is now on display at the Smithsonian Institute as the first fuel-cell-powered vehicle.

Many of the concepts that have been discussed are incorporated into the hydrogen–oxygen fuel cells developed to provide reliable electric power for manned space craft. Liquid hydrogen and oxygen were chosen because they produce a large amount of energy per unit mass and because the water from this reaction is potable. Moreover these two materials are used in propellent systems.

The complete fuel cell systems include the following components:

1. Cryogenic hydrogen and oxygen storage containers
2. Pressurization and feed systems
3. Reactant preheater to vaporize and warm the hydrogen and oxygen
4. Fuel cell modules mounted in cylindrical tanks. A duplicate unit is included for reliability.
5. Cooling system including a secondary coolant circulated through the cell modules to remove heat and carry it to a space radiator. Part of the cooling fluid many pass through the reactant preheater.
6. Water accumulator
7. Electrical controls and monitoring system

These components are shown in Fig. 5-13 for the General Electric solid polymer electrolyte system. Some auxiliaries are not included.

Individual sandwich fuel cells are stacked in series to meet voltage requirements. Each stack is actually a self-contained 350 W unit. A 1 kW module contains three such stacks in parallel. The general specifications for a module are given in Table 5-5.

All necessary wiring and valving connections are located on an accessory pad on the side of the unit. An electrical monitoring

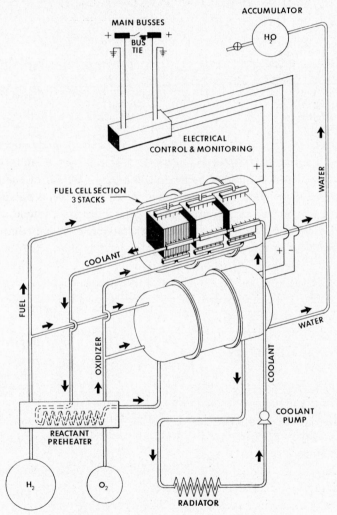

FIG. 5-13   Space fuel cell system (General Electric Co.).

control unit monitors the performance status of individual stacks. This can be automated to schedule periodic removal of inert gases from the fuel system and to isolate out-of-limit components in a redundant system. No other control functions are required in this design.

TABLE 5-5 GENERAL ELECTRIC SPACE FUEL CELL MODULE

Cell active area	7×7.5 in.
Power per stack	350 W
Number of stacks	3
Power per module	1 kW
Module size	2 ft $\times$ 1 ft diameter
Cooling	circulating liquid at 120 °F
Heat rejection	40 thermal watts per module

A dual-porosity diffusion-electrode fuel cell system is being developed for Apollo by the Pratt & Whitney Aircraft Division. Sintered nickel plates are used and a perforated nickel plate supports the porous structure of the oxygen electrode. These are 14 in. diameter by 0.07 in. disks with an active area 10 in. in diameter. The electrodes are assembled into 0.75 in. thick cells that are stacked into modules producing 30 V. Bolts tie the module together inside a 17 in. diameter tank. The electrolyte, 85 percent potassium hydroxide and 15 percent water, is contained between the electrodes. At the 500 °F operating temperature, electrical conductivity of the electrolyte and the chemical reaction rates are high. In addition, peroxide is rapidly decomposed at this temperature so that polarization losses are minimum. The measured open-circuit potential is 1.1 V. An important advantage of the high-temperature operation is that water is easily removed and excess heat can be rejected to a radiator of minimum size. Excess hydrogen circulated through the fuel electrodes removes heat and water vapor.

Current density is an important variable in determining the optimum system design. At high rates the cell is smaller. However, the accompanying decrease in efficiency makes it necessary to reject additional heat. Then there is an increase in weight due to the heat transfer equipment. The optimum design point for the diffusion electrode power system is about 150 A/ft² even though much higher rates can be obtained from the cell. To achieve reliability, three modules are installed instead of the two that provide the required power. However efficiency is higher when all

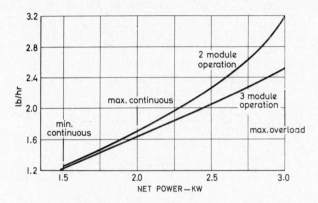

FIG. 5-14 Total oxygen and hydrogen consumption (Pratt & Whitney Aircraft Division).

three modules are operating because of the lower current density. The oxygen and hydrogen consumption for these two modes of operation is shown in Fig. 5-14.

CERAMIC ELECTROLYTE

A zirconium oxide–yttrium oxide ceramic known as Nert's mixture conducts an electric current by transferring oxygen ions through the crystal lattice. There is very little electronic conductance through this remarkable material. High-temperature fuel cells that uses this ceramic electrolyte have been demonstrated. High reaction rates (current density of 700 A/ft²) have been obtained. The elevated temperature at which this cell can be operated without the usual corrosion problems makes it of interest for hydrocarbon oxidation.

FUSED CARBONATE ELECTROLYTE

A high temperature (700 °C) fuel cell with molten carbonate electrolyte contained within a ceramic matrix is being developed for the oxidation of inexpensive fuels such as carbon monoxide–hydrogen mixtures produced from carbon or hydrocarbons by the water–gas reaction. A mixture of about 50 percent magnesium

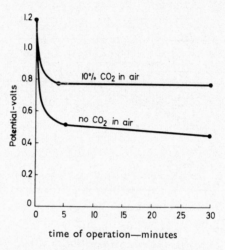

Fɪɢ. 5-15   Effect of CO_2 in air on carbonate cell.

oxide powder and about 50 percent lithium–sodium–potassium carbonate (m.p. 490 °C) can be pressed at 500 °C into disks or tubes. The product behaves as a solid although the volume fraction of molten carbonate is about 65 percent. It is dense and homogeneous. The electrical conductance is also about 65 percent of the pure liquid phase conductance. The material is contained between porous metal electrodes.

With this electrolyte, carbon dioxide must be added to the inlet air to produce the carbonate (CO_3^{--}) ion at the oxygen electrode

$$\tfrac{1}{2}O_2 + CO_2 + 2e^- \rightarrow CO_3^{--}$$

This carbonate ion is then transported through the electrolyte to react at the fuel electrode with hydrogen or carbon monoxide,

$$H_2 + CO_3^{--} \rightarrow H_2O + CO_2 + 2e^-$$

$$CO + CO_3^{--} \rightarrow 2CO_2 + 2e^-$$

This effect of carbon dioxide at the oxygen electrode is illustrated in Fig. 5-15.

With sintered nickel fuel electrodes and silver air–carbon dioxide electrodes, Broers at the Central Technical Institute TNO, The Hague, Netherlands, has obtained current densities of 150 A/ft^2 at 0.7 V using water gas containing 20 percent hydrogen, 10 percent carbon monoxide and 70 percent carbon dioxide. However the operation of the cell, deteriorates due to changes in the silver electrode. Otherwise this fuel cell has many desirable characteristics including the use of inexpensive fuels at high efficiency.

DISSOLVED FUEL

Some liquid fuels are soluble in the electrolyte of a fuel cell. These include methyl alcohol, hydrazine hydrate, ethylene glycol and even sugar. The fuel electrode then can be a metal plate coated with a catalyst such as platinum black or paladium. The oxygen electrode is usually a porous structure impregnated with some different catalyst that is inactive with the fuel. These electrodes are immersed in the fuel-electrolyte solution as indicated in Fig. 5-16. Justi in Germany and investigators at the Allis–Chalmers Mfgr. Co. and at Esso Research and Development Co. have described fuel cells using various dissolved fuels. The Allis–Chalmers Mfgr. Co. has demonstrated a golf cart and a lift truck powered with hydrazine hydrate fuel cells of this type.

The use of water-soluble liquid fuels offers many practical advantages in storage and handling as compared to hydrogen. Furthermore some of the liquid fuels such as methyl alcohol can be produced in nearly unlimited quantity and at reasonable cost as discussed in Chapter 4.

The carbon compounds may be completely oxidized to carbon dioxide. This will dissolve in an alkaline electrolyte to form a carbonate salt and for continuous operation, this carbonate must be removed. Several possible methods for carbonate removal have been suggested. This carbonate problem can be avoided by the use of acid electrolyte systems. These reject carbon dioxide to the atmosphere and no regeneration is required. However, there are difficult corrosion problems at the electrodes. Also the oxygen electrode catalysts are less active in an acid electrolyte.

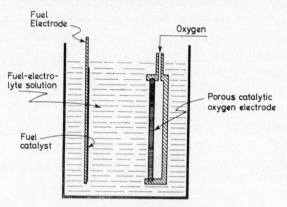

FIG. 5-16   Dissolved fuel system.

The rate of the electrochemical reaction is usually high at the fuel electrode and current densities of 1000 A/ft² have been reported. Certain compounds such as acetone or other partially oxidized products can reduce the reaction rate and these materials must be removed from the electrolyte. Hydrazine hydrate fuel has the advantage that it is oxidized to nitrogen and water without troublesome intermediate or final oxidation products.

HYDROCARBONS

The use of inexpensive hydrocarbons in fuel cells has long been a research objective. Indirect processes (reaction of the hydrocarb onwith steam to form hydrogen and carbon monoxide, or its partial oxidation to produce these gaseous fuels for electro-chemical reaction) or the direct electrochemical oxidation of the hydrocarbon at an electrode are pursued.

High temperature (500–800 °C) electrode reactions will proceed at a useful rate. At these temperatures a ceramic or molten (alkali or carbonate) electrolyte must be used. A molten alkali 1.5 kW fuel cell that oxidized carbon with air was made by Jacques in 1896. The current densities were over 100 A/ft^2 and the potential was 1 V. However, the carbon dioxide produced sodium carbonate and no good method of regenerating the sodium hydroxide was found. Therefore the idea of operating a streetcar system from a power station of this type was abandoned.

The direct oxidation of propane and other hydrocarbon gases at low (100 °C) temperatures in an alkaline electrolyte fuel cell was announced in 1960 by the Esso Research and Development Company. Again the sodium hydroxide in the electrolyte was consumed by reaction with carbon dioxide to form the carbonate. Also gum formation on the catalyst is understood to have caused a rapid decrease in reaction rate. These problems have prevented the exploitation of this important advance in electrode catalysis.

A carbon dioxide rejecting acid–electrolyte fuel cell for the direct oxidation of common liquid fuels such as diesel oil and gaseous hydrocarbon fuels (propane and natural gas) was des-cribed by the General Electric Research Laboratories in April 1963. This cell operates at an intermediate temperature of 150–250 °C. Platinum catalysts are used in special form in a porous electrode. This electrocatalysis involves the following steps:

(1) Chemisorption of the fuel molecules on the electrode sur-face in the presence of the electrolyte.

(2) Formation of active intermediate compounds by dehydro-genation.

(3) Electrochemical oxidation of these active intermediate compounds.

(4) Desorption of oxidation products from the electrode sur-face.

Phosphoric acid is the electrolyte in the cell shown in Fig. 5-17. Here a porous electrode admits oxygen from the air. The hydrocarbon is oxidized at a rate that produces 50 A/ft^2 of electrode

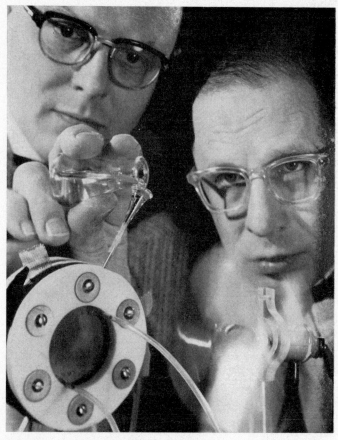

FIG. 5-17   General Electric hydrocarbon cell. Dr. Thomas Grubb is pouring diesel oil into the cell with Dr. Leonard Niedrach on the left.

area at a potential of 0.5 V. This corresponds to a cell efficiency of 40 to 50 percent. This development is supported by the U.S. Army Engineer Research and Development Laboratory.

THERMALLY REGENERATIVE FUEL CELLS

Metal hydrides such as calcium or lithium hydride can be decomposed at an elevated temperature of about 900 °C producing hydrogen and the metal. These can be separated and recombined in an electrochemical reaction at a lower temperature of some 350 °C to produce electrical energy. Other metal halides can be used similarly but at somewhat different temperatures. By carrying out these processes continuously, a system for converting thermal energy into electrical energy is possible. Although electrochemical processes are involved, such a system is limited in efficiency to a fraction of the Carnot efficiency since the process involves the conversion of thermal energy into electrical energy.

The electrochemical reaction between hydrogen and the metal to produce the hydride can be carried out with an electrolyte composed of the chlorides of the alkali metals. However, preliminary investigations indicate that thermal losses would make the overall efficiency of the hydride system low even though the many technical problems were solved. The use of metal halides in a thermally regenerative fuel cell appears more attractive and both the heavy metal iodides and chloride systems have been studied in detail.

A concentration cell also could be thermally regenerative since a current-carrying ion changes in chemical activity over a temperature interval.

BIOCHEMICAL FUEL CELLS

The use of biological materials to produce electrical energy could have many applications. Thus research on biochemical fuel cells is of interest to manned space flight and to industrial operations. Perhaps waste materials will be disposed of by oxidation to carbon dioxide and water with the useful production of electrical energy.

Food materials—carbohydrates, lipides and proteins—can be classed as primary fuels. These can be hydrolyzed by biologically produced hydrolytic enzymes to produce secondary foods. These simpler molecules include glucose, fatty acids and amino acids which are more active chemically that the primary foods. By partial oxidation and other processes tertiary foods such as alcohols, hydrogen, urea and ammonia are produced from the secondary foods. These tertiary foods are electrochemically reactive in a fuel cell and thus can be used to produce electrical energy. Some secondary foods also will react in a fuel cell.

Biological metabolism in a fuel cell can convert a primary food into a tertiary form for subsequent oxidation at an electrode to produce electrical energy. This biological conversion of the primary food can take place in a separate vessel or near the surface of the electrode. However the conditions near the electrode usually are not optimum for both processes. For example carbohydrates can be decomposed to simple alcohols by bacteria. These alcohols can then serve as the fuel for the electrochemical cell. A protein may produce urea which is electrochemically active. Although these tertiary foods produce less energy than the primary foods, their chemical activity is greatly increased by the biological metabolism.

A more direct but much more difficult biochemical fuel cell would use electrochemical metabolism of the primary food to produce electrical energy. The enzymes required for these reactions must be produced by bacteria living on a part of the primary food. The electrochemical metabolism must take place on the surface of the electrode. Although simple in concept, the electrochemical metabolism involves complex processes.

PRIMARY BATTERIES

LECLANCHÉ CELL

The conventional dry cell is made from a zinc can lined with a paper separator wet with mercuric chloride solution to amalgamate the surface of the zinc. This can is filled with a mixture of manganese dioxide and carbon moistened with a solution of ammonium chloride and zinc chloride. A carbon rod serves as the positive central electrode. The container is sealed with pitch leaving space for expansion; or, if the outside of the zinc can is protected by steel, the cover can be attached with a crimped seal (Fig. 5-18).

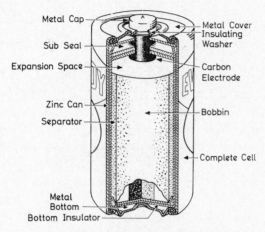

FIG. 5-18   Leclanché dry cell (Eveready).

The chemical reaction is usually written as

$$Zn + 2MnO_2 \rightarrow ZnO + Mn_2O_3$$

The actual chemistry of the Leclanché cell is more complicated than indicated by this reaction, and the products formed depend upon the acidity of the electrolyte. The electrode reactions can be written as

$$Zn \rightarrow Zn^{++} + 2e^-$$

$$2MnO_2 + Zn^{++} + 2e^- \rightarrow ZnO + Mn_2O_3$$

Thus, zinc is consumed at the negative electrode and manganese dioxide is reduced at the positive electrode.

Other forms of construction include the flat cell (Fig. 5-19). Here there is neither an expansion chamber nor a carbon rod. Thus there is a greater amount of the manganese oxide mix per unit cell volume to increase the energy content.

Another form of construction that gives even higher energy to weight and volume ratios is known as the cathodic envelope. In cells of this type, both surfaces of the zinc plate are covered by two flat cakes of the manganese dioxide mixture. This sandwich is encased by the cathode collector, a special, carbon-

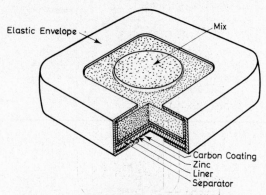

FIG. 5-19   Flat Leclanché dry cell (Eveready).

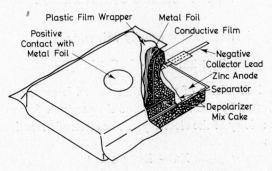

FIG. 5-20   Cathodic envelope cell (Eveready).

impregnated conducting film of flexible plastic and metal foil. This collector is bonded to the plastic envelope that seals the cell.

Dry cells are made in many sizes. The nominal voltage of an individual cell is 1.5, but assemblies of cells (batteries) are made with potentials up to 510 V. The total energy delivered by a battery is a function of temperature, rate of discharge and duty cycle (hours per day of operation). Although other types of cells may deliver more energy per unit weight, the Leclanché cell is a reliable and inexpensive portable source of electrical energy that is used widely.

ALKALINE BATTERY

Heavy or continuous currents can be supplied economically by a modification of the Leclanché cell—the alkaline battery. Here the anode of pressed zinc powder gives a high surface area. The manganese dioxide cathode lines the inner wall of the steel container and a potassium hydroxide solution provides good electrical conductivity. With this alkaline electrolyte the final reaction product is sodium zincate although the chemical reaction is usually written the same as for the Leclanché cell.

The cell produces a nominal 1.5 V. Some models are rechargeable, if only partly discharged. Although the cycle life of the alkaline battery is shorter than some other secondary batteries, its specific power is unusually high and it is inexpensive.

AIR-DEPOLARIZED BATTERY

A battery that uses oxygen from air as the cathode material can provide long reliable life for communications and similar applications where low power is required at nearly constant voltage. Air-depolarized batteries might even be classified as a fuel cell, since the reactant at the cathode is continuously supplied from the atmosphere. A porous graphite electrode coated on the electrolyte side with a waterproofing agent and containing a catalyst permits oxygen to diffuse into the battery. A zinc anode is used with a caustic electrolyte. The cell reaction is written as

$$Zn + \tfrac{1}{2}O_2 \text{ (air)} \rightarrow ZnO$$

The final reaction product with caustic is sodium zincate, Na_2ZnO_3, as in the alkaline battery.

This battery supplies nearly constant voltage provided the maximum ability of the carbon electrode to absorb atmospheric oxygen is not exceeded. It is also rugged with little deterioration when not in use. It is shipped dry since the loss of water from the porous electrode during storage could be a problem. To activate the battery, the seal is broken and water is added. Additional water may be required periodically depending upon conditions.

MERCURY CELLS

The mercury cell contains a mercuric oxide cathode, an amalgamated zinc anode and a concentrated aqueous electrolyte of potassium hydroxide saturated with potassium zincate. The cathode and anode are pressed shapes in a sealed steel container. The chemical reaction is written as

$$Zn + HgO \rightarrow ZnO + Hg$$

A permeable barrier of microporous plastic prevents migration of any material in the cell, thereby contributing to long shelf and service life. Mercury batteries give high capacity per unit volume since the active materials are dense and are efficiently used. This type of battery will function over a wide temperature range of $-65\,°F$ to $160\,°F$ with only a slight decrease in voltage at the low temperature, if only a small current is drawn. Mercury cells are used on small instruments including hearing aids because their capacity is high and they are durable.

INDIUM CELL

Very small batteries for electric wrist watches have been developed using indium with mercuric oxide. The chemical reaction is written as

$$2In + 3HgO \rightarrow 3\,Hg + In_2O_3$$

These cells can be completely sealed and used at very low current drains for longer periods of time than the similar zinc–mercuric oxide cells, since indium is more resistant than zinc to corrosion. Also indium cells give nearly constant voltage at low current drains.

HIGH CAPACITY DRY CELLS

Aluminum and magnesium as anode materials can release much more energy per unit mass than zinc. These higher energy metals are used with silver oxide and with organic oxidizers such as dinitrobenzene. Corrosion is often a difficult problem with magnesium and aluminum because these metals are water reactive unless there is a protective oxide film. Zinc, however, is stable in water.

SEA-ACTIVATED BATTERIES

Reserve primary batteries that activate when immersed in sea water were developed during World War II. They have become important power sources for special apparatus such as remote weather and oceanographic equipment. Military uses include buoys, radiosonde equipment and torpedoes. The batteries are stored dry in sealed containers. They have the advantage that the electrolyte — sea water — need not be transported.

FIG. 5-21   SEACEL water-activated torpedo battery (Yardney Electric Corp).

Sea-activated batteries have magnesium electrodes that are oxidized by silver chloride. Such batteries as shown in Fig. 5-21 are made in sizes ranging from 0.2 to 100 Ah. They can be activated in sea water ranging from 28 °F to 85 °F, and once activated the batteries can be successfully discharged at low ambient temperatures. Very high-rate batteries are designed for a flow of sea water through the cells to obtain close regulation of temperature and voltage. These can be activated in less than 10 sec and energy densities up to 70 Wh per pound of dry battery have been obtained under favorable conditions. Water adds from 5 to 30 percent to the mass.

WET PRIMARY CELLS

The Lalande cell with zinc anode, cupric oxide cathode and sodium hydroxide electrolyte in a glass jar supplies a heavy current for transportation and mine signalling systems that must have reliable but inexpensive power supplies. One form of this battery was invented by Thomas Edison as a power source for the laboratory development of the electric light. The battery produces 0.5 to 0.7 V at high current drains. Since the cathode after discharge can be rejuvinated by placing the electrode in a furnace to reform the cupric oxide, the battery might be considered in part a fuel cell. Only the zinc anodes are consumed.

MOLTEN SALT BATTERIES

Fused electrolytes can provide higher electrical conductance than aqueous solutions. Also, electrode reactions in molten salts not only take place at remarkably high rates, but in many cases they are nearly reversible. As a result, batteries with molten salts can produce heavy currents with only small polarization losses.

An example is the heat-activated thermal battery. Calcium or magnesium anodes are used with alkali–metal halide electrolytes. The cathodes may be chromates, oxides or halides. Since the cell is inert at room temperature, it can be stored for long periods without deterioration or danger from short circuits. As soon as the temperature is raised above the melting point of the electrolyte, heavy currents can be drawn until the metals are exhausted.

The reactions of the light metals in molten salt systems release a large amount of energy per unit mass: consequently such systems can be high performance electrical energy sources.

SOLID-ELECTROLYTE CELLS

Silver halide crystals can conduct electricity by silver ion diffusion. Although this process is relatively slow, assemblies of solid electrolyte cells for producing high potentials for instruments that require only a very small current (microamperes) are made commercially. The cells have silver anodes, silver bromide or iodide solid electrolyte, and cupric bromide or iodide cathodes.

SECONDARY BATTERIES

LEAD–ACID BATTERY

An electrochemical device for storing energy was invented in 1859 by Planté. He observed that two lead plates immersed in dilute sulfuric acid would produce a current after being charged. Many improvements were made including the use of a paste of lead oxide on a lead lattice as the active material and separators of wood or porous rubber.

By 1890 lead–acid batteries of "modern" construction giving high capacity were produced. As a result of their excellent performance and low cost, these batteries are used to start automobile engines, provide power for electric trucks and materials handling equipment, and serve as standby power sources.

Batteries for different applications have special design features. For automobile starting, for instance, thin plates provide a high current for a short time (usually only a few seconds). The service life is some 200 to 300 deep discharge cycles and there is a 20 to 30 percent energy loss per month from self-discharge. Batteries for trucks with electric motor drives must supply energy for 8 to

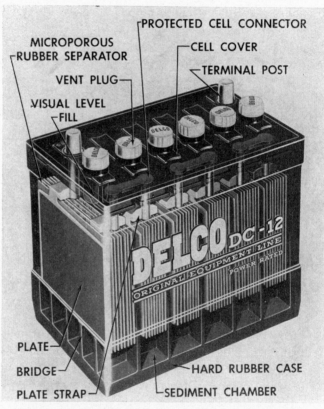

FIG. 5-22   Lead–acid battery (Delco Remy Div., GMC).

10 hr with nearly complete discharge daily. Thicker electrodes are used and means are provided to hold the lead oxide on the positive plate. These batteries are more expensive, but they will last for several years with proper care. Stationary batteries for standby power are designed for a life of 8 to 15 years and special lead alloys give them a low self-discharge rate. Aircraft batteries

have arrangements to prevent the loss of electrolyte through vents when inverted.

The electrochemical reaction in the lead acid battery is written as

$$Pb + PbO_2 + 2H_2SO_4 \rightleftharpoons 2\ PbSO_4 + 2H_2O$$

Spongy lead at the anode is oxidized to lead sulfate and the lead oxide at the cathode is reduced. It also produces lead sulfate with the consumption of sulfuric acid. The removal of acid from the solution during discharge reduces the specific gravity of the electrolyte. This change provides a convenient means for measuring the charge. In a typical battery at 70 °F the specific gravity is 1.26 at full charge and 1.07 at complete discharge.

A car battery can be recharged at a high rate for a short time without damage. However, charging at a much lower rate is necessary to reach maximum capacity. During overcharge, most of the electrical energy is consumed by the decomposition of water into hydrogen and oxygen. Water must therefore be added to make up for this loss.

NICKEL–IRON BATTERY

The first of the secondary batteries that use alkaline electrolyte is the nickel–iron battery. It was discovered by Edison and placed in production about 1908 after some ten years work. There have been few changes in the battery since. The cathode plates are perforated tubes filled with nickel hydroxide mixed with metallic flakes of thin nickel to improve conductivity. The negative electrodes are plates with rectangular pockets containing iron oxide that charging reduces to spongy iron.

The chemical reaction in which trivalent hydrated nickel oxyhydroxide, $NiO(OH)_2(H_2O)_n$, is reduced to the divalent form is usually written as

$$2Ni(OH)_3 + Fe \rightarrow Fe(OH)_2 + 2Ni(OH)_2$$

Since the exact composition of the nickel compound is not certain, the equation is written with the hydroxide to show that there is no reaction with the electrolyte. The electrolyte concentration remains unchanged during charge and discharge except for decomposition of water to hydrogen and oxygen during overcharge or self-discharge.

Nickel–iron batteries are rugged. They resist both mechanical and electrical abuse. Also they can maintain nearly constant ampere-hour discharge capacity at high discharge rates. However the voltage drops at high rates. Because they are more expensive than the lead–acid battery and do not perform as well at low temperatures, they are not used for automobile starting. Nickel–iron batteries are preferred, however, for electric-powered trucks and other heavy industrial work.

NICKEL–CADMIUM BATTERY

The nickel–cadmium battery, because of the superior electrochemical properties of cadmium, performs better than the nickel–iron battery, though at added cost. Advantages in performance include a very low rate of self-discharge and an operating temperature range of $-65\,°F$ to $180\,°F$.

Sintered porous metal plates are preferred for the nickel-cadmium battery, because thinner electrodes with larger reaction surface areas are needed for high performance. Again the electrochemical reaction is written as

$$2Ni(OH)_3 + Cd \rightarrow 2Ni(OH)_2 + Cd(OH)_2$$

Although the hydrated nickel oxyhydroxide has been identified as the trivalent nickel compound reacting with cadmium, the reaction is written in this form to indicate no change in the electrolyte. Since the measurement of the charge level is important for some uses, a third electrode has been developed to determine the level of charge in sealed cells.

These sealed cells require other special features to prevent the accumulation of hydrogen and oxygen during overcharge. The generation of hydrogen at the cadmium electrode is prevented by putting greater capacity into this electrode than in the nickel electrode. This results in the production of oxygen at the nickel electrode during overcharge, while some cadmium oxide still remains to be reduced on the cadmium electrode. Here the oxygen reacts with cadmium to form addition cadmium oxide. If the rate of overcharge is not excessive, this oxygen production and consumption dissipates the electrical energy without the accumulation of gas to increase the pressure above the design pressure of the cell.

The number of charge–discharge cycles possible with the nickel–cadmium battery depends, as in other batteries, upon the temperature and the rate and depth of discharge. This battery, however, is superior to others in cycle life and charge retention. It has been used in many space power applications because of these properties and the high reliability obtained with sealed cells.

Nickel–cadmium cells are made in three basic configurations—buttons, cylinders and rectangles. These cells are assembled into batteries to provide the required voltage. Careful attention must be given to circuits with several sets of batteries since parallel connections are not recommended. Minor differences in internal resistance of the cells after cycling may result in extreme variations in the state of charge of individual cells and polarity reversal in others.

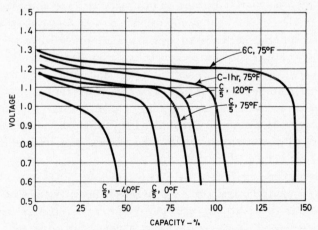

FIG. 5-23 Discharge characteristics of nickel–cadmium battery at various discharge rates and temperatures.

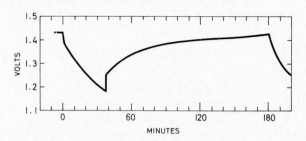

F<small>IG</small>. 5-24   Charge–discharge characteristics of nickel–cadmium battery.

These batteries have a high effective capacitance in circuits and sometimes are used as the equivalent of capacitance for filtering ripples out of direct current power.

SILVER OXIDE–ZINC BATTERY

The silver oxide–zinc reaction produces a high energy output per unit weight. With this system, both primary and secondary batteries have been developed having high current rates as well as high specific energy. These batteries have found extensive use in missiles and spacecraft where the requirement for higher performance can be met only by this relatively expensive type of battery. There is a limited commercial market for rechargeable silver oxide–zinc batteries for special applications such as instruments. Although this electrochemical system long has been known to have advantageous properties, it was not until 1941 that the separator problem was solved sufficiently to permit a practical battery to be made. By the use of cellophane as a semi-permeable membrane, H. G. André was able to limit the passage of colloidal silver and prevent the growth of long zinc whiskers (treeing) that can short out a cell.

Silver oxide may exist with two valences. These are silver monoxide, Ag_2O, and the divalent silver oxide, AgO, which is sometimes referred to in the older literature as silver peroxide. Later studies have shown that this is not a true peroxide. The divalent silver oxide yields 2 faradays of electricity per gram-atom of silver and the silver monoxide yields half this amount. These compounds may be made chemically or by the electrolytic oxidation of silver.

The chemical reaction proceeds in two steps, starting with divalent silver oxide

$$2AgO + Zn \rightarrow ZnO + Ag_2O$$

Then the monovalent oxide is reduced to silver

$$Ag_2O + Zn \rightarrow ZnO + 2Ag$$

As in other alkaline cells with zinc, the soluble zincate ion ZnO_2^{--} is formed from the oxide ZnO

$$ZnO + 2OH^- \rightarrow ZnO_2^{--} + H_2O$$

This soluble zincate can cause migration of zinc away from the anode with resulting losses during the recharging process.

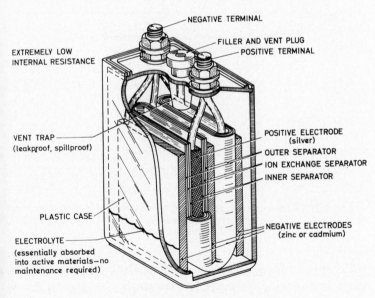

FIG. 5-25   Cut-away view of rechargeable alkaline cell (Yardney Electric Corporation).

A typical charge–voltage curve for a silver oxide–zinc battery is shown in Fig. 5-26. This stepped voltage characteristic corresponds to the formation of silver monoxide during the first step followed by conversion to divalent silver oxide. The discharge

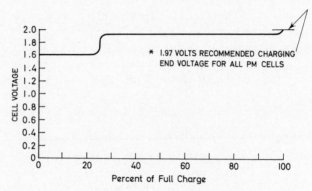

FIG. 5-26 Typical charge curve of silver oxide–zinc system (Yardney Electric Corporation).

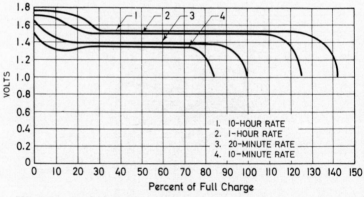

FIG. 5-27 Typical discharge curves for the silver oxide–zinc system (Yardney Electric Corporation).

curve, Fig. 5-27, is similar, but depends on the rate of discharge. The stepped voltage discharge characteristic may be avoided where precise voltage control is essential, by limiting the charge potential or by partially discharging the battery to the plateau voltage before use. Primary batteries of high capacity made with chemically prepared divalent silver oxide, have nearly constant discharge voltage without the step change.

Both the silver oxide and the zinc electrodes are made with porous high-surface area pressed material using pure silver grids for both electrodes. Other less expensive grid materials are silver plated nickel screen at the positive electrode and copper screen at the negative electrode. The electrolyte used is an aqueous solution of potassium hydroxide. Usually layers of several separator materials are used to obtain the required performance. These may include regenerated cellulose materials and woven nylon cloth. Chemical reactions of the electrolyte and the silver oxide with the separator materials limit the life of the cell particularly at elevated temperatures.

Fig. 5-28 Rechargeable silver oxide–zinc aircraft battery (Yardney Electric Corporation).

In the development of sealed silver oxide–zinc cells, a number of difficulties have been overcome including the reaction of zinc to produce hydrogen from the electrolyte. Also the oxygen recombination reaction used in the cadmium cells during overcharge does not proceed readily with silver. However, sealed batteries have been developed for space applications. The operating conditions are more restrictive than for cadmium batteries and some venting may be required although much higher capacity can be obtained.

High capacity zinc–silver oxide batteries may be shipped dry for manual activation just prior to use to prevent loss of capacity while standing in the activated condition. This activation usually is accomplished just prior to the firing of a missile. The requirement for high capacity batteries for missiles which must be in the ready condition for long periods of time such as defensive missiles, has led to the development of automatically activated batteries. The batteries can be activated by an electrical signal. After a few seconds required for the automatic filling with electrolyte and soaking of the separator material, the batteries are in a fully active condition. There is no deterioration during the dry storage

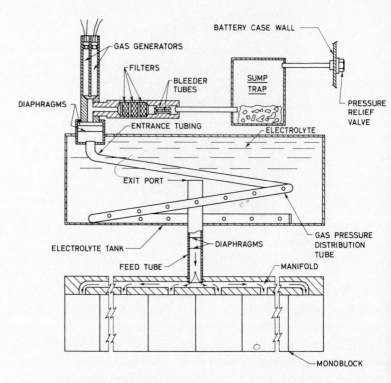

FIG. 5-29   Schematic diagram of automatically activated primary silver oxide–zinc battery (Yardney Electric Corporation).

and there is a considerable safety factor in having an inert battery during standby conditions. The electrolyte reservoir in which the potassium hydroxide solution is stored is connected by a manifold to each cell of the battery. The activation device may use a solid-

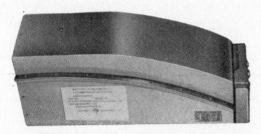

FIG. 5-30 Automatically activated primary silver oxide–zinc battery curved to fit missile skin (Yardney Electric Corporation).

FIG. 5-31 Automatically activated primary silver oxide–zinc battery (Yardney Electric Corporation).

propellent gas generator to force the liquid into the cells at a high rate, however, some batteries depend upon gravity flow. A typical design is shown in Fig. 5-29. The activation time of this battery can be varied from a fraction of a second up to five minutes. The battery may have more than 24 hr of wet stand time after activation before the performance degraded below a useful level.

SILVER OXIDE-CADMIUM BATTERY

The excellent electrochemical properties of the cadmium elec-trode are combined with the high capacity of the silver oxide system in this recently developed battery dating from 1955. Sealed cells with long cycle life are now available and are used in space-craft and other advanced applications requiring superior perform-ance.

Similar to the silver oxide–zinc cell the chemical reaction pro-ceeds in two steps with voltage plateaus corresponding to the di-valent and monovalent silver oxides

$$2AgO + Cd + H_2O \rightarrow Ag_2O + Cd(OH)_2$$
$$Ag_2O + Cd + H_2O \rightarrow 2Ag + Cd(OH)_2$$

The active materials of the electrodes may be in a porous sinter-ed matrix or pressed onto a metal grid. The electrolyte is an

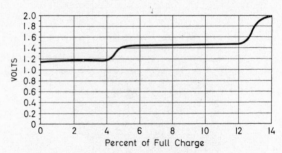

FIG. 5-32   Typical charge curve for the silver oxide–cadmium system (Yardney Electric Corporation).

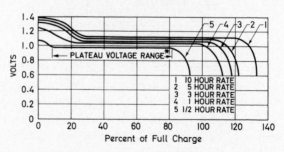

FIG. 5-33   Typical discharge curves for the silver oxide–cadmium system (Yardney Electric Corporation).

aqueous solution of potassium hydroxide. Construction of the cells is similar to that of other alkaline batteries with multiple layers of cellophane and nylon separator material being used to

FIG. 5-34 Silver oxide–cadmium button cells (Yardney Electric Corporation).

FIG. 5-35 Silver oxide–cadmium battery for TV service (Yardney Electric Corporation).

prevent ion migration. The same arrangements for sealing are used as for the nickel–cadmium battery. Oxygen removal at the cadmium electrode permits continuous overcharge without excessive pressures; however, charging should be limited to 1.5 to

1.6 V for sealed cells. Silver oxide–cadmium cells have provided more than 7000 cycles to 50 percent capacity during each discharge without failure.

Being self-contained, batteries are less sensitive to environmental conditions than some other sources of power. Even the absence of a gravity field (zero-*g*) does not cause serious difficulty for batteries used for space power. Here sealed cells are required to operate in the reduced pressure. However, an emergency vent may be used to release any excessive pressure that might be produced by abnormal conditions such as reverse charging.

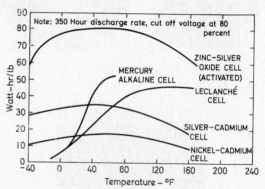

FIG. 5-36   Maximum battery capacity vs. temperature (Electro-Optical Systems, Inc.).

Temperature, however, changes battery characteristics as shown in Fig. 5-36. The total energy delivered decreases at low temperature and may have a maximum value near room temperature. However, maximum battery power increases with temperature because the chemical reaction rates increase and the electrical resistance of the electrolyte decreases. Relations between discharge rate, capacity and temperature are provided in Figs. 5-37, 5-38 and 5-39. Self-discharge also increases with temperature, although the rate of loss depends upon the type of cell, its con-

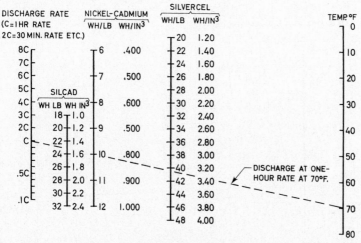

FIG. 5-37 Comparison of the specific energy of silver oxide–zinc, silver oxide–cadmium and nickel–cadmium systems (Yardney Electric Corporation).

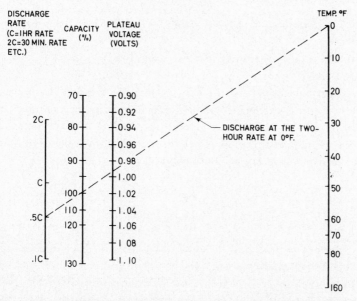

FIG. 5-38 Performance characteristics of the silver oxide–cadmium battery. To find the capacity and plateau voltage, draw a straight line between the discharge rate and the ambient temperature (Yardney Electric Corporation).

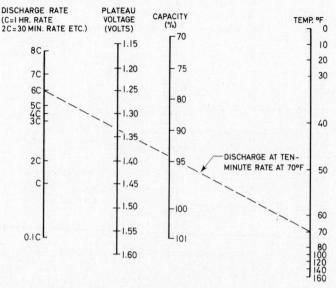

FIG. 5-39 Performance characteristics of the silver oxide–zinc battery. To find the capacity and plateau voltage, draw a straight line between the discharge rate and the ambient temperature (Yardney Electric Corporation).

struction and operating history (some typical values of time to 50 percent charge retention are shown in Fig. 5-40).

Thermal control of the battery may be required to prevent temperature extremes. Greater efficiency can be obtained by avoiding low temperature operation. Cooling of large batteries may be required to remove heat produced during operation since excessive temperatures could result.

BATTERY CHARACTERISTICS

Battery performance is shown by curves of discharge voltage at different discharge rates and temperatures, such as Fig. 5-33. From the curves it is seen that the voltage initially drops to a nearly constant value until the battery is exhausted. After the "knee" of the discharge curve, the voltage drops abruptly and the battery is "dead".

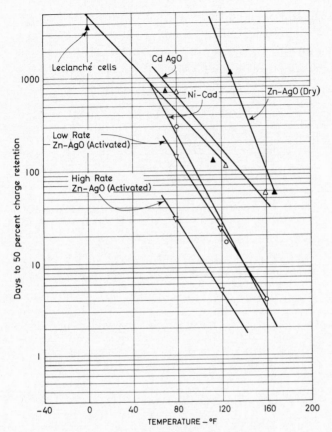

Fig. 5-40 Battery shelf line (approximate) (Electro-Optical Systems, Inc.).

Battery capacity is the total output of electricity (ampere-hours). It is usual to quote capacity to some terminal voltage or to the projected knee of the curve. This capacity decreases at high discharge rates due, in part, to inefficient use of the active material. This efficiency and the cell capacity can be increased by reducing the current density (amperes per unit electrode area). Thus by increasing the electrode surface area in a cell, greater capacity through more complete utilization of active material results.

Various analytical expressions have been suggested for relating battery capacity to discharge rate. However only Peukert's law for lead–acid batteries has been found adequate and convenient. This now has been extended to apply to other secondary batteries. In this equation the current I and the discharge time t appear with two empirical constants n and C

$$I^n t = C$$

The validity of this is demonstrated if a plot of $\log I$ vs. $\log t$ yields a straight line. The slope of this line is $-\dfrac{1}{n}$. Knowing n, the value of C can be obtained.

TABLE 5-6   ANALYTIC REPRESENTATION OF DISCHARGE CHARACTERISTICS OF SECONDARY BATTERIES

Type	Nominal capacity	Temperature (°C)	n	C	Capacity $I \times t$
Lead–acid	45	25	1.37	73.0	$73I^{-0.37}$
Lead–acid	120	25	1.50	378.0	$378I^{-0.50}$
Sintered Ni–Cd	20	24	1.06	23.4	$23.4I^{-0.06}$
Sintered Ni–Cd	20	24	1.07	21.8	$21.8I^{-0.07}$
$Ag_2O–Zn$	5	−18	1.14	4.93	$4.93I^{-0.14}$
$Ag_2O–Zn$	60	−18	0.98	54.6	$54.6I^{+0.02}$
$Ag_2O–Zn$	60	0	1.07	83.6	$83.6I^{-0.07}$
$Ag_2O–Zn$	60	30	1.07	84.1	$84.1I^{-0.07}$
Ni–Fe alkaline	100	22	1.02	105.0	$105I^{-0.020}$

Values for these constants depend on the size and construction of the battery. Table 5-6 shows that n for lead–acid batteries is of the order of 1.4 whereas for alkaline batteries n is about unity. Thus the capacity of the lead–acid battery decreases with rate of discharge while the capacity of the alkaline batteries is more constant. For the silver oxide–zinc cell at −18 °C n is indicated as slightly less than unity. Here the capacity should increase slightly with an increasing rate of discharge (this might be the result of internal heating from large currents). The quantity C is obviously related to size, and the capacity becomes identical to C when n is unity.

Other useful relations can be derived from Peukert's law. For example, the capacity of a battery It (ampere-hours) is

$$It = CI^{1-n}$$

Also the rates of change of effective capacity with respect to current and time are

$$\left[\frac{\partial(It)}{\partial I}\right]_t = (1-n)CI^{-n}$$

$$\left[\frac{\partial(It)}{\partial t}\right]_I = \frac{n-1}{n}\,C^{1/n}t^{-1/n}$$

ENERGY AND POWER

The power EI (watts) and the total energy EIt (watt-hours) delivered by a battery are usually more important than capacity (It). Therefore an expression for the average potential $\bar{E}$ as a function of current is needed.

Discharge data show that the voltage decreases during discharge at constant current and that this can be approximated by a straight line up to the "knee" of the discharge curve. The midpoint of this line is used as the average potential $\bar{E}$. From values of $\bar{E}$ as a function of current, the average potential at zero current E^* is estimated. Then an internal resistance for the cell is obtained from

$$R_i = \frac{E^* - \bar{E}}{I}$$

$$\bar{E} = E^* - IR_i$$

So the battery power P is

$$P = E^*I - I^2R$$

From this relation the maximum power is obtained

$$\frac{d(P)}{dI} = E^* - 2IR_i = 0$$

$$I = \frac{E^*}{2R_i} \text{ (max. power)}$$

The maximum power is then

$$P_{max} = \frac{(E^*)^2}{2R_i} - \frac{(E^*)^2}{4R_i} = \frac{(E^*)^2}{4R_i}$$

The power delivered by a battery increases with the current up to this maximum value. At this point the resistance of the external circuit just equals the internal resistance of the battery.

Unfortunately, the internal resistance of a battery is not constant and may even decrease with load. Therefore a more accurate method for obtaining maximum power and energy has been developed. For several types of secondary batteries the average potential $\bar{E}$ can be related to the current by an expression of the form

$$\bar{E} = E^* - BI^{-m}$$

Here E^*, B and m are constants. Then the power becomes

$$P = I(E^* - BI^{-m})$$

From this the total energy is found to be

$$Pt = CI^{1-n}(E^* - BI^{-m})$$

Also the maximum power is

$$P_{max} = -mB\frac{E^*}{(1-m)B}^{\frac{1-m}{m}}$$

TABLE 5-7 ANALYTIC EXPRESSION
OF AVERAGE VOLTAGE

Battery type	Average voltage
Lead–acid at 25 °C	$\bar{E} = 1.978 - 0.0103\ I^{0.964}$
Nickel–cadmium with sintered plates, at 24 °C, 5 cells	$\bar{E} = 6.25 - 0.086\ I^{0.470}$
Nickel–iron at 22 °C	$\bar{E} = 1.323 - 0.00446\ I^{1.005}$

Test data on various types of cells are represented in Table 5-7. It is seen that pertinent information from a whole series of curves has been reduced to a concise algebraic form.

TABLE 5-8   PRIMARY CELL CHARACTERISTICS

Type	Open-circuit voltage	Average voltage	Capacity at low current		Shelf life (years)	Operating temp. limits °F
			Wh/lb	Wh/in³		
Air cell	1.5	1.25	65	2.2	5 (dry)	40 to 140
Alkaline	1.52	1.25	44	3.8	2	−40 to 140
Indium	1.37	1.15	23	2.1	1 to 3	−20 to 190
Leclanché	1.5 to 1.65	1.25	43	3.5	1	0 to 120
Magnesium–silver chloride	1.6	1.3	40	3.0		28 to 85
Silver oxide–zinc	1.86	1.5	65	4.6	3 (dry)	−20 to 160
Solid electrolyte	0.69			1.5	0.1	20	−65 to 170
Thermal	3.0			4		10	−65 to 165

TABLE 5-9   SECONDARY CELL CHARACTERISTICS

Type	Average voltage	Open-circuit voltage	Charge loss per month (percent)	Charge-discharge cycles	Specific energy at low drain	
					$\frac{Wh}{lb}$	$\frac{Wh}{in^3}$
Nickel–iron	1.2	1.34	30	2000	11	0.9
Lead–acid (automotive)	2.0	2.14	25	300	15	1.3
Nickel–cadmium	1.2	1.34	2	2000	12	0.9
Silver oxide–cadmium	1.1	1.34	3	2000	24	2.4
Silver oxide–zinc sealed	1.45	1.86	3	100	20–50	1.3–3.1
Silver oxide–zinc primary	1.45	1.86	—	—	55	3.6

REQUIRED BATTERY CAPACITY

The secondary battery in a system must have capacity to meet requirements when primary power is not available. The maximum recharging current is limited to a value related to capacity. Also the energy that can be drawn is restricted to a fraction of total capacity for long cycle life. Therefore the total installed capacity is usually much larger than that required just for energy storage. For example, a secondary battery may be required in a satellite that passes into the earth's shadow on every orbit for a period t_d. Solar cells generate a current I_s during the charge period t_c to recharge the battery and to supply the base load I_l. The amount of electricity produced by the primary source $I_s t_c$ minus the amount delivered to the base load during the charge period must equal or exceed the requirements for battery charging. There is an allowance β for overcharge and for losses in order to ensure maximum charge for each cycle so that

$$I_s t_c - I_l t_c = I_l t_d (1 + \beta)$$

System analysis is complex is cases where the load varies. Where many functions are to be performed, a power control system may be necessary to regulate the battery charging current and to limit the discharge cycle. This power control system may detect failed components and disconnect them from the circuit.

REFERENCES

1. W. R. MENETREY and J. CHRISNEY, "Chemical Systems", *Energy Conversion Handbook*, Electro-Optical Systems, WADD Technical Report 60–699 Vol. VI, 1960.
2. B. R. STEIN, "Status Report on Fuel Cells", Army Research Office Report No. 1, 1959.
3. J. E. McCORMICK, "Fuel Cell Systems", RADC-TN-60-118, Rome Air Development Center, USAF, 1960.
4. D. R. ADAMS, P. Y. CATHOU, R. E. GAYNOR, R. D. JACKSON, JR., J. H. KIRSCH, L. L. LEONARD, G. S. LOCKWOOD, JR., W. P. WARNOCK, and R. E. WILCOX, JR., *Fuel Cells—Power for the Future*, 1960.
5. G. J. YOUNG, *Fuel Cells*, New York, Reinhold, 1960.

6. E. W. Justi and A. W. Winsel, *Kalte Verbrennung*, Wiesbaden, Franz Steiner, 1962.
7. General Electric, "Some Plain Talk About Fuel Cells", 1961.
8. J. L. Platner and P. D. Hess, "Static Moisture Removal for Hydrogen Oxygen Capillary Fuel Cell", Allis–Chalmers, 1963.
9. S. S. Tomter and A. P. Antony, "Hydrazine Fuel Cell", Allis–Chalmers, 1963.
10. C. H. J. Broers, "High Temperature Cells with Carbonate Paste Electrolyte", *Fuel Cells*, Chem. Engr. Prog., New York, 1963.
11. M. Shaw, "Biochemical Fuel Cells", 17th Annual Power Sources Conference Proceedings, PSC Publications Committee, Red Bank, New Jersey.
12. R. C. Shair, "Electrochemical Cells for Space Power", Am. Rocket Society Paper No. 2165–61.
13. H. T. Francis, "Space Battery Hand Book", Armor Research Foundation, Chicago, 1963.
14. C. K. Morehouse, R. Glickman and G. S. Lozier, "Batteries", *Selected Papers on New Techniques for Energy Conversion*, S. N. Levine, ed., New York, Dover Publications, 1961.
15. G. W. Vinal, *Storage Batteries*, 4th Edition, New York, Wiley, 1955.
16. S. M. Selis and C. R. Russell, "An Analytic Representation of the Discharge Characteristics of Commercial Secondary Batteries", *Electrochemical Technology*, I, No. 3–4, pp. 77–81, 1963.

CHAPTER 6

SOLAR ENERGY*

INTRODUCTION

The sun is an essentially inexhaustible source of energy. It is the indirect source of the energy stored in fossil fuels. Solar concentrators for operating heat engines or static thermal energy converters (thermoelectric or thermionic generators) have been developed. Heating with solar energy has been studied at length, however other energy sources usually are more practical.

The major advance in utilizing solar energy to produce power came in 1954 with the discovery of the silicon solar cell at The Bell Telephone Laboratories. Solar cells operate radios and provide emergency power, but one of their most important applications is generating electrical energy in space vehicles. The weight and complexity of a chemical or nuclear fuel is avoided and solar cells will produce electrical energy as long as they are illuminated. They are reasonably efficient (up to about 14 percent) and reliable.

SOLAR CONSTANT

Radiation from the sun that is received outside the earth's atmosphere ranges from soft X-rays (0.001 microns) and extreme ultraviolet to beyond the infrared (more than 2 microns). The longer wavelength region is closely approximated by the radiation

---

* Extensive material for this chapter has been drawn from Ref. 6-1, W. Evans and W. R. Menetrey (Electro-Optical Systems Inc.) "Direct Solar Conversion", *Energy Conversion System Reference Handbook*, W. R. Menetrey, ed., WADD-TR 60-699.

from a black body at 6000 °K. Both have peak intensity at about 0.5 microns. At this temperature, the solar radiation, however, has less short wavelength radiation than a black body.

The earth's atmosphere filters out part of this radiation in selective absorption by oxygen, nitrogen, water vapor and dust. The amount of absorption depends on the altitude, humidity, and the angle of the sun θ from the zenith. Solar radiation can be expressed in terms of the atmosphere thicknesses (m) it traverses, so that

$$m = \frac{1}{\cos \theta}$$

When the sun is 60° from the zenith,

$$m = 2$$

Outside the atmosphere, m is obviously zero. Values of the solar radiation for various conditions are given in Table 6-1.

TABLE 6-1   SOLAR RADIATION

m	Condition	W/m²
0	Outside atmosphere	1400
1	Sea level, sun at zenith	920
2	Sea level, sun at 60° from zenith	740
1	Cloudy day	120

Radiation intensity varies with fluctuations in the sun. These can be as much as ±3.5 percent. Radiation also varies with distance from the sun, decreasing inversely as the square of this distance. Therefore, the solar radiation intensity at other planets may be greater or less than at earth depending on distance from the sun (Table 6-2). At the distance of Mars, for example, the intensity is 43 percent of that at the distance of the Earth.

TABLE 6-2 DISTANCE FROM THE SUN

Planet	Millions of miles
Mercury	36
Venus	67
Earth	93
Mars	142
Jupiter	483
Saturn	886

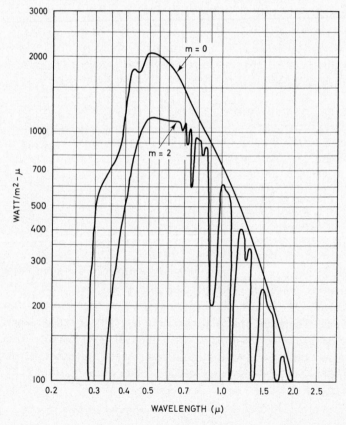

FIG. 6-1 Solar radiation above the atmosphere and the sea level (Allison).

BASIC SEMICONDUCTOR SOLAR CELL CONCEPTS

A metal may be described as a material in which some of the electrons associated with the constituent atoms always are free to move about. An insulator has all the electrons bonded firmly to the atoms so that the electrons cannot move about. A semiconductor then is a material in which no electrons are free at a temperature of absolute zero, but an increasing number become free to move about as the temperature rises. The energy that binds the electrons in a semiconductor is relatively small. This is called the band gap or forbidden energy band. The average energy of the electrons rises as the temperature rises. As a result, the number of electrons possessing enough energy to be free increases. Thus the conductivity of a semiconductor increases with temperature.

The average energy of the electrons in a material is determined by its temperature T. The fraction of electrons having energy equal to or greater than E is

$$f = e^{-E/kT}$$

where k is the Boltzmann constant. This quantity is seen often in semiconductor equations.

An electron also may acquire energy through its interaction with a photon. Photon energy is

$$E_f = hv$$

where h is Planck's constant and v is the light frequency. This energy must be greater than the energy gap of the electron, E_g, for the electron to become free.

When an electron has been excited and freed from an atom, a vacancy is left. In the presence of an electric field, this vacancy can be filled by a bound electron from an adjacent atom, leaving another vacancy. In effect, the vacancy propagates in an electric field in a direction opposite to that of the electron flow. It is characteristic of most semiconductors that these vacancies, called holes, move in a field almost as readily as electrons, acting very much like positively charged particles.

A trace of foreign material (dope) in a semiconductor crystal may produce charge carriers in either of two ways:

(1) Provide extra electrons that are easily excited into a free state.
(2) Present vacancies or holes in the crystal.

Crystals that contain impurities of the first type have more free electrons present than free holes. This is designated n- (negative) type. Conversely, crystals of the second type having more free holes than electrons are called p- (positive) type. Semiconductors that contain a substantial amount of impurity (heavily doped) conduct current almost exclusively with only one type of charge carrier—negative or positive. In crystals that have no impurities, the number of holes and electrons is equal. It is this number per unit volume that is called the intrinsic carrier concentration.

A doped crystal contains more charge carriers of one type than of the other. The concentration of the majority type charge carriers per unit volume is signified by n_n or p_p for n- or p-type crystals. The corresponding concentrations of the minority charge carriers are p_n and n_p.

The mobility μ_p of holes and μ_n of electrons describes the ease with which carriers move when influenced by an electric field. The mobility is the average carrier velocity divided by the applied field (cm^2/V-sec).

A charge carrier concentration gradient in a crystal will cause the carriers to diffuse just as heat diffused under a gradient of temperature. The diffusion coefficient, D, for a semiconductor has the same role as the diffusion coefficient in the heat diffusion equation. Units are usually cm^2/sec.

When a carrier is excited into the free state, it remains in this state for a finite length of time. The lifetime τ_n or τ_p is defined as the times required for the number of excited carriers to decay to $1/e$ of the previous values. In equilibrium, of course, the rate at which carriers are being formed just equals their rate of decay.

Carriers diffuse under a concentration gradient and recombine (return to the unexcited state). The average length that carriers travel before recombining is called the diffusion length—L_n for electrons and L_p for holes. The electrical properties of semiconductors can be described in terms of these parameters (μ, D, τ, and L).

THE SEMICONDUCTOR JUNCTION

A semiconductor may have the impurities so distributed that the crystal is n-type on one side and p-type on the other. Then the region where the two types meet is called the junction. If both n- and p-type impurities are present throughout the crystal, the junction occurs where their effective concentrations are equal. The potential energy of the electrons is greater in the p-region than in the n-region. Similarly, the potential energy of the holes is greater in the n-region than in the p-region. Therefore, the junction represents a potential barrier to both electrons and holes (Fig. 6-2).

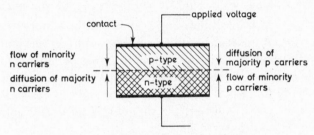

FIG. 6-2   Semiconductor junction.

The nonequilibrium distribution of carriers results in their diffusion across the junction. This diffusion, however, produces a charge distribution and a resulting field. The field then causes a current to flow in a direction opposite to the diffusion current. At equilibrium the diffusion and the field currents are equal. The availability of minority carriers determines the equilibrium conditions. If the flow by diffusion of majority carriers exceeds that of minority carriers, the junction potential barrier will rise. This will reduce the flow of majority carriers until their flow equals that of the minority carriers. This equilibrium current is referred to as the saturation current I_0.

The potential gradient between the n- and p-regions is concentrated in a region that is very close to the junction. This region is called the depletion region. Any minority carriers reaching this region are swept across the junction by the electric field. Increasing the intensity of the field will not increase this current since all minority carriers that reach the junction are swept across anyway. However, the flow of majority carriers can be increased. These currents are limited by the junction barrier. Therefore, decreasing the barrier will increase sharply the majority carrier flow. The rectifying properties of semiconductor junctions now become apparent. When no field is applied externally across the junction, the net current is zero. In fact, the potential barrier cannot be measured externally because of similar, exactly equal and opposite potential barriers, that appear in the contacts made to the semiconductor for the measurements.

An external potential difference applied in a direction to cause minority carrier flow will increase the fields in the depletion region. As mentioned previously, however, the minority carrier flow will not increase but will remain equal to I_0. The majority carrier current, equal in equilibrium to I_0, will be further reduced by the increased potential barrier, so that the maximum current measured externally is I_0. When the field is applied in the majority carrier direction, however, the situation is quite different. The barrier will be lowered and the majority carrier current will increase exponentially with applied voltage; thus, the majority carrier current, I_m, becomes

$$I_m = Ae^{(\alpha V)}$$

where A and α are constant and V is the externally applied voltage. At zero applied voltage

$$I_m = I_0$$
$$A = I_0$$

Also, α is the electronic charge q divided by kT, where again k is the Boltzmann constant. Thus the current–voltage relation for an ideal diode is given by

$$I = I_m - I_0 = I_0 e^{(qV/kT)} - I_0$$

THE SOLAR CELL

Photons impinging upon the semiconductor junction can excite new p- and n-carriers. Each photon with more energy than the band-gap E_g will produce one minority and one majority carrier in either the p- or the n-region. Any of these minority carriers that reach the junction will be swept across by the field. This lowers the potential barrier across the junction until majority carriers flow just equals the additional minority carrier flow from the photons. Now the decrease in the potential barrier can be seen externally; in fact, the situation actually is described by the circuit shown in Fig. 6-3. Here the diode represents the junction (before

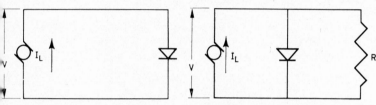

FIG. 6-3   Solar cell equivalent circuit (no external load).

FIG. 6-4   Solar cell equivalent circuit (with external load).

the photon-generated carrier current appears) and the current generator represents the photon-generated current. The voltage V appears externally and can be measured. It is sufficient just to make the diode current equal to the added photon-generated minority carrier current, I_L, so that

$$I_0 e^{qV/kT} - I_0 = I_L$$

When the semiconductor junction is short circuited, the junction potential barrier can be only that normally present without illumination. This potential cannot be measured externally because of the compensating barriers in the contacts, as mentioned previously. However, if the external circuit is a resistor, the photon-generated current is divided between the diode and this resistor. The equivalent circuit is shown in Fig. 6-4. Current I_{ex} in the external load is now I_L minus the diode current, or

$$I_{ex} = I_L - I_0(e^{qV/kT} - 1)$$

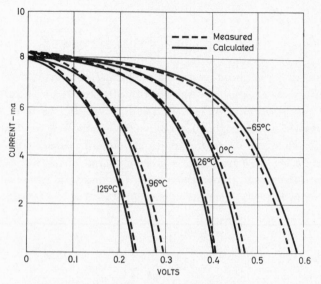

FIG. 6-5 Typical current–voltage characteristics vs. temperature for silicon
solar cell (WADD TR 60-699).

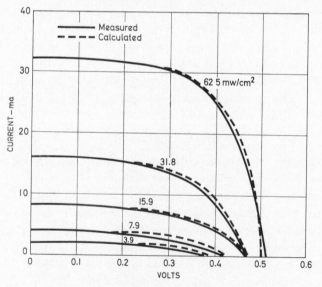

FIG. 6-6 Typical current–voltage characteristics vs. intensity for a silicon
solar cell (WADD TR 60-699).

This is the fundamental idealized solar cell operating equation.

The current–voltage characteristics of actual solar photovoltaic cells are described more accurately by the relation

$$I_{ex} = I_L - I_0[e^{q(V - IR_s)/nkT} - 1]$$

where R_s is the internal cell series resistance. The dimensionless parameter n accounts for space charge generation and other effects. Its value usually is greater than unity and is nearly constant with voltage. The value of n decreases with temperature and with intensity of illumination (insolance). Typical cell performance is illustrated in Figs. 6-5 and 6-6.

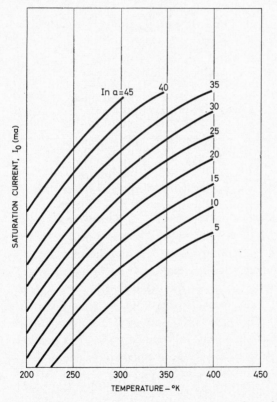

FIG. 6-7 Saturation current vs. temperature for various values of a (WADD TR 60-699).

The saturation current I_0 per unit cell area is given approximately by

$$I_0 = q\left[p_n\left(\frac{D_p}{\tau_p}\right)^{\frac{1}{2}} + n_p\left(\frac{D_n}{\tau_n}\right)^{\frac{1}{2}} \right]$$

It is thus a function of equilibrium densities of carriers, diffusion rates and carrier lifetimes. This saturation current is a sensitive function of temperature as shown in Fig. 6-7 and by the relation

$$I_0 = aT^3(e^{-qE_g/kT})$$

where E_g is the effective thermal band gap (approximately 1.1/eV for silicon). The value of a is determined by the semiconductor properties.

TABLE 6-3   TYPICAL SILICON SOLAR
CELL PARAMETERS

τ_p	10^{-7} sec
ϱ	0.1 ohm-cm
D_p	10 cm²/sec
μ_n	700 cm²/V-sec
$a = q/kt$	40 V^{-1}
I_0	10^{-6} mA
L_D	10^{-3} cm
E_g	1.1 eV
p_n	10^5 cm^{-3}
I_L	100 mW/cm²

The open-circuit voltage V_∞ is determined by light density and by the semiconductor properties. These include the series resistance, the mobility of carriers and the energy gap. To obtain a large voltage, the semiconductor should have a large band gap, low resistance, low carrier mobility and long carrier lifetime. However, it can be shown that for maximum power in the solar spectrum, the band gap should have a value between 1.0 and 1.2 eV. Thus silicon with an band gap of 1.1 is a preferred material. The open-circuit voltage (I equals zero) is found to be

$$V_\infty = \frac{nkT}{q} \ln\left(\frac{I_L}{I_0}\right)$$

This voltage decreases with increasing temperature (Fig. 6-8).

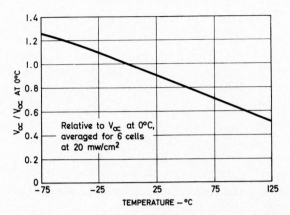

FIG. 6-8   Open-circuit voltage vs. temperature for typical silicon cell
(WADD TR 60-699).

The short-circuit current (V equals zero) is given by the relation

$$I_{sc} = I_L - I_0(e^{-qIR/nkt} - 1)$$

Since the series resistance R_s is small for cells of high quality, it
follows that

$$I_{sc} \cong I_L$$

The power P delivered by the cell is

$$P = IV = V\left[I_L - I_0(e^{q(V-IR)/nkT} - 1)\right]$$

By matching the load resistance to the cell, power equal to 60 to
80 percent of the product of the open-circuit voltage and the
short-circuit current can be extracted.

CELL MATCHING

High efficiency results only when all the cell parameters — surface conditions, junction depth, and crystal perfection — are very
close to optimum. Solar cells with high efficiency have almost
identical characteristics. Lower efficiency cells, however, exhibit
quite a significant divergence of characteristics.

Since mismatched cells unduly reduce efficiency, each cell's performance is measured under standard conditions. Cells of high efficiency are used where their premium cost is justified. Other cells can be matched and combined into modules. The circuit may require adjustment according to the measured characteristic of each module.

SILICON CELL

A typical p–n silicon cell is made from a slice of silicon 20 mil thick. The silicon crystal from which this flat wafer is cut contains a uniformly distributed impurity of the n-type. The wafer then is heated in an atmosphere of the p-type impurity (boron) so that this element diffuses into the surface. When the concentration of boron near the surface becomes much greater than that of the n-type atoms, the surface of the wafer becomes p-type. The zone

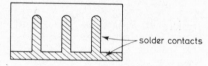

FIG. 6-9   Gridded cell.

at which the diffused concentration of p-type material equals that of the n-type material is defined as the junction. After the back and edges are cleaned, a narrow solder contact is applied to the surface and over the entire back. A grid of solder or wires can be added to the surface to minimize losses in collecting the current (Fig. 6-9).

OTHER MATERIALS

Efficient cadmium sulfide solar cells were reported at about the same time as the first silicon units. The physical processes in the two types of cell are different, however. The CdS cells are constructed so that a barrier layer appears at a contact (usually copper) and the voltage is generated across this barrier layer.

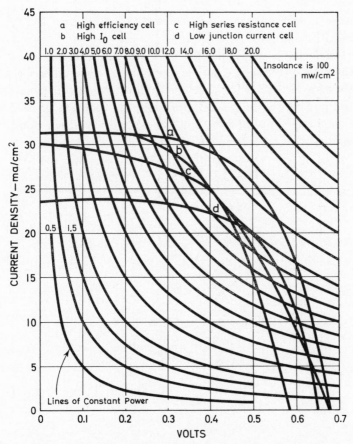

FIG. 6-10   Typical silicon solar cell performance curves showing efficiency
degradation (WADD TR 60-699).

Cells of this type are easier to make than are silicon cells. Although
the band gap of cadmium sulfide is 2.4 eV, its spectral response
is more indicative of a material with a band gap of 1.3 eV. Since
the rate of efficiency degradation with temperature appears to be
lower than for silicon cells, CdS cells may find applications where
higher temperatures are required or where radiation of longer
wavelength is to be converted. A possible application is the ther-
mal-photovoltaic converter for producing electricity directly from
thermal radiation from a heated surface or flame. However, in

the solar spectrum, the efficiency of CdS solar cells is less than that of silicon cells.

Intermetallic semiconductor cells such as gallium arsenide (band gap 1.4 eV) should have improved high-temperature operating characteristics. Their development has been delayed by severe metallurgical problems and the difficulty of producing large crystals suitable for solar cells. Some of the types of semiconductor materials that have been studied are listed in Table 6-4.

TABLE 6-4   SOLAR CELL MATERIALS

Material	E_g eV
Ge	0.7
Si	1.1
InP	1.3
GaAs	1.4
CdTe	1.4
AlSb	1.6
CdSe	1.8
AlAs	2.2
GaP	2.4
CdS	2.4

COMPOSITE CELLS

A semiconductor material with a single band gap can convert efficiently only energy from a relatively narrow portion of the entire solar spectrum. Photons with less energy than the band gap will not excite hole–electron pairs in the semiconductor, whereas photons with higher energy will convert part of their energy to heat and will be absorbed nearer the surface of the solar cell. In the silicon solar cell the spectral efficiency (that is, the fraction of total energy in the solar spectrum that is actually imparted to the carriers) is less than 50 percent. This can be increased, however, by making it possible to convert photons into electrical carriers at more than one band gap.

In principle, a single-band-gap semiconductor material is transparent to photons with less energy than the band gap. Actually, this is true only for relatively pure and well developed materials such as germanium and silicon. Since the ideal semiconductor material will transmit energy at wavelengths longer than the cut off wavelength, it should be possible to have a stacked photovoltaic energy converter. The high-energy photons then are converted at the top of the stack and the low energy photons are converted in the layers below.

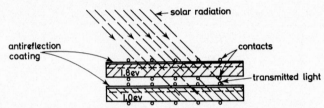

FIG. 6-11   Composite energy gap solar cell (WADD TR 60-699).

A semiconductor with a higher band-gap energy could be advantageous to use with silicon in the fabrication of a multi-layered photovoltaic cell. Gallium arsenide, aluminium antimonide and gallium phosphide have band-gap energies that appear attractive for composite cells. Each of these can convert solar energy into electrical energy efficiently only within a narrow band of wavelengths near the absorption edge.

The high band-gap components must transmit the long wavelength radiation, if a composite cell is to operate well. Also the surfaces of the cells must be treated to minimize reflection and scattering. Silicon monoxide, arsenic trisulfide, or magnesium fluoride can be used as antireflection coatings.

Another approach to the composite cell used a dichroic mirror. This directs the longer and shorter wavelength radiations to the proper cells mounted at right angles to each other (Fig. 6-12). The solar radiation is incident on the dichroic mirror at an angle of 45 degrees. Overall efficiency now depends only upon the transmissive and reflective characteristics of the dichroic mirror. This type of generator could have an efficiency approaching 20 percent.

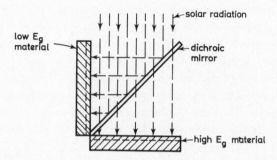

FIG. 6-12   Reflective composite solar cell (WADD TR 60-699).

TEMPERATURE CONTROL

The performance of silicon solar cells degrades significantly as the temperature increases (Fig. 6-13). Therefore, it is imperative that these systems be designed to operate at the lowest possible temperature consistent with mission and vehicle requirements. Temperature can be controlled through radiation, conduction, convection, thermoelectric heat transfer, or combinations of these. Radiation and conduction are used for thermal control in satellites.

The basic parameters that describe the radiative properties of a surface are absorptivity α and emissivity ε. At a particular wavelength, these are equal:

$$\alpha(\lambda) = \varepsilon(\lambda)$$

The reflectance r is equal to $(1-\alpha)$. This is measured readily with a spectrophotometer and the values are used to determine absorptivity and emissivity. The total absorptivity and emissivity over any given spectral distribution can be found by integration. Total emissivity is defined using the black-body spectrum, which is a function of temperature. Therefore, total emissivity is itself a function of temperature. Absorptivity of many materials has been determined for the solar spectrum. A typical value for an untreated silicon solar cell surface is 0.94.

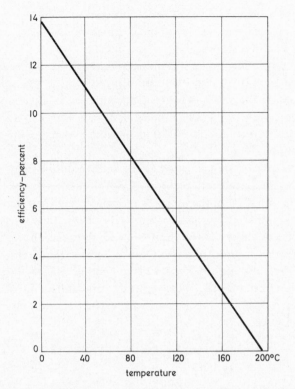

FIG. 6-13 Efficiency vs. temperature of a silicon solar cell.

The total power P radiated from a surface of area A is

$$P = A\varepsilon\delta T^4$$

where ε is the total emissivity at the absolute temperature T, and δ is the Stefan–Boltzman constant, 5.67×10^{-12} W/cm² °K⁴. The equilibrium temperature for a panel oriented at an angle θ from the sun is found by equating the total rate of energy absorption with the sum of power emitted and the electrical power produced:

$$A\alpha H \cos \theta = A\varepsilon\delta T^4 + P_{\mathrm{elec}}$$

Here H is the solar constant of 1400 W/m² outside the earth's atmosphere. A space vehicle usually will have several surfaces with various angles of orientation to the sun and with different values of ε and α. For each panel, the sum of the rate of energy absorption must equal the sum of the power radiated and the electrical power produced.

Thermal conduction paths may be provided to carry heat away from solar cells through the supporting structure. The solar cell temperature can be lowered significantly by connecting them through conduction paths to good emitting surfaces. A variety of materials have emissivities of 0.95 or greater at the temperatures of interest.

Cover glasses are cemented to the surface of the solar cells to provide environmental protection and to reflect much of the incident radiation in the longer wavelengths that the silicon solar cells cannot use to produce electricity. Also a blue dye on the glass covers filters out the short wavelength radiation that would damage the organic adhesive used to cement the covers to the cells. The glass surface emits a maximum amount of black body radiation from the cell. These spectral temperature control techniques are effective in reducing the operating temperature of the cells in space.

CELL MOUNTING

The most frequently used method of assembling and mounting cells consists of soldering five cells together to form a strong and rigid shingle (Fig. 6-14). A series connection of five cells thus is

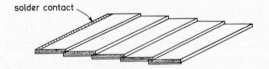

solder contact

FIG. 6-14 Series submodule.

provided. When they are mounted on an electrically conductive surface, an insulating adhesive must be used. Alternatively, modules of parallel-connected cells can be made (Fig. 6-15). Then the cells are mounted flat on the substrate and can be soldered to it for good thermal and electrical contact.

The optimum series–parallel arrangement of cells in a large array is determined by considerations of the panel configuration, required voltage and essential reliability. In general, cell failures, whether from environmental damage or fabrication errors, result in open circuits rather than short circuits. Thus, to reduce the effect of failures, the basic grouping should be cells in parallel. However, the shingle submodule usually is preferred because it uses the panel area more efficiently.

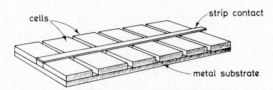

FIG. 6-15   Parallel submodule.

The substrate material for mounting the cells may itself be rigid or it may be made rigid by a supporting frame structure. Double-faced aluminum honeycomb sheet provides a high strength-to-weight ratio but it has poor thermal conduction properties compared to a metal sheet supported by a framework. Nonmetallic structural materials such as fiberglass and pressed compositions are electrical insulators but they are poor thermal conductors. The surface of the vehicle itself may be used as the substrate, if its shape, size and temperature characteristics are favorable.

Solar-cell arrays large enough to produce a kilowatt of power are expensive to make because each cell is small and costly. Also a large array with covers for radiation shielding and support structure is heavy and difficult to package as rigid panels in a spacecraft, particularly during launch. Therefore, much attention is given to the development of large-area, thin-film photovoltaic cells. These might be made by evaporating a thin layer of semiconductor material onto a flexible substrate of thin metal or plastic that could be rolled up into a small volume for stowage during launch. Evaporation processes would be well suited to low-cost production of large area cells. Thin film cadmium sulfide cells have been made on a flexible sheet as large as 6 in. square. Even though the efficiency of such cells is only about 2 percent, a reduction in panel weight is possible. Furthermore, these cells are resistant to radiation damage. Other semiconductor materials that are being studied for making thin-film cells include cadmium telluride and gallium arsenide.

ENVIRONMENTAL EFFECTS

The space environment is detrimental to solar cells, their supporting structure and any auxiliaries such as concentrators. It does not appear that operating in a vacuum seriously degrades the cells. However, meteoroids, high energy proton and electron bombardment and exposure to X-rays are damaging.

With several cells series-connected in a module and a number of modules parallel-connected on each panel, a large meteoroid impact damaging one cell sufficiently to produce an open circuit will not cause complete failure. Performance of the panel deteriorates, however, because of the loss of a module and the resulting mismatch between modules. The probability of this type of damage in multiple units is low. More likely is damage from "sand blasting" by many small meteoroids. However, cells protected by glass or quartz covers should not deteriorate from this type of damage by more than 15 percent in long-term (months) space operation.

The solar corona consists of out-streaming particles—proton and electrons—moving at high velocity. During solar flares the intensity and energy of this flux greatly increase. The proton kinetic energy may vary between 2 and 20 keV which is sufficient to produce radiation damage in silicon solar cells. The electron kinetic energy from this source is below the radiation damage threshold. Glass or quartz covers will absorb the proton energy and protect the cells although the covers may become spattered with some reduction in light transmission. Radiation damage will also result from exposure to X-rays from the sun and to cosmic radiation from space. Studies have shown that these radiations seriously degrade cell performance only after an exposure of several years.

More serious radiation damage comes from electrons and protons in the Van Allen belts, and from radioactive material produced by high altitude nuclear weapons tests. There are intense fluxes of electrons and protons with sufficient energies to change the properties of semiconductor materials in regions near the earth. Glass or quartz covers again provide some protection. Also, some other types of solar cells are more resistant to this radiation than p-on-n-type silicon cells. For example, by changes in the manufacturing procedures, n-on-p-type semiconductors have been produced with improved resistance to radiation. Other semiconductor materials are being studied and although the efficiencies of both gallium arsenide and cadmium sulfide cells are lower than that of silicon solar cells, they have been found to be resistant to radiation damage.

SOLAR CONCENTRATORS

Optical devices can collect solar radiation and focus it onto a relatively small area. This concentrated energy then may be used by solar cells, static thermal energy conversion devices (thermoelectric or thermionic generators) or in an absorber to heat a working fluid in an engine.

From the earth's vicinity, the sun appears as a circular disc subtending an arc of approximately 32 min. Therefore, a solar concentrator cannot concentrate solar radiation to a vanishingly small area. The actual size and shape of the image depend on the geometry of the concentrator.

The devices that have been suggested for solar energy concentration include paraboloids of revolution, parabolic cylinders, hemispheres, circular cylinders, Fresnel lenses and mirrors, conical mirrors and dual mirror systems that use paraboloidal or hemispherical primary mirrors. These basic shapes are illustrated in Figs. 6-16 and 6-17. Each type forms a focal image of a certain shape. The paraboloid of revolution, for example, forms a disc image at the focal point of the parabola, whereas the spherical mirror forms a circular rod image along the principal axis of the hemisphere. Variations of these basic shapes include toroidally shaped mirrors with circular or parabolic cross sections. Approxi-

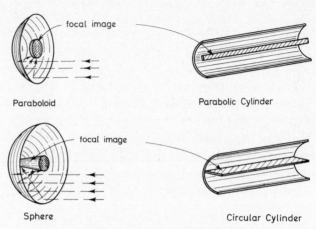

Fig. 6-16   Basic mirror shapes (WADD TR 60-699).

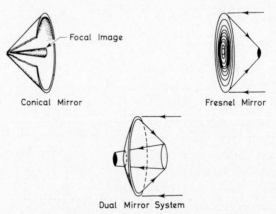

Fig. 6-17   Basic mirror shapes (WADD TR 60-699).

mations of these shapes have been made with segmented mirrors consisting of a multitude of small, flat plates. An umbrella-type structure can approach a paraboloid by a series of parabolic cylindrical shapes (Figs. 6-18 and 6-19).

FIG. 6-18   10-foot umbrella type solar collector (NASA Langley Research Center).

FIG. 6-19   Sunflower solar-mercury turbine power system (Thompson Ramo-Wooldridge).

The cross-section of a paraboloid reflector is shown in Fig. 6-20. The properties of the reflector are expressed in terms of the diameter D_m, the focal length f, and the rim angle θ_m between the optical axis of the reflector and the reflected ray from the rim. The aperture ratio D_m/f is the inverse of the familiar f-number of lenses. The image produced by a cone of light reflected from a

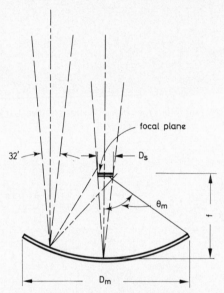

FIG. 6-20   Solar reflector cross-section.

point on the mirror forms an ellipse on the focal plane. The diameter of the theoretical solar image is D_s. The performance of various reflector geometries can be compared on the basis of the concentration factor C defined as the ratio of the total projected area of the reflector to the total area of energy interception in the focal place. Values of the concentration factor for various geometries and of the equivalent black body temperature are compared in Fig. 6-21. Here n is the number of sections in an umbrella reflector and m is the number of equal length serrations in a Fresnel reflector. It is seen that the paraboloid of revolution offers the best performance. Fresnel mirrors, although of lower

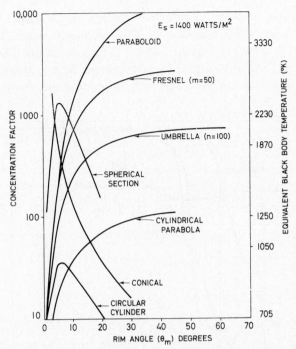

FIG. 6-21 Concentration factors and equivalent black body temperatures for various geometries (Allison).

performance than paraboloids, have advantages for folding and storage.

Other basic shapes such as the spherical mirror and cylindrical mirror have low concentration ratios. Dual mirror systems are extremely sensitive to errors in alignment. Consequently, most development effort has been spent on reflectors that are paraboloids of revolution in a form that can be folded including Fresnel mirrors.

SURFACES AND COATINGS

Several types of coatings are available for reflective surfaces. Coatings usually are applied directly to the reflector face after it is formed. However, in a process such as electroforming, it would be possible to place the reflective coatings on the master before building up the reflector face. Then the reflector face and coatings would be removed together. Other processes include chemical polishing, brightening, and vacuum coating. Several metals have been vacuum-deposited successfully to produce specularly reflec-

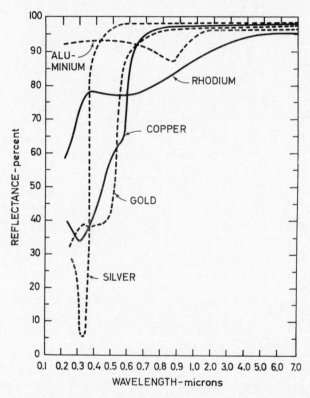

FIG. 6-22   Reflectance of evaporated films of metals (WADD TR 60-699).

tive surfaces for concentrators—the most important of these are aluminum, silver, gold, copper and rhodium. The reflectance of evaporated films of these metals as a function of wavelength is illustrated in Fig. 6-22. Here it is seen that aluminum is the only metal with a high reflectance in all useful regions (visible, ultraviolet, and infrared). The reflectance of the other metals drops rapidly in the visible or ultraviolet. This very property makes gold useful for thermal control because it reflects short wavelength light and emits thermal radiation.

The concentrated solar energy from an optical reflector is received by the absorber at the focal plane. Here the light energy is transferred to a working fluid or to an energy converter. The design of the absorber depends on the size, shape and accuracy of the mirror and on the temperature, and surface properties of the absorber.

Several absorber configurations have been suggested including a black body cavity, a flat plate and both convex or concave surfaces (Fig. 6-23). Under most conditions, a cavity absorber is the most efficient.

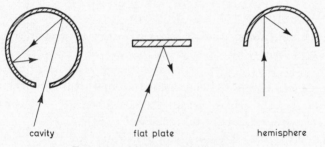

cavity   flat plate   hemisphere

FIG. 6-23   Absorber configurations.

An enclosure with a small opening approaches a black body absorber. Radiation entering through the opening is reflected repeatedly before being absorbed or escaping back through the opening. If the interior cavity wall has an absorptivity of 0.9, it will absorb 0.999 of the radiation after three reflections. The amount of radiation escaping back through the opening can be made very small by using a small opening or by inserting a quartz window. Cavity shapes that have been studied in detail include cylinders, spheres, hemispheres, and cones. The spherical absorber is slightly more efficient than the others for a ratio of window area to surface area that is more than 0.02. At smaller values, the efficiencies of the various shapes coalesce. The selection of the absorber design then can be based on other factors. Local hot spots in the cavity can be controlled by using a cavity liner material with a thermal energy emissivity of 0.3 to 0.4.

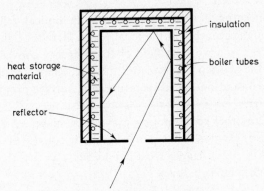

FIG. 6-24 Cylindrical cavity boiler.

When an absorber is used with a dynamic heat engine, a fluid is heated (usually boiled) in tubes that surround the cavity. The cavity walls may contain a thermal storage material to provide energy for peak power and to reduce hot spots. Insulation on the outside surfaces limits thermal losses. A schematic arrangement for a cylindrical cavity is illustrated in Fig. 6-24.

When absorbers are used with thermionic and thermoelectric converters, the converter elements can be mounted in the cavity walls. The converter is thus an integral part of the cavity structure. The outer wall may be used as the radiator for heat rejection.

REFERENCES

1. W. Evans and W. R. Menetrey (Electro-Optical Systems, Inc.), "Direct Solar Conversion", *Energy Conversion Systems Handbook*, WADDTR 60–699.
2. D. H. McClelland and C. W. Stevens, "Solar–Thermal Energy Sources", ibid.

3. D. L. DRESSER, E. H. HIETBRINK, R. B. MCCLURE, and R. O. WHITAKER, *Allison Research and Development of Solar Reflectors*, EDR No. 1826, Vol. I, 1960.
4. NASA, *Power for Spacecraft*, SP-21, Washington D.C., 1960.
5. P. MOON, "Proposed Standard Solar-Radiation Curves for Engineering Use.", *J. of Franklin Inst*. Nov. 1940.
6. *Proceedings of a Conference on Energy Conversion and Storage*, W. L. INVILLE ed., Oklahoma State University, 1963.
7. D. M. CHAPIN, C. S. FULLER, and G. L. PEARSON, "A New Silicon *p–n* Junction Photocell for Converting Solar Radiation into Electrical Power", *New Techniques for Energy Conversion*, S. N. LEVINE, ed., New York, Dover, 1961.
8. C. W. STEVENS, "Photovoltaic Converters", *An Analysis of Solar Energy Utilization*, Vol. II, Part 3, WADC TR 59–17 Feb. 1949.
9. P. DUWEZ, "Utilization of Solar Furnaces in High Temperature Research", ASME Paper No. 56-AV-17 1956.
10. G. HELLER, "Thermal Control of the Explorer Satellites", *ARS J*. Vol. 30, No. 4, 1960.

CHAPTER 7

THERMOELECTRICITY*

INTRODUCTION

Electric generators based upon the thermoelectric effect are particularly useful where small amounts of power are required from reliable static units. Small generators heated with kerosene lamps or propane burners have been produced in some quantity to power radios in remote areas away from public utilities. A typical unit is shown in Fig. 7-1. The most extensive use of thermoelectric generators, however, is in the automatic control system of gas heated appliances. Here the current from the thermoelectric elements when heated by the pilot flame must hold the main valve open against a closing force. The semiconductor materials developed for this purpose made possible the early production of radioisotope thermoelectric generators for space.

Semiconductor materials for thermoelectric applications produce higher voltages and higher ratios of electrical to thermal conductivity than do metals. Heat conducted along the elements in a generator represents a loss that is minimized by the use of semiconductors. In this way the efficiency of energy conversion has been increased by more than an order of magnitude. Further substantial increases in efficiency have been expected from the improved materials developed with the help of advanced semiconductor theory; however, the actual progress has been slow compared to the considerable development effort expended and

---

* Material for this chapter has been taken at length from J. Blair and J. D. Burns, Electro-Optical Systems, Inc., "Static Thermal Converters", *Energy Conversion Systems Reference Handbook*, W. R. Menetrey, ed., WADD TR 60-699, Sept. 1960.

FIG. 7-1 Thermoelectric generator (Minnesota Mining and Manufacturing Co.).

the exhaustive theoretical studies made. Nevertheless, thermo-electricity continues to find new applications where moderately efficient small static generators are required.

The discovery and development of thermoelectricity has been reviewed by Joffe in Ref. 7-2. Seebeck in 1821 observed that a compass needle near a circuit made of different conductors was deflected when one of the junctions was heated. Concluding that magnetism was produced by a temperature difference he attempted to relate these observations to the magnetic forces of the earth on the basis of the temperature differences between the equator and the poles. In trying to prove this theory of thermomagnetism, Seebeck investigated many materials including metal oxides, minerals, and other compounds now classified as semiconductors. With some of these he achieved efficiencies of about 3 percent in converting thermal energy into electricity. This efficiency was comparable to that of steam engines of that period. Unfortunately this discovery was not recognized as a means for producing useful electricity because of the misconceptions and controversies concerning thermomagnetism and thermoelectricity. As a consequence, until the development decades later of practical batteries and electromagnetic generators, the only source of electricity was the cumbersome electrostatic generators. Electrochemical preparations of some elements were accomplished with the minute currents produced in this way. The only use of thermoelectricity over the next century was for temperature measurements. Even in this application the important advantages of Seebeck's mineral semiconductors were overlooked.

The next step in the history of thermoelectricity came in 1834 when Peltier, a French watchmaker, observed that a thermal effect is produced by an electric current flowing through a junction of dissimilar conductors. However, Peltier also failed to comprehend the fundamental nature of his observation. He concluded only that Ohm's law might not apply for very weak currents.

A revival of interest in thermoelectric power came with the development after 1939 of synthetic semiconductor materials having thermoelectric effects orders of magnitude greater than those in metals. The application of these new materials to thermoelectric systems was recognized by Maria Telka who made a generator of some 5 percent efficiency using zinc antimonide and lead sulfide.

THERMOELECTRIC PHENOMENA

The flow of heat and the flow of electrons through a material are related. The flow of electrons transports some thermal energy and the flow of heat transports some electricity. In addition are the irreversible conversion of electrical energy into heat by electrical resistance, designated as Joule or I^2R heating, and the irreversible flow of heat by thermal conduction.

A thermoelectric generator is illustrated in Fig. 7-2. Two dissimilar materials, n and p, are connected by metal conductors making good thermal and electrical contact at the hot and cold junctions. The electrical energy generated from thermal energy does work in an external circuit; the remainder of the thermal energy is rejected from the cold junction at T_0. The potential depends upon both the temperature difference and the properties of the materials.

The Seebeck effect or thermoelectric power of the junction is defined in terms of the Seebeck coefficient, α. This is the rate of change of thermoelectric force with temperature

$$\alpha = \lim_{\Delta T \to 0} \left(\frac{\Delta V}{\Delta T} \right)$$

The dimensions of α are voltage divided by temperature. The potential difference across the generator is then

$$\Delta V = \int_{T_0}^{T} \alpha dT$$

An average value of the Seebeck coefficient can be found from

$$\bar{\alpha} = \frac{\Delta V}{\Delta T}$$

The value of the coefficient is a function of temperature and for many metals a linear relation is used

$$\alpha = a + bT$$

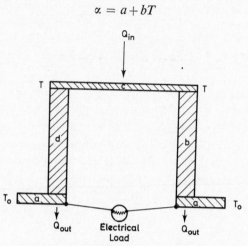

FIG. 7-2 Thermoelectric circuit.

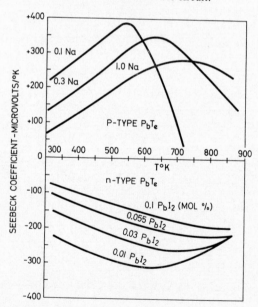

FIG. 7-3 Seebeck coefficient of lead telluride vs. temperature (Minnesota Mining and Manufacturing Co.).

However, for semiconductors of interest for power generation, the Seebeck coefficient is highly nonlinear with temperature passing through a maximum and then decreasing (Fig. 7-3). There is therefore an optimum temperature for the operation of each material. Some typical values for the Seebeck coefficient measured at 100 °C with lead as the reference junction material are given in Table 7-1.

The Seebeck coefficient is measured at zero current. Therefore the term "thermoelectric power" applied to this coefficient is a misnomer. Also the contact materials in Fig. 7-2 do not contribute to the thermoelectric effect when these junctions between dissimilar materials have no temperature gradient.

TABLE 7-1   SEEBECK COEFFICIENT AT 100 °C
(LEAD REFERENCE MATERIAL)

Aluminium	$-0.20 \ \mu V/°K$
Carbon	14.6
Constantan	-47.0
Copper	3.5
Germanium	375
Iron	13.6
Mercury	-12.1
Nichrome	25.0
Nickel	-22.0
Platinum	-5.2
Silicon	-455

The potential difference at a thermoelectric junction can be explained by the diffusion of charge carriers from hot to cold areas. An n-type semiconductor with conductance electrons free to diffuse then becomes positive at the hot junction. This property can be imparted to lead telluride by adding a small amount (0.01 mol. %) of lead iodide. The opposite effect is produced by adding 0.1 mol. percent of sodium to the pure semiconductor material— then the positive carriers diffuse to the cold area. There is also an opposing flow of charge carriers resulting from the thermal gradient. Thus the maximum potential is a function of the thermal transport properties.

PELTIER EFFECT

An electric current through a junction of dissimilar materials will absorb or liberate heat depending upon the direction of flow. This reversible conversion of electrical and thermal energy is termed the Peltier effect (Fig. 7-4). The Peltier coefficient is defined by

$$\pi_{ab} = \frac{-Q}{I_{ab}}$$

It has the units of watts per ampere or volts. The magnitude of the Peltier coefficient depends upon the materials at the junction

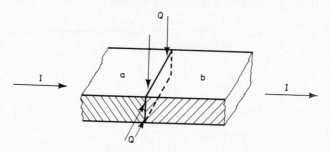

FIG. 7-4   Peltier effect.

and the temperature. The convention has been adopted that I_{ab} is positive when the current flows from a to b. Q is heat absorbed from the surroundings. This may include Joule heating from junction resistance.

The Peltier coefficient is related to the Seebeck coefficient by

$$\pi_{ab} = T\alpha_{ab}$$

(This relation will be discussed in a following section.)

THOMSON EFFECT

A third thermoelectric effect exists although it is not of primary importance in thermoelectric devices. This is the reversible absorption or liberation of heat in a homogeneous conductor when a temperature gradient and an electric current are imposed simultaneously. This is illustrated for the one-dimensional case in Fig. 7-5.

The Thomson coefficient τ is defined by

$$\tau = \frac{Q}{I \Delta T}$$

Here Q is the heat absorbed when the current flows toward the higher temperature region. The units are the same as the Seebeck

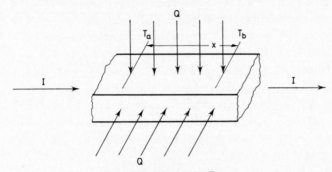

FIG. 7-5   Thomson effect.

coefficient (V/°K). As the electric current moves from the lower to the higher temperature region, heat must be added to raise the temperature of the charge carriers. This amount of heat must be equal to the number of charge carriers multiplied by their "specific heat." Thus the Thomson coefficient is the specific heat of electricity, and the units used may be joules per coulomb per degree Centigrade or joules per electron per degree Centigrade.

The Thomson coefficient is related to the Seebeck coefficient by

$$\tau = T \frac{d\alpha}{dT}$$

(This equation will be discussed in a following section.) For many metals and some other materials where the Seebeck coefficient can be expressed as a function of temperature by

$$\alpha = a + bT$$

the Thomson coefficient becomes

$$\tau = bT$$

Values of b are available in tables of thermoelectric properties.

KELVIN RELATIONS

The relations between thermoelectric effects were published by Lord Kelvin (W. Thomson) in 1854. His analysis provides a simple and accurate description of thermoelectricity. However, the assumption that the reversible thermoelectric processes can be separated thermodynamically from irreversible thermal conduction and joule heating is difficult to justify, even though the relations derived with this assumption certainly are correct.

In the thermoelectric circuit shown in Fig. 7-2, an electrical charge q will be transferred around the circuit a-b-c-d-a. As this charge is moved, heat must be added or removed to maintain the original thermal condition.

At the junction a-b, electrons will be "evaporated" from a and "condensed" on b both at T_0, to transfer the charge. The heat that must be added is

$$Q_{ab} = -q\pi_{ab}$$

where π is the Peltier coefficient. This is the difference between the heats of "evaporation" of the electron charge for the two materials at T_0.

The charge is moved next in material b from a region at T_0 to the higher temperature T. The heat that must be added is

$$Q_b = q \int_{T_0}^{T} \tau_b dT$$

where τ_b, the Thomson coefficient, is the "specific heat" of the electron charge.

Transferring the charge from material b to material d through material c involves the same energy change as moving the charge directly from b to d. This follows from the concept that the heats of "condensation" and "evaporation" of the charge to and from material c are identical is absolute magnitude, leaving the difference in heats of "evaporation" between materials b and d at the temperature T. The heat added is then

$$Q_{bd} = -q\pi_{bd-T}$$

Next the charge is transferred in material d from the hot region at T to the lower temperature T_0. The energy that must be removed from element d during this process is

$$-Q_d = q \int_{T_0}^{T} \tau_d dT$$

Finally the charge is transferred from material d to material a both at T_0. Here the energy change is

$$Q_{da} = -q\pi_{da-T_0}.$$

This can be combined with the energy change in the initial step Q_{ab} by considering the charge to be transferred directly from material d back to material b, both at T_0, so that

$$Q_{db} = -q\pi_{dbT_0}.$$

The system has now been restored to its initial condition. External work, W, has been done by the system in moving the charge q across the potential difference, V_{db}, between elements d and b. This work is

$$W = -qV_{bd}$$

The first law of thermodynamics provides the relation

$$\Delta U = Q - W$$

Since there is no change in the condition of the system as a result of this cyclic process, the change in internal energy ΔU is zero. The heat added to the system must equal then the work done, or

$$Q = W = -qV_{bd}$$

The heat added, Q, is found by a summation of the heat added in each step of the charge transfer

$$\sum Q = q \int_{T_0}^{T} \tau_b dT - q\pi_{bdT} - q \int_{T_0}^{T} \tau_d dT - q\pi_{db T_0} = -qV_{bd}$$

Substituting the equivalent

$$\pi_{db T_0} = -\pi_{bd T_0}$$

the potential difference V is found to be

$$V_{bd} = -\int_{T_0}^{T} (\tau_b - \tau_d)dT + \pi_{bdT} - \pi_{bd T_0}$$

The thermoelectric processes just considered are reversible. If there were no other effects, the total entropy change would be zero and simple relations between the thermoelectric coefficients would follow; but there are the irreversible processes of heat conduction from the hot to the cold junctions and the joule (I^2R) heating. Kelvin made the difficult assumption that the reversible and the irreversible processes could be considered separately. Then the entropy change for the reversible processes is

$$\Delta S = \sum \frac{dQ}{T} = -\int_{T_0}^{T} (\tau_b - \tau_d)\frac{dT}{T} + \frac{\pi_{bdT}}{T} - \frac{\pi_{bd T_0}}{T_0} = 0$$

Differentiating this relation with respect to T gives

$$\frac{-(\tau_b - \tau_d)}{T} + d\left(\frac{\pi_{bd}}{T}\right)/dT = 0$$

By differentiating the equation for the potential V with respect to T,

$$\frac{dV_{bd}}{dT} = -(\tau_b - \tau_d) + d(\pi_{bd})/dT$$

Eliminating the term $(\tau_b - \tau_d)$ between these relations gives the Seebeck coefficient in terms of the Peltier coefficient

$$\frac{dV_{bd}}{dT} = \frac{\pi_{bd}}{T} = \alpha_{bd}$$

The Thomson coefficient becomes

$$\tau_b - \tau_d = Td(\alpha_{bd})/dT$$

Although the assumption of separating the reversible and irreversible processes is difficult to support, the results of this derivation are accurate.

IRREVERSIBLE PROCESSES

Attempts to justify the assumption made by Kelvin have led to the formulation of the thermodynamics of irreversible processes. This applies to systems with flows of heat and electricity in irreversible processes. Classical thermodynamics described only the equilibrium state and reversible processes.

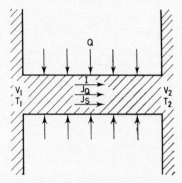

FIG. 7-6   Related flows.

The electrical current through a conductor (Fig. 7-6) with both electrical and thermal gradients is determined by both these driving forces, or

$$I = L_{iV}\Delta V + L_{iQ}\Delta T$$

Here L_{iV} and L_{iQ} are constants. By considering an isothermal system ($\Delta T = 0$) the value of L_{iV} can be determined. Then

$$I = \frac{\Delta V}{R}$$

and

$$L_{iV} = \frac{1}{R} = C$$

This constant is the electrical conductance, C.

The thermal current, J_Q, is determined by these same driving forces, so that

$$J_Q = L_{QV}\Delta V + L_{QT}\Delta T$$

Where there is no potential difference, the thermal current becomes

$$J_Q = L_{QT}\Delta T = \frac{kA\Delta T}{x} = K\Delta T$$

The thermal conductivity k, the cross-sectional area A, and the path length x, determine this coefficient, and

$$L_{QT} = K$$

An entropy current, J_S, can be defined similarly by

$$J_S = \frac{J_Q}{T} = L_{SV}\Delta V + L_{ST}\Delta T$$

The values of the coefficients are

$$L_{SV} = \frac{L_{QT}}{T}$$

and

$$L_{ST} = \frac{L_{QT}}{T} = \frac{K}{T}$$

The electrical, entropy and thermal currents are therefore linear functions of the driving forces ΔV and ΔT. Because special relations exists between the electrical and the entropy currents, this pair is termed conjugate flows. The equations are again

$$I = L_{iV}\Delta V + L_{iT}\Delta T$$

and

$$J_S = L_{SV}\Delta V + L_{ST}\Delta T$$

According to the Onsager reciprocal relation, for these conjugate flows the coefficients L_{iT} and L_{SV} are equal

$$L_{iT} = L_{SV}$$

The other coefficients are known from the electrical and thermal properties and physical dimensions. In this way the thermodynamics of irreversible processes provides the relations between entropy and other currents necessary for the rigorous derivation of the Kelvin equations.

PERFORMANCE ANALYSIS

The performance of a single-stage thermoelectric generator will be considered with reference to Fig. 7-7. The elements are assumed to be of uniform cross-section, homogeneous, and perfectly insulated on their sides. There are thermal and electrical currents therefore only in the x-direction. The connecting straps are as-

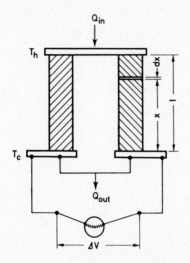

FIG. 7-7 Thermoelectric generator.

sumed also to be perfect conductors of electricity with negligible thermal capacity. These assumptions usually are not significant limitations particularly under static conditions.

The temperatures at any point x and at time t in each of the elements are designated by $T_n(x, t)$ and $T_p(x, t)$. The common cold junction temperature $(x = 0)$ is $T_c(t)$ and that of the hot junction $(x = 1)$ is $T_h(t)$.

The heat conduction rate in the x-direction at the lower face of an infinitesimal section through an element is

$$Q_{kx} = -kA \frac{\partial T}{\partial x}$$

At the upper face of this section, this rate has changed to

$$Q_{k(x+dx)} = -kA\left[\frac{\partial T}{\partial x} + \frac{\partial}{\partial x}\left(\frac{\partial T}{\partial x}\right)dx\right]$$

The net heat addition into this section is then

$$Q_{k\,net} = \frac{\partial}{\partial x}\left(kA\frac{\partial T}{\partial x}\right)dx$$

The joule heating in this section is

$$Q_j = I^2\frac{\varrho}{A}\,dx$$

where ϱ is the electrical resistivity. Heat transported into this section by the electric current (the Thomson effect) is

$$Q_\tau = \tau I\left(\frac{dT}{dx}\right)dx$$

The sum of the heat addition rates must equal the rate of change of internal energy of the material in the section, or

$$Q_U = \frac{\partial}{\partial t}(C_p A T)\,dx$$

where C_p is the heat capacity. Partial differential equations can be written relating temperature with position and time in each element as follows

$$\frac{\partial}{\partial x}\left(k_p A_p \frac{\partial T_p}{\partial x}\right) + \tau_p I\frac{\partial T_p}{\partial x} + \frac{\varrho_p}{A_p}I^2 = \frac{\partial(C_p A_p T_p)}{\partial t}$$

$$\frac{\partial}{\partial x}\left(k_n A_n \frac{\partial T_n}{\partial x}\right) - \tau_n I\frac{\partial T_n}{\partial x} + \frac{\varrho_n}{A_n}I^2 = \frac{\partial(C_p A_n T_n)}{\partial t}$$

In the steady-state case $\left(\dfrac{\partial T}{\partial t} = 0\right)$, and when thermoelectric parameters do not vary appreciably with temperature ($\tau = 0$), these equations reduce to the much simpler forms,

$$k_p A_p \frac{d^2 T_p}{dx^2} + \frac{\varrho_p}{A_p}I^3 = 0$$

$$k_n A_n \frac{d^2 T_n}{dx^2} + \frac{\varrho_n}{A_n}I^2 = 0$$

Solutions to these linear differential equations with constant coefficients can be obtained for the following boundary conditions

$$T_p(0) = T_n(0) = T_c$$
$$T_p(1) = T_n(1) = T_h$$

These solutions are

$$T_p(x) = T_c + \Delta T\left(\frac{x}{1}\right) + \frac{1}{2} I^2 \left\{ \left(\frac{\varrho_{p1}}{A_p}\right)\left(\frac{1}{k_p A_p}\right)\left[\frac{x}{1} - \left(\frac{x}{1}\right)^2\right]\right\}$$

$$T_n(x) = T_c + \Delta T\left(\frac{x}{1}\right) + \frac{1}{2} I^2 \left\{ \left(\frac{\varrho_{n1}}{A_n}\right)\left(\frac{1}{k_n A_n}\right)\left[\frac{x}{1} - \left(\frac{x}{1}\right)^2\right]\right\}$$

The temperature profiles in the thermoelectric elements are therefore quadratic functions of the position parameter $\left(\dfrac{x}{1}\right)$ (Fig. 7-8). Without the joule heating, the temperature distribution would, of course, be linear.

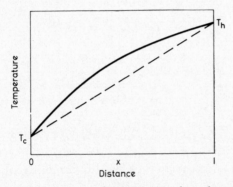

FIG. 7-8   Temperature distribution along element.

The rate of thermal energy input to the hot junction Q_h is the sum of the Peltier heat removed

$$-Q_\pi = \alpha T_h I$$

and the rate of heat conduction away through the two elements

$$-Q_p = k_p A_p \frac{dT_p}{dx}\bigg|_{(x=1)}$$

$$-Q_n = k_n A_n \frac{dT_n}{dx}\bigg|_{(x=1)}$$

The total heat input, then, is

$$Q_h = \alpha T_h I + k_p A_p \left.\frac{dT_p}{dx}\right|_{(x=1)} + k_n A_n \left.\frac{dT_n}{dx}\right|_{(x=1)}$$

Similarly, at the cold junction, the rate of heat rejection is

$$-Q_c = \alpha T_c I + k_p A_p \left.\frac{dT_p}{dx}\right|_{(x=0)} + k_n A_n \left.\frac{dT_n}{dx}\right|_{(x=0)}$$

Values of the temperature gradients $\left(\dfrac{dT_p}{dx}\right)$ and $\left(\dfrac{dT_n}{dx}\right)$ at each end of the elements can be obtained from the previous relations for the temperature distribution. Using these values, the rates of heat addition and rejection are found

$$Q_h = \alpha T_h I + K \Delta T - \tfrac{1}{2} I^2 R$$
$$-Q_c = \alpha T_c I + K \Delta T + \tfrac{1}{2} I^2 R$$

where

$$\Delta T = T_h - T_c$$

$$R = 1\left(\frac{\varrho_p}{A_p} + \frac{\varrho_n}{A_n}\right)$$

$$K = \left(\frac{k_p A_p}{1} + \frac{k_n A_n}{1}\right)$$

This shows that exactly half the joule ($I^2 R$) heat generated in the elements flows to each junction.

ELECTRICAL CHARACTERISTICS

The voltage at the external load is given by

$$V = \alpha \Delta T - IR = V_0 - IR$$

where V_0 is the open circuit voltage ($I = 0$). Voltages, then, is a linear function of the temperature difference between the hot and cold junctions.

The generator produces maximum electric power when the resistance of the external load R_L just equals the net thermocouple resistance,

$$R_L = R$$

The maximum power delivered by the generator is therefore

$$P_{\max} = \frac{V_0^2}{4R} = (\alpha \Delta T)^2 / 4\,R$$

POWER DENSITY

The thermoelectric generator power density is defined as the ratio of the maximum electrical power output to the total volume of the elements. This power density σ_p is found from previous relations to be

$$\sigma_p = \frac{P_{\max}}{(A_p + A_n)l} = \tfrac{1}{4}\frac{\alpha^2 \Delta T^2}{l^2(A_p + A_n)\left(\dfrac{\varrho_p}{A_p} + \dfrac{\varrho_n}{A_n}\right)}$$

The power density thus varies as the reciprocal of the squared length of the thermoelements. Therefore the thermoelements should be as short as possible to reduce the amount of thermoelectric material. This minimum length is established by limitations of electrical and thermal contact resistance and by system design.

CONVERSION EFFICIENCY

Efficiency in converting thermal energy into electricity is

$$\eta = \frac{VI}{Q_h}$$

This efficiency can be expressed in terms of temperature difference and material properties by using previous relations for V and Q_h

$$\eta = \frac{\alpha \Delta T I - R I^2}{\alpha T_h I + K \Delta T - \tfrac{1}{2} R I^2}$$

The efficiency can be maximized with respect to the current I for a constant temperature difference ΔT. This maximum occurs when the current is

$$I = \frac{\alpha \Delta T}{R(1 + M)}$$

where M is defined as

$$M = \sqrt{1 + Z\left(\frac{T_h + T_c}{2}\right)}$$

Z is the thermoelectric figure of merit describing the element properties and it is defined by

$$Z = \frac{\alpha^2}{\left(\dfrac{\varrho_p}{A_p} + \dfrac{\varrho_n}{A_n}\right)(k_p A_p + k_n A_n)}$$

The figure of merit is thus a function of the area ratio A_p/A_n and Z is maximum for

$$A_p/A_n = \sqrt{\frac{\varrho_p k_n}{\varrho_n k_p}}$$

Then the maximum value of Z is

$$Z_{\max} = \frac{(|\alpha_n| + |\alpha_p|)^2}{(\sqrt{k_p \varrho_p} + \sqrt{k_n \varrho_n})^2}$$

The maximum value of Z therefore is independent of the dimensions of the thermoelements. It is a function only of the material properties α, ϱ, and k.

The maximum efficiency is

$$\eta_{\max} = \frac{T_h - T_c}{T_h} \cdot \frac{M - 1}{M + T_c/T_h}$$

The maximum efficiency is seen to be the product of the Carnot efficiency and a second factor embodying the materials parameters. The dependence of maximum efficiency on Z and T_h is shown in Fig. 7-9, where T_c has a value of 300 °K.

The conditions for maximum efficiency can be expressed in terms of the optimum electrical load resistance. The current as a

THERMOELECTRICITY

function of load resistance is

$$I = \frac{\alpha \Delta T}{R(1 + R_L/R)}$$

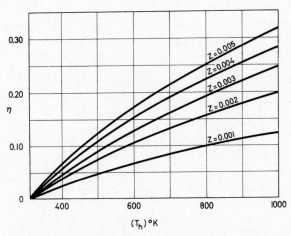

FIG. 7-9 Thermoelectric generator efficiency as a function of Z and T_h (WADD TR 60-699).

The optimum value of the load resistance is

$$R_{L\,\text{opt}} = MR = R\sqrt{1 + Z\left(\frac{T_h + T_c}{2}\right)}$$

This value of the load resistance for maximum efficiency is larger than the value for maximum power.

AVERAGE PARAMETERS

The analysis that has been presented is based on parameters that do not change significantly with temperature and therefore they can be assumed to be constant. This simple analysis can be adopted for temperature-dependent parameters by defining approximate average values over the temperature range of interest.

The average figure of merit is

$$Z_{\mathrm{av}} = \left[\frac{|\bar{\alpha}_n| + |\bar{\alpha}_p|}{\sqrt{\bar{\varrho}_p \bar{k}_p} + \sqrt{\bar{\varrho}_n \bar{k}_n}} \right]^2$$

An average value of each property can be obtained by integrating its point values over the temperature interval and dividing by the temperature difference. For example, the average value of the Seebeck coefficient is

$$\bar{\alpha} = \frac{\displaystyle\int_{T_c}^{T_h} \bar{\alpha}\, dT}{T_h - T_c}$$

Performance calculations based upon the average parameters are surprisingly accurate. Errors of less than 7 percent have been observed, even where there are strongly temperature-dependent parameters.

MULTIPLE STAGE GENERATORS

The efficiency of a thermoelectric generator can be increased by staging as shown in Fig. 7-10. Heat rejected from the first stage flows through the second. The operation of the generator

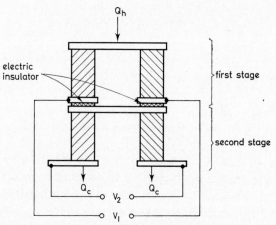

FIG. 7-10   Two-stage generator.

then is divided into two temperature ranges. Optimum thermo-electric materials now can be selected for each stage. In addition, the size of the second stage can be reduced by an amount corres-ponding to the energy converted into electricity in the first stage. Overall efficiency is greatest when the efficiency of each stage is maximum. Selection of the intermediate temperature and of the element geometry in each stage is determined in part by the mate-rials used.

The elements in a multistage generator can be connected electric-ally in various ways. However it usually is necessary to electric-ally insulate each stage with a material that has high thermal but low electrical conductivities. These conflicting requirements pres-ent a difficult materials problem. As a result, the thermal and electrical contact losses may limit the number of stages.

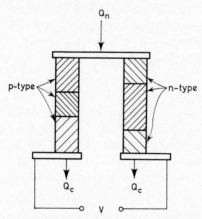

FIG. 7-11 Segmented generator.

Another arrangement of elements is shown in Fig. 7-11. This is termed a segmented generator. Its theoretical efficiency is less than that of the corresponding multistage generator. There are practical advantages, however, to be obtained with segmented generators that could outweigh their theoretical limitations.

THERMOELECTRIC MATERIALS

Thermal conductivity k, electrical resistance ϱ and the thermo-electric coefficient α are combined in the "figure of merit" Z for a single material as

$$Z = \frac{\alpha^2}{\varrho k}$$

The Seebeck coefficient decreases in value as the concentration of charge carriers increases. Metals have many free electrons. A low value of α results because these free electrons behave somewhat like a free gas within the metal with only small changes in concentration resulting from a temperature gradient. Semiconductors and semimetals have not nearly so many free charge carriers and a larger concentration gradient results from a temperature gradient. This corresponds to a larger thermoelectric voltage and larger Seebeck coefficient.

The thermal conductivity k is the sum of lattice conductivity k_L and the electronic conductivity k_{el} or

$$k = k_L + k_{el}$$

Lattice thermal conductivity results from crystal lattice vibrations. It may increase, decrease, or pass through a maximum with increasing temperature, depending upon the material and the temperature range. In several materials of interest, the lattice conductivity is inversely proportional to the absolute temperature. The heavy elements have low values of k_L. Charge mobility and associated electrical conductivity also are greater in materials made from the heavy elements. Elements near the middle of the periodic table are usually preferred. Their lattice thermal conductivity can be reduced further by additives (doping).

Electronic thermal conductivity is determined by the concentration of charge carriers and their mobility. A useful relation between the conduction of electricity and the electronic thermal conduction is the Wiedeman–Franz law expressed by the relation

$$k_{el} = \frac{L}{\varrho}$$

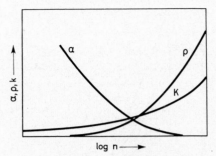

FIG. 7-12 Properties vs. electron concentration.

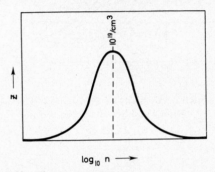

FIG. 7-13 Figure of merit vs. electron concentration.

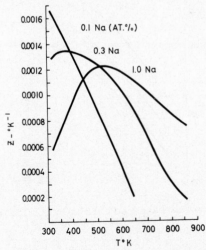

FIG. 7-14 Figure of merit of p-type PbTe vs. temperature (Minnesota Mining and Manufacturing Co.).

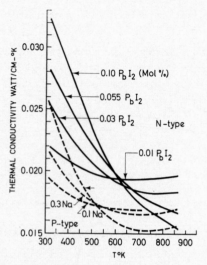

Fig. 7-15　Thermal conductivity of PbTe vs. temperature (Minnesota Mining and Manufacturing Co.).

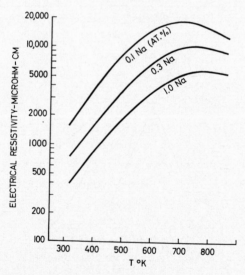

Fig. 7-16　Electrical resistivity of p-type PbTe vs. temperature (Minnesota Mining and Manufacturing Co.).

where L is a constant and $1/\varrho$ is the electrical conductivity. Thus the electronic thermal conductivity of a material is directly proportional to its electrical conductivity.

Variations in the properties of thermoelectric materials caused by the concentration of charge carriers (number per cm³) are shown in Figs. 7-12 and 7-13. An optimum concentration about 10^{19} per cm³ is indicated. This is much less than the concentration

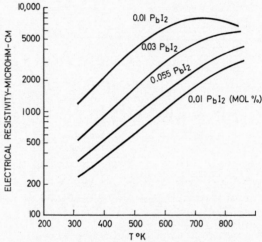

FIG. 7-17 Electrical resistivity of *n*-type PbTe vs. temperature (Minnesota Mining and Manufacturing Co.).

in metals but it does correspond to the carrier densities in some semiconductors and semimetals. The concentration in semiconductors may be increased by the addition of impurities (doping). Insulators have too few free electrons to be effective as thermoelectric materials. They correspond to the areas to the far left on Figs. 7-12 and 7-13.

Intermetallic compounds and alloys of the heavy elements have received much study for thermoelectric applications. These elements include lead, bismuth, antimony, tellurium, and selenium. Some typical properties of lead telluride and shown in Figs. 7-14, 7-15, 7-16 and 7-17.

THERMOELECTRIC CALCULATIONS

The application of the thermoelectric relations that have been developed can be illustrated in the analysis of a typical power problem. In this example, the size and number of lead telluride elements required to produce 100 W (e) at 12 V are determined for a system with the characteristics listed in Table 7-2.

TABLE 7-2   POWER SYSTEM CHARACTERISTICS

t_h	482 °C (900 °F)
t_c	149 °C (300 °F)
ΔT	333 °C
α_p	2.35×10^{-4} V/°C
ϱ_p	3.39×10^{-3} ohm-cm
k_p	1.67×10^{-2} W/cm °C
α_n	2.43×10^{-4} V/°C
ϱ_n	2.79×10^{-3} ohm-cm
k_n	1.96×10^{-2} W/cm °C

The figure of merit is found by a substitution of values from this table into the equation

$$Z = \frac{(|\alpha_n| + |\alpha_p|)^2}{(\sqrt{k_n\varrho_n} + \sqrt{k_p\varrho_p})^2}$$
$$Z = 1.03 \times 10^{-3}/°C$$

Using this value of Z, the parameter M is calculated

$$M = \sqrt{1 + Z(T_h + T_c)/2}$$
$$M = 1.268$$

This parameter determines the optimum ratio of the load resistance R_L to the internal resistance R_i

$$M = R_L/R_i = 1.268$$

The open-circuit voltage produced by the thermocouple is

$$V_0 = \alpha\Delta T = 4.79 \times 10^{-4} \times 333 = 0.159 \text{ V}$$

The external voltage is found from

$$V = V_0 - IR_i = \frac{V_0 R_L}{R_L + R_i} = 0.0887 \text{ V}$$

This value determined the number of thermocouples connected in series to produce 12 V, or

$$N = \frac{12}{0.0887} = 135 \text{ couples}$$

Thus the electric power delivered per couple is

$$\frac{P}{N} = \frac{100}{135} = 0.74 \text{ W/couple}$$

Since the electric power is also given by

$$\frac{P}{N} = \frac{E^2}{R_L} = 0.74 \text{ W/couple}$$

the external resistance is found to be 0.0106 ohms. The internal resistance is then determined

$$R_i = \frac{R_L}{M} = 0.0084 \text{ ohms}$$

Internal resistance is the sum of the resistance of each element plus that of the contact and connector. These additional resistances are assumed to be negligible. Then the electrical resistance of the thermocouple becomes

$$R_i = \frac{\varrho_n l_n}{A_n} + \frac{\varrho_p l_p}{A_p} = 0.0084 \text{ ohms}$$

The calculation of the maximum value of the figure of merit is based upon the value of the area ratio A_p/A_n of

$$\frac{A_p}{A_n} = \sqrt{\frac{\varrho_p k_n}{\varrho_n k_p}} = 1.19$$

The length of each element is given as 3 cm. Using this value the

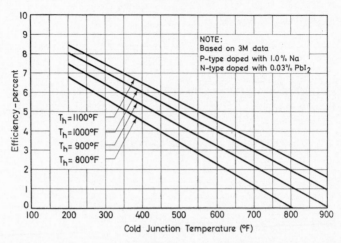

NOTE:
Based on 3M data
P-type doped with 1.0% Na
N-type doped with 0.03% PbI$_2$

FIG. 7-18   Efficiency of PbTe elements vs. hot and cold junction temperatures (The Martin Company).

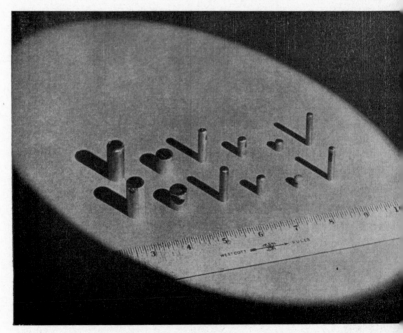

FIG. 7-19   Thermoelectric generator elements (Minnesota Mining and Manufacturing Co.).

cross-sectional area of each element can be calculated

$$R_i = \frac{2.79 \times 10^{-3} \times 3}{A_p/1.19} + \frac{3.39 \times 10^{-3} \times 3}{A_p} = 0.0084 \text{ ohms}$$

$$A_p = 2.394 \text{ cm}^2$$

$$A_n = 2.013 \text{ cm}^2$$

The total thermocouple area at the hot junction is

$$A_{\text{total}} = 4.407 \times 135 = 595 \text{ cm}^2$$

The efficiency of energy conversion is found from

$$\eta = \frac{VI}{Q_h}$$

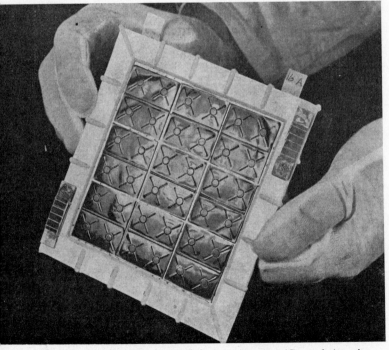

Fig. 7-20 Solar thermoelectric panel for space power (General Atomics Division, General Dynamics Corp.).

Since the electric power output is 100 W and the rate of heat addition at the hot junction is

$$Q_h = N(\alpha T_h I + K\Delta T - \tfrac{1}{2} I^2 R_i)$$
$$Q_h = 135 \times 11.56 = 1560 \text{ W}$$
$$\eta = \frac{100}{1560} = 0.064$$

REFERENCES

1. J. BLAIR and J. D. BURNS, Electro-Optical Systems, Inc., "Static Thermal Converters", *Energy Conversion Systems Reference Handbook*, W. R. MENETREY , ed., WADD-TR 60-699, Sept. 1960.
2. A. F. JOFFE, "The Revival of Thermoelectricity", *Scientific American*, Vol. 199, No. 5, Nov. 1958.
3. F. E. JAUMOT, JR., "Thermoelectric Effects", *Proc. IRE*, Vol. 46, No 3, 1958.
4. A. F. JOFFE, *Semiconductor Thermoelements and Thermoelectric Cooling*, London, Inforsearch Ltd, 1957.
5. C. A. DOMENICALI, "Irreversible Thermodynamics of Thermoelectricity", *Rev. Mod. Phys.*, Vol 26, p. 237, 1954.
6. S. R. DEGROOT, *Thermodynamics of Irreversible Processes*, New York, Interscience, 1951.
7. N. F. MOTT and R. W. GURNEY, *Electronic Processes in Ionic Crystals*, 2nd ed., London, Oxford, 1950.
8. R. W. URE, JR., "Semiconductor and Semi-Metals", *Science and Engineering of Thermoelectricity*, R. R. HEIKES and R. W. URE, JR., ed., New York, Interscience, 1961.
9. R. W. URE, JR., and R. R. HEIKES, "Theoretical Calculations of Device Performance", ibid.
10. J. G. MORSE, The Martin Co., "Radioisotope System Design", *Energy Conversion Systems Reference Handbook*, W. R. MENETREY, ed., WADD-TR 60-699, Sept. 1960.

CHAPTER 8

THERMIONIC GENERATORS*

INTRODUCTION

The thermionic generator contains a hot cathode that emits electrons and a cold anode that collects them, as in the closely related vacuum tube diode. The basic process was discovered by Thomas Edison when he observed that electricity moves from a hot filament to a cold filament in a vacuum light bulb; only recently has the active development of thermionic generators been pursued.

This generator operates at high temperatures. The cathode temperature may be the order of 2000 °K, with the heat rejection temperature at the anode about 1000 °K. This high heat rejection temperature permits the use of lightweight radiators. Also, thermionic generators can be operated in series with lower temperature conversion devices to obtain improved efficiency. Such combinations are particularly attractive for use with future high temperature nuclear reactors. Here the diode could be part of the fuel element, and a secondary coolant could transfer heat from the anode to a conventional power plant.

THERMIONIC EMISSION

The rate of emission of electrons from a hot surface in a vacuum is given by the Richardson–Dushman equation,

$$I = AT^2 e^{-e\varphi/kT}$$

* Extensive materials for this chapter has been drawn from J. B. Burns, Electro-Optical System, inc., "Thermionic Emitters", *Energy Conversion Reference Handbook*, W. R. Menetry, ed., WADD-TR 60–699, Ref. 2.

FIG. 8-1 Thermionic generator with cesium tube (General Electric Co.).

where I is the saturation current (A/cm^2), A is the Richardson constant (A/cm^2 $^\circ$K^2), and k is the Boltzmann constant. The quantity $e\phi$, is the energy required to "evaporate" an electron from the surface—the "work function". The units of $e\phi$ are energy units (electron volts, ergs, etc.). For some purposes it may be desirable to express ϕ in volts, and e in electron charge units. These work function units must be consistent with those of the Boltzmann constant for the total exponent to be dimensionless.

Tables of the work function for various materials are available in the literature. Some typical values are listed in Table 8-1. For the elements, there is a systematic variation in the work function according to position in the periodic table. The electron emission rate and the corresponding value of the work function can be modified greatly by additives to the surface. For example, thorium added to a tungsten electrode will increase the emission rate by a factor of several orders of magnitude. A monomolecular layer of cesium on tungsten will produce an even greater effect. Cathodes coated with oxides of barium, calcium and strontium have high emission rates and mixed oxide coatings are used in vacuum tubes. However, some contaminants such as oxygen can drastically reduce the electron emission rate.

These effects can be expressed in the Richardson–Dushman equation as changes in the work function. Thus, coating a tungsten cathode with cesium reduces the work function.

TABLE 8-1   THERMIONIC WORK FUNCTION

Platinum	5.32 eV
Palladium	4.99
Tungsten	4.52
Copper	4.47
Molybdenum	4.20
Tantalum	4.19
Zirconium	4.12
Silicon carbide	3.5
Thorium	3.4
Tungsten–uranium	2.8
Tungsten–thorium	2.7
Cesium	1.81
Tungsten–cesium	1.5
Barium–strontium oxide	1.0

Electrons within the electrode can escape when they approach the surface with an energy greater than the work function. Their number increases exponentially with temperature. For example, the rate of emission from a pure tungsten electrode is negligible below 2500 °K; but between 3000 °K and 3500 °K, the saturation current density increases by more than an order of magnitude.

The reference electron energy in a conductor is the Fermi level — this is the energy state with a 50 percent probability of being occupied. This reference energy level is determined by the temperature and by the material. After an energetic electron has overcome the work function barrier and escaped, its kinetic energy is reduced by the amount of the work function. However,

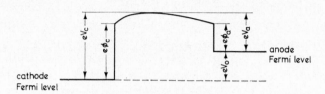

FIG. 8-2   Energy diagram.

the potential energy of the electron is increased by this same amount. The total energy with reference to the Fermi level—the sum of the kinetic and potential energies—thus remains unchanged. If the electron is reflected and falls back to the electrode, the potential energy is recovered and the electron returns to its original energy level. Should the electron enter an electrode with a lower work function, only the amount of this work function is converted to kinetic (thermal) energy. Any remaining energy can do external work (Fig. 8-2).

SPACE CHARGE

The escape of an electron leaves the cathode with a positive charge. This produces an electrostatic force that tends to hold electrons in the vicinity of the cathode. The resulting cloud of electrons creates a space charge that retards further electron emissions. In moving against the electrostatic force from this space charge, the kinetic energy of an electron is reduced and its potential energy increased. After moving past the charged zone, the electron is accelerated and its potential energy is decreased (Fig. 8-2).

The space charge can control the electron flow from the cathode and thus limit the performance of the thermionic generator. This limiting effect of the space charge can be reduced by placing the electrodes very close together (0.001 cm) as shown in Fig. 8-3 for a vacuum diode. However, this close spacing is difficult to main-

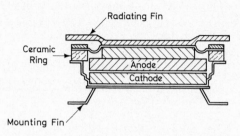

FIG. 8-3   Vacuum diode (WADD TR 60-699).

tain in a high temperature device of practical size. Small changes in this spacing have a large effect on power output and efficiency. Thus there may be large variations in performance between vacuum diodes produced to the same specifications.

PLASMA DIODE

Difficulties with the vacuum diode encouraged the development of other means for reducing the space charge effect. The most important of these is the addition of an easily ionized vapor to produce positive ions that will neutralize the space charge.

Cesium vapor is well suited for this purpose since it will ionize when atoms strike the hot cathode. Positive cesium ions are generated by this and other mechanisms. The concentration of positive ions near the cathode depends on the concentration of cesium vapor (vapor pressure) and the cathode temperature. The ions drift towards the anode and create a positively charged plasma between the electrodes. This positive space charge can increase the electron emission rate, although the flow of electrons to the anode is impeded by scattering processes between the electrons and the cesium molecules.

Cesium has other effects on the operation of the diode. For example, the work function of the electrodes is reduced by a surface layer of cesium, as mentioned, thus increasing the electron emission rate. This reduction in the work function of the anode material also can increase the efficiency of energy conversion.

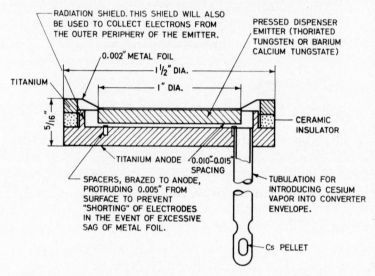

FIG. 8-4   Cesium thermionic generator (General Electric Co.).

Cesium is evaporated into the system from a controlled-temperature reservoir. In a typical design (Fig. 8-4) the cesium reservoir is a thin nickel tube. A glass capsule containing the cesium is at the end of the tube during assembly. Afterward the capsule is moved to a position about 1 inch from the radiator and the remainder of the tube is pinched off. Then the stem is pressed to crush the capsule and release the cesium.

The performance of a cesium thermionic generator as a function of cesium reservoir temperature is shown in Fig. 8-5. This illustrates the effects of space charge neutralization and of impedance due to cesium scattering.

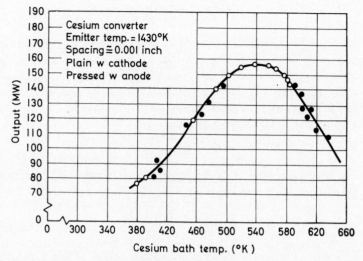

FIG. 8-5 Output of cesium thermionic generator vs. cesium temperature
(General Electric Co.).

ANODE POTENTIAL

The electron emission rate given by the Richardson–Dushman equation is a limiting value based upon a positively charged anode. As the anode potential becomes more negative, the emitted electrons are repelled and fall back to the cathode. Thus current can become a sensitive function of plate voltage. This retarded current, I_R, becomes

$$I_R = AT^2(e^{-e\varphi/kT})(e^{-eV/kT})$$
$$I_R = I_s e^{-eV/k}$$

where V is the anode voltage and I_s is the saturation current.

The three distinct regimes of diode operation are (1) saturation current when there is no space charge or anode retardation, (2) space charge limited current, and (3) retarded field current. The mathematical analysis of thermionic generator operation to determine optimum operating conditions becomes complex when all of these effects are considered.

ENERGY RELATIONS

The useful electrical work that can be done by an electron is

$$W = eV_c - eV_a = eV_0$$

where eV_c and eV_a include the work functions and any space charge effects at the cathode and anode respectively. The output voltage is V_0. The net electric power is

$$P_e = I(V_0 - IR)$$

The internal resistance of the leads is R. For a flow of heat into the cathode of Q, the efficiency η is

$$\eta = \frac{P_e}{Q} = \frac{I(V_0 - IR)}{Q}$$

This heat Q provides the heat of evaporation q_1 of the electrons from the cathode surface; the additional kinetic energy q_2 of the electrons; the net thermal radiation q_3 between the cathode and anode; heat conduction and ohmic losses q_4 through the lead to the cathode; heat conduction q_5 from the cathode through the cesium vapor to the anode; the cesium ionization energy, q_6; and ohmic losses, q_7, in this cesium vapor. The total heat flow is then

$$Q = q_1 + q_2 + q_3 + q_4 + q_5 + q_6 + q_7$$

The total power of the electrons leaving the cathode surface is

$$q_1 + q_2 = I(\phi_c + 2kT_c)$$

The term $2kT$ represents the sum of the kinetic energy of motion of the electrons in each of three directions.

The net thermal radiation between the cathode and anode is

$$q_3 = \delta A(T_c^4 - T_a^4) \left(\frac{1}{\varepsilon_c} + \frac{1}{\varepsilon_a} - 1 \right)^{-1}$$

where δ is the Stefan–Boltzmann constant (5.67×10^{-12} W/$^\circ$K^{4}cm^2), A is the area (cm^2), and ε_c and ε_a are the emissivities of the cathode and anode respectively. The cathode emissivity is evaluated at the cathode temperature, whereas the anode emissivity must be evaluated at the average temperature $(T_c + T_a)/2$.

The lead losses are

$$q_4 = \frac{\varkappa_1 \times A_1}{l} (T_c - T_{amb}) - I^2 R_1/2$$

where $\varkappa_1$ is the thermal conductivity of a lead of cross-sectional area A_1 and length l. The ambient temperature is T_{amb}. Since the ohmic loss contributes to the heating of the cathode, only half of this quantity is subracted from the lead loss. It is noted that the lead material and lead size represent a compromise between thermal and electrical losses. Usually the ohmic loss in the lead is one-tenth of the heat conduction loss.

The heat conduction through the cesium vapor is

$$q_5 = \frac{\varkappa_{cs} A}{x} (T_c - T_a)$$

where $\varkappa_{cs}$ is the thermal conductivity (watts/cm^2 °K/cm) of the cesium vapor and x is the electrode spacing.

The significance of each of these quantities for a typical cesium thermionic generator is indicated in Tables 8-2. Here it is seen that the three major paths of heat loss from the cathode are (1) electron evaporation, (2) thermal radiation and (3) terminal lead conduction.

TABLE 8-2　CATHODE ENERGY LOSSES

Electron evaporation	43 percent
Electron kinetic energy	7
Thermal radiation	27
Terminal lead loss	16
Cesium heat conduction	1
Cesium ionization	1
Cesium ohmic loss	5
	100 percent

Many variables and material properties influence the performance of a thermionic generator. Efficiency and maximum power both increase with cathode temperature. Using optimistic values for work functions and emissivities, the best efficiencies that can be expected have been estimated. These values are compared with the limiting Carnot cycle efficiencies in Table 8-3.

TABLE 8-3   PROBABLE LIMITS OF EFFICIENCY OF
THERMIONIC GENERATORS VS. TEMPERATURE

Cathode temperature	Anode temperature	*TI*	Carnot
3500 °F	1160 °F	0.33	0.59
3000	1160	0.27	0.53
2500	1160	0.19	0.45
2000	1160	0.10	0.34

Performance data from thermionic generator tests (Fig. 8-6) show that power densities from 1 to 11 W/cm² have been obtained. An efficiency of over 16 percent was observed at 3300 °F.

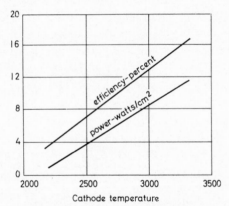

FIG. 8-6   Demonstrated performance.

Even higher performance is expected to result from the addition of hydrogen to the cesium since this has been observed to reduce the work function.

NUCLEAR THERMIONIC POWER

Nuclear fuels such as uranium oxide can operate at high emitter temperatures and these fuels are compatible with refractory metals such as molybdenum and tungsten. The heat transfer rate

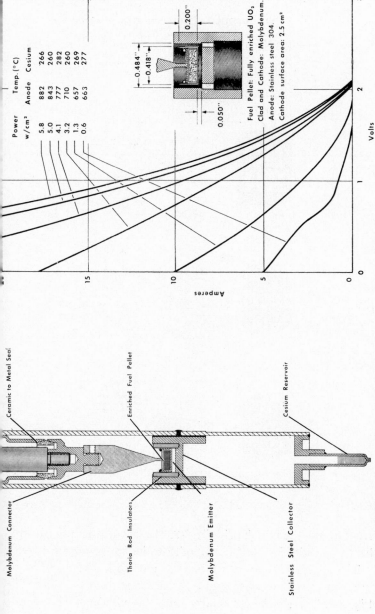

FIG. 8-7 Plasma diode assembly (General Electric Co.). FIG. 8-8 Output curves for in-reactor converter (General Electric Co.).

is matched to the generation of thermal energy in a nuclear fuel by enclosing it within the cathode (Fig. 8-7). Experimental nuclear diodes of this type, operated in the neutron flux of a nuclear

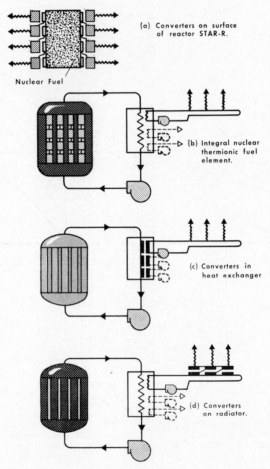

FIG. 8-9   Comparison of nuclear thermionic systems (General Electric Co.).

reactor, produced the data in Fig. 8-8. The rate of generating fission heat was varied by moving the unit relative to the reactor core.

Thermionic generators can be combined with nuclear reactors nto power systems of several types. Four of these are shown in Fig. 8-9. The simplest, a reactor with thermionic converters on the outer surface and anodes cooled by direct radiation, is being developed for space power. Surface-to-volume relations limit this particular design to less than 100 kW. Reactors that are not

FIG. 8-10 SNAP 13 radioisotope thermionic generator (Thermo Electron Eng. Corp., Martin Marietta Corp.).

limited in size could be made with integral nuclear thermionic fuel elements throughout the core. In these, circulating liquid metal would cool the anodes, carrying the waste heat to a heat engine for the generation of additional power from this high temperature waste heat. In this way, the efficiency of thermal energy conversion could be increased. In another nuclear thermionic power system design, a liquid metal transfers heat from the reactor at very high temperatures to operate external thermionic units.

FIG. 8-11 Cascade thermionic-thermoelectric generator (Thermoelectron Engineering Co. — Minnesota Mining and Mfg. Co.).

Compact nuclear thermionic generators for space power offer many advantages. As a result of their efficiency and high temperature of heat rejection, radiator size can be reduced. Estimates based on thermionic test data indicate that power units that will weigh less than 10 lb per kilowatt of electrical power are possible.

Radioisotope-heated thermionic generators offer similar advantages. A thermionic generator heated with curium-242 is being developed to demonstrate thermionic power (Fig. 8-10). It will produce 12 W for a 90-day lunar mission.

A cesium thermionic–thermoelectric cascade generator (Fig. 8-11) has been constructed and operated successfully. The thermionic generator, in the shape of a tapered plug, fits inside the thermoelectric generator. The waste heat rejected from the thermionic unit operating at 1400 °C passes directly to the hot junction of the thermoelectric generator at a temperature of about 500 °C. Cascade units of this type may be developed to have an efficiency of 10 to 12 percent.

REFERENCES

1. W. L. KNECHT, "Thermionic Energy Conversion", WADD-TR 60–128, Mar. 1960.
2. J. B. BURNS, Electro-Optical Systems, Inc., "Thermionic Emitters", *Energy Conversion Systems Reference Handbook*, W. R. MENETREY, ed., WADD-TR 60–699, Sept. 1960.
3. V. C. WILSON and J. LAWRENCE, "Test of a Cesium Thermionic Converter Designed to Utilize Solar Energy in Outer Space", GE Report No. 60-RL-2518 E, Sept. 1960.
4. E. N. GYFTOPOULOS and G. N. HATSOPOULOS, "Thermionic Nuclear Reactor", AIEE District Meeting Paper DP 62-919, May 1962.
5. L. W. PERRY, "Status of Thermoelectrics and Thermionics", SAE Paper 783 B, Jan. 1964.
6. B. G. VORHEES, "Progress Toward Nuclear Thermionic Power", ARS Paper 2577, Sept. 1962.
7. E. I. BLOUNT, "Thermionic Conversion", *Thermoelectricity: Science and Engineering*, R. R. HEIKES and R. W. URE, JR., ed., New York, Interscience, 1961.
8. V. L. STOUT, "Thermionic Emission and Thermionic Power Generation", *Thermoelectricity*, P. H. EGLI, ed., New York, Wiley, 1960.

CHAPTER 9

RADIOISOTOPE POWER
SOURCES*

INTRODUCTION

There are many requirements for small, long-life power sources for remotely operated devices particularly in space where the performance of most systems is limited by the available energy. The development of radioisotope auxiliary power units for satellites was initiated in 1955. Many applications now are being found for these compact reliable sources of electrical energy having useful lives of months or even years without maintenance or refueling.

There are several ways to convert the energy released by a radioisotope into electrical energy and a type of nuclear battery was suggested by Mosley in 1913 (Ref. 2). Using a nuclide that emits an electrically charged particle within an evacuated metal container, and with the source insulated from the container as shown in Fig. 9-1, several thousand volts can be produced. The charged particles are driven away from the source by their high kinetic energy and collect on the metal wall. The current from this type of battery is small (micro-microamperes) however, the device is useful in certain instruments as a high voltage reference source. Other types of nuclear batteries can be made using the radiation from the radioisotope to activate a semiconductor junction or heat a thermocouple. A gas ionized by radioactivity will produce a potential in contact with two electrodes of different

---

* Extensive material for this chapter has been drawn from J. B. Weddell W. M. Bowes, W. R. Corliss and G. P. Six, The Martin Company and Electro-Optical Systems Inc., "Radioisotope System Design", *Energy Conversion Systems Reference Handbook*, W. R. Menetrey, ed., WADD-TR 60-699.

work functions. Also the radioisotope can be used to produce light in a phosphor and this light can activate a photosensitive material. Such a nuclear battery, the size of a dime was developed in 1953 to power an electric wristwatch. This unit produces 20 microwatts from a promethium-147 source (Ref. 2).

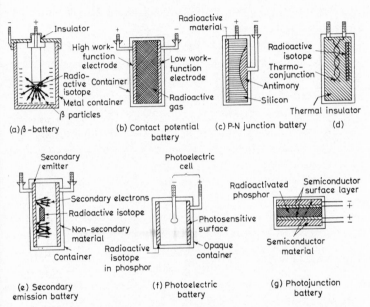

FIG. 9-1 Nuclear batteries. Reproduced from R. I. Sarbacher, *Encyclopedic Dictionary of Electronics and Nuclear Engineering*, Prentice-Hall.

The initial development of isotopic power sources capable of producing larger amounts of power might be identified with a radioisotope electric generator built in late 1953 by the Mound Laboratory (Ref. 3). This unit was used to publicize power generated from nuclear energy, during discussions with representatives from the utilities regarding their part in the development of commercial nuclear power. The unit was not intended for practical power generation.

The Mound Laboratory, where this generator was built, is operated for the U.S. Atomic Energy Commission by the Monsanto Research Laboratories, Inc., and has extensive facilities for the separation and loading of polonium-210. This is a remarkable energetic radioisotope. Very special precautions and equipment are required to handle plutonium safely until it is sealed into a capsule; once it is sealed, little harmful radiation is produced outside the capsule. Because of the large amount of energy produced with little external radiation, polonium-210 is suited for use in small power sources.

A toy steam engine made by the Jensen Manufacturing Co., Jeannette, Pennsylvania was modified for this power demonstration unit. The electric strip heater was removed from the boiler and three brass thimbles silver soldered into the boiler to receive the radioisotope fuel rods. Insulation was added and an armature from a small Delco Appliance permanent-magnet motor was substituted in the generator. These modifications (Fig. 9-2) increased the efficiency of the system to 0.25 percent.

The design of the fuel rods presented a special problem because of the hazards associated with the polonium-210. Three fuel rods containing a total of about 2000 curies of radioactivity and producing 70 W of thermal energy were used. The fuel rods were 5/8 in. in diameter and 6.5 in. long and had a wall thickness of 1/8 in. Close to 60 curies of polonium-210 was loaded into each of several hollow iron spheres (about 0.42 in. in diameter) that were sealed by nickel plating. After measuring the polonium-210 content calorimetrically, thirteen of the spheres were loaded into each fuel rod and embedded in solder. The end of the fuel rod was sealed by seating a threaded stainless steel cap against a soft aluminum gasket and then soldering the cap in place. This solder also served as a visual indication that the fuel rod had not overheated. Figure 9-3 shows a partial section of developmental rod.

A meter calibrated to read engine speed, was connected to the generator along with a light bulb to demonstrate the production of nuclear power. It was found that a distance of one foot from the model loaded with the fuel rods, the radiation level was 20 mr/hr. This dose rate is not considered excessive since observers would be more than 2 ft away and the exposure would be limited to occasional short demonstrations.

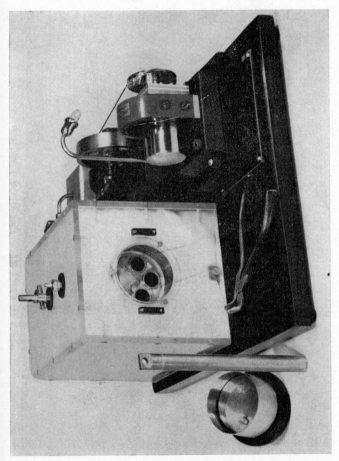

FIG. 9-2 Radioisotope heated steam generator set (Monsanto Research Corporation, Mound Laboratory).

A carrying case (shown in Fig. 9-4) contained an aluminum plate to which the fuel rods were clipped when not in use. By radiation and convection this plate dissipated the heat from the fuel rods without excessive temperatures.

Although this simple nuclear-power steam engine was built in a short time without much development, it was the unheralded

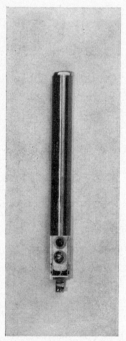

FIG. 9-3   Polonium-210 fuel capsule (Monsanto Research Corporation, Mound Laboratory).

forerunner of an important class of power sources for space and for remote locations on earth.

Also early in 1954 a radioisotope heated thermoelectric generator was constructed by using a reject fuel sphere from the steam engine. This method of converting the heat from radioactive decay into electrical energy is described in Ref. 4. Other radioisotope thermoelectric generators were constructed as a possible but unused display at the Brussels World Fair.

This first application of radioisotope power in space came in the successful launching and operation of TRANSIT IV-A in June 1961 (Ref. 5). These satellites transmit data with which

FIG. 9-4   Radioisotope generator in case (Monsanto Research Corporative Mound Laboratory).

mariners more accurately can determine at any time the positions of ships, and TRANSIT IV-A is a preliminary model of this satellite system. By comparing the Doppler frequency changes, which occur as the satellite approaches and recedes from the ship, with a known computation of the satellite's orbit, the navigator can calculate his position within one tenth of a mile. An operational TRANSIT system with four satellites will provide accurate navigational coverage to any spot on the earth.

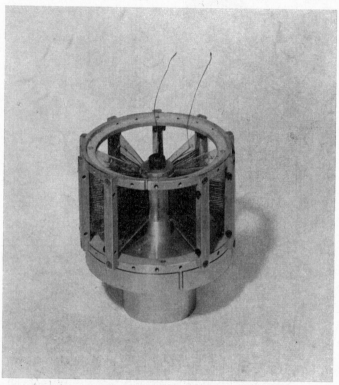

FIG. 9-5 Polonium-210 thermoelectric generator (Monsanto Research Corporation, Mound Laboratory).

Two of the four transmitters on TRANSIT IV-A are powered by a radioisotope–thermoelectric generator with an output of 2.7 W. Plutonium-238 provides the heat for the generator which was designed for a life of at least five years, even though the half-life of plutonium-238 is much longer (89.6 years). Since the thermal heat release drops only 4 percent in five years, a thermal control device is unnecessary.

This isotope was selected for its long half-life, its low gamma radiation level, and its high power density. The plutonium-238 fuel capsule is designed to withstand any fires or explosions that might occur during launching. The generator and fuel capsule is expected to burn up during re-entry into the earth's atmosphere dispersing the radioactive material at altitudes so high than atmospheric contamination will not become a hazard.

The generator consists of an encapsulated radionuclide heat source, a heat source support, a thermoelectric energy conversion system, a radiator, insulation, and an external housing that is approximately a $5\frac{1}{2}$ in. sphere (Fig. 9-20).

RADIOACTIVITY

Many nuclides, decay and emit energy. Such radioactive materials occur naturally, particularly in thorium and uranium minerals. Radioactive materials also may be produced by nuclear fission, by the absorption of neutrons, or by other radiations. Since there are a large number of radionuclides whose properties vary greatly in rate of energy release and types of radiations produced, a detailed study of the production and properties of radioactive materials is required before selecting a radioisotope and designing a heat source for a power unit. Some important considerations in the selection of a radioisotope are the types of radiations it released, its rate of decay, its physical properties, availability, and cost.

Each chemical element is characterized by the number of positive nuclear particles, protons, in the nucleus. The electrons (which determine chemical properties) must equal the protons in number for a neutral charge. The number of protons in the nucleus is designated by Z, the atomic number of the element. Neutrons which have no electrical charge but a mass nearly the same as that of the proton, make up the remainder of the nucleus and the sum of the number of neutrons and protons is the atomic weight.

Three types of ionizing radiation were identified from early studies of the rays from natural radioactive materials. It was found that not all types of radiation are emitted simultaneously by all radioactive substances. The radiations identified were alpha-particles that have a four-unit mass (corresponding to the helium atom) and a positive charge of two; beta-particles which have the negative charge and the mass of an electron; and gamma-rays which are similar to X-rays.

The two principal types of radionuclides suitable for high thermal energy release are the beta- and alpha-emitters. The other unstable nuclides (i.e. K-electron capture, L-electron capture, internal conversion or isomeric transition) are not sufficiently energetic to be usable for power generation. Whether or not gamma-radiation will be produced by beta or alpha emitters depends upon the radionuclide. The beta-particles emitted by most radionuclides have energies that are continuously distributed over a range which extends to the maximum value characteristic of each species. The maximum energy for many of the radionuclides that emit beta particles is less than 3 MeV—a value below 1 MeV is typical. The beta-ray range in air for a maximum energy of 1 MeV is about 12 ft although most of the particles are absorbed within 5 ft. Because the maximum range of high energy beta-rays in solid materials is only a few centimeters, the absorption of the beta-rays by the fuel and encapsulating material is not a difficult problem.

Alpha-particles are emitted at specific energy levels which have been carefully measured and studied. Only a few mils of material are required for the absorption of alpha-rays and the range of a 6 MeV alpha-particle in air is less than 2 in. However, a radiation hazard can be created by a possible secondary reaction between alpha-particles and low atomic weight elements to produce neutrons.

Since gamma-radiations are electromagnetic waves, the processes for absorption are quite different from those for the electrically charged beta- and alpha-particles. Gamma-rays are much more penetrating. The intensity of gamma-radiation decreases exponentially as it passes through any material; theoretically, therefore, only an infinite thickness of material will completely absorb this type of radiation. Energetic gamma-rays can travel more than

1000 ft in air or pass through several inches of solid material before being greatly attenuated.

The quantity of radiation from a sample of radioactive material decreases exponentially with time while the energies of the radiations emitted remain unchanged. The number of atoms which will disintegrate during a time interval is directly proportional to the number of atoms of the species present at that time. If the number of atoms present is A, the rate of decay (energy release rate) is $\dfrac{dA}{dt}$ or

$$\frac{dA}{dt} = -\lambda A$$

where λ is a constant characteristic of each radioactive species. The value of this constant cannot be changed by ordinary physical conditions such as temperature or chemical combination. Integration of the above relation leads to the exponential form

$$A(t) = A(0)e^{-\lambda t}$$

where $A(t)$ is the number of atoms of species A at a time t and $A(0)$ is the number of atoms initially present ($t = 0$).

Another constant frequently used is the half-life, the time required for half the atoms in a sample to decay or for the rate of energy release (power) to decrease to half its original value. The half-life is related to the disintegration constant by

$$t_{1/2} = \frac{0.693}{\lambda}$$

The value of the half-life may vary from a small fraction of a second (3×10^{-7} sec for polonium-212) to billions of years (for uranium-238).

The curie, a unit used to describe the rate of radioactive events is defined as 3.7×10^{10} disintegrations per second. When disintegrations occur at this rate in a radioactive material, it is said to have one curie of activity. The curie is based on the activity of 1 g of radium; 1 g of radium has 1 curie of activity.

328 ELEMENTS OF ENERGY CONVERSION

There is a coincidental but useful relation between the curie and the energy released by fissioning of an atom of nuclear fuel. Since about 200 MeV of energy are released per fission, and taking a curie as 3.7×10^{10} nuclear events per second, it follows that one

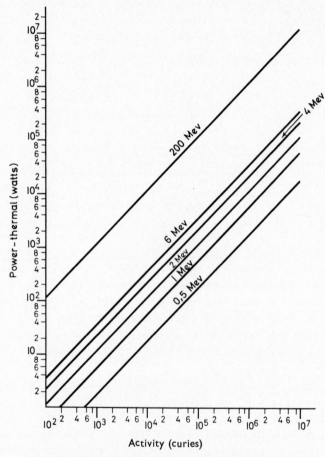

FIG. 9-6 Thermal power from radioactivity.

curie of fissions (actually 1.19 curies of fissions) releases one watt of power (thermal). Extending this relation to a radioisotope heat source which releases 2 MeV per atomic decay heating an electric generator with an efficiency of 10 percent, then a curie (1.19 curies) of this radioactive material will produce a milliwatt of electrical power. These relations are convenient in estimating both the amount of radioactive material required for power sources and associated problems of radiation. Figure 9-6 shows the thermal power released by radioactive material for several decay energies.

The absorption of electrons of high energies will produce penetrating electromagnetic radiations similar to X-rays and called bremsstrahlung. This radiation originates with the accalaration of electrons in the process of being absorbed and the term, bremsstrahlung, means breaking radiation. The flux and energy of this radiation depend upon the energy of the beta radiation and, to a lesser extent, on the type of material absorbing the electron energy. The heavy elements (materials of high atomic number) produce more radiation than the light elements. Although the bremsstrahlung may be important in determining shielding requirements, the radiation is a minor energy loss from a beta source. The energy spectrum of these X-rays produced by the absorption of beta-radiation is continuous over a broad range with the maximum energy approaching that of the beta-particle and the average energy much less than this. When the high energy beta-rays from strontium-90 and yttrium-90 (2.26 MeV) are absorbed in a heavy element such as lead, they will produce intense X-rays important in shielding design. A proper choice of absorbing material will minimize the amount of X-rays. Because beta-particles having energies less than 1 MeV do not produce intense bremsstrahlung, the shielding problem can be minimized by selecting lower-energy beta sources and absorbing materials of low atomic weight.

Alpha-particles do not produce X-radiations by the bremsstrahlung process. However, secondary radiations from alpha-emitters may include decay gammas, fission product gammas, neutrons from spontaneous fission and neutrons from reactions of alpha-particles with low atomic weight materials. Impurities such as carbon, aluminum, and oxygen can be of significance in an alpha source. For example, the average neutron production in a polonium source may be 100 to 200 neutrons per second per curie because of inherent impurities. Other light elements that may produce neutrons include boron, hydrogen, beryllium, nitrogen and fluorine. The yield from polonium-210 alphas with the light elements is shown in Fig. 9-7.

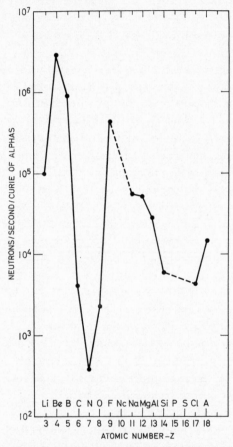

FIG. 9-7 Neutron yield from polonium-210 alphas (5.3 MeV) with light elements (The Martin Company).

In some cases, the radiation dose from spontaneous fission neutrons can exceed that of the total gamma radiation. For example, curium-242, with a spontaneous fission half-life of 7×10^6 years, will have a neutron dose rate exceeding that of the gamma dose rate for as long as 5 years; after that the gamma dose rate overtakes and dominates the neutron dose rate through buildup of fission products. In the case of plutonium-238, the gamma dose predominates over that from spontaneous fission neutrons.

PRODUCTION OF RADIOISOTOPES

The nuclides of interest as sources of thermal energy are produced by fission or are formed by neutron absorption in some target material that is irradiated in a reactor. Although radioisotopes can be made with cyclotrons and other types of accelerators, the large quantities of material required for power generators are produced in nuclear reactors. (The cyclotron is particularly useful for making isotopes by deuteron — heavy hydrogen — reactions, but these isotopes are used for other purposes.)

By the absorption of a neutron, a nuclide is transformed into the isotope of the same element but one with a greater mass (by one unit), and gamma-radiation is emitted. The synthesized isotope may or may not be radioactive. For the case where the new isotope decays by emission of a beta-particle, a second new isotope will be formed with the same mass (nearly) as its parent but with an atomic number one unit greater since one additional positively charged nuclear particle (proton) is created in the emission of a negative beta-particle. For example, uranium-238 may be converted to uranium-239 by the absorption of a neutron. Uranium has an atomic number of 92. The daughter of uranium-239 by beta-emission is neptunium-239 which has an atomic number of 93. This in turn decays again by beta-emission to plutonium-239 which has an atomic number of 94. This chain of reactions can be extended (Fig. 9-8) to include the formation of curium-242 — an important isotopic fuel for power sources. Other processes, including fissioning by absorption of fast and slow neutrons result in the destruction of nuclides in this chain. It is estimated that 1000 g of plutonium-239 containing 1 percent of plutonium-241 will produce about 0.5 g of americium-241 by neutron irradiation in a reactor.

Formation of Curium-242

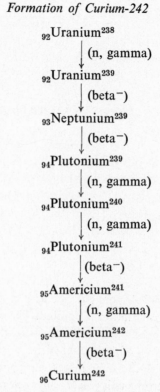

$_{92}$Uranium^{238}

$\downarrow$ (n, gamma)

$_{92}$Uranium^{239}

$\downarrow$ (beta$^-$)

$_{93}$Neptunium^{239}

$\downarrow$ (beta$^-$)

$_{94}$Plutonium^{239}

$\downarrow$ (n, gamma)

$_{94}$Plutonium^{240}

$\downarrow$ (n, gamma)

$_{94}$Plutonium^{241}

$\downarrow$ (beta$^-$)

$_{95}$Americium^{241}

$\downarrow$ (n, gamma)

$_{95}$Americium^{242}

$\downarrow$ (beta$^-$)

$_{96}$Curium^{242}

Fig. 9-8   Formation of curium-242.

The probability that a neutron will be absorbed by an atom of a material is expressed in terms of the absorption cross-section σ_a in units of barns (10^{-24} cm^2 per nucleus); this area might be considered the target area to be hit by the neutron and hence the term "barn". If there are N target nuclei per cubic centimeter, the product $N\sigma_a$ is called the macroscopic cross section $\sum_a$ for neutron absorption,

$$N\sigma_a = \sum_a$$

The neutron density, n (neutrons per cm^3), multiplied by the average neutron velocity, v, gives the neutron flux, ϕ (neutrons per cm^2-sec). The rate of formation of the nuclide A_f per unit

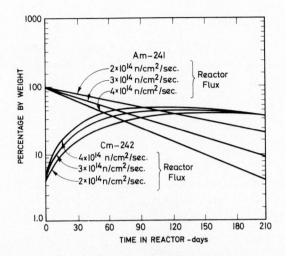

FIG. 9-9   Rate of conversion of americium to curium-242 in a reactor
(The Martin Company).

FIG. 9-10   Isotope face of Oak Ridge reactor (Oak Ridge National Laboratory).

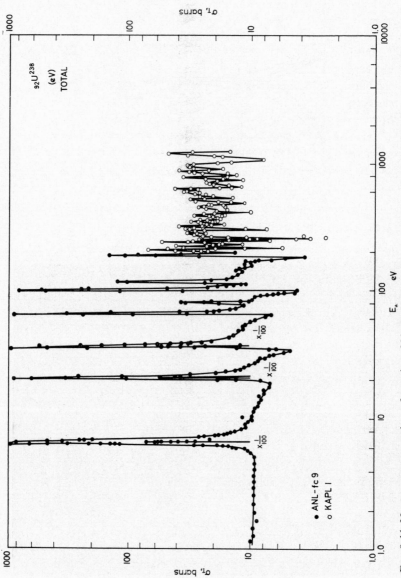

FIG. 9-11 Neutron cross-section of uranium-238. Reproduced from *Neutron Cross Sections*, by D. J. Hughes and R. B. Schwartz, Brookhaven National Laboratory Report 325, Supplement 1.

volume by absorption of neutrons, is, therefore,

$$\frac{dA_f}{dt} = N\sigma_a \cdot \phi = \Sigma_a \phi$$

The neutron absorption cross-section varies greatly between different elements and isotopes and typical values may range from 0.032 barns for bismuth which forms polonium-210 to 2×10^6 barns for xenon-135. The absorption cross-section also depends upon the energy of the neutron, and for many isotopes the absorption decreases with neutron velocity. However, some materials have strong absorption peaks at certain neutron energies as shown for uranium-238 in Fig. 9-11.

FISSION PRODUCTS

Radioisotopes useful as heat sources also are produced by the fissioning of nuclear fuel in a reactor. An atom of fissionable material can break in many different ways in the fission process, although two primary fission product nuclides are always formed in addition to neutron, gamma-, beta- and neutrino-radiations, and energy in the form of kinetic energy of the fission fragments. The weight of a pair of fission fragments plus the neutrons equals the weight of the fissioned atom with a very small allowance for the energy released. Fission products with atomic weights over the range from 72 (zinc) to 160 (gadolinium) have been identified, however, most (97 percent) of the species falls into a light group with masses from 85 to 104 and a heavy group with atomic weights from 130 to 149. By defining fission yield as the proportion of nuclear fissions yielding a particular species, the sum of all fission yields is 200 percent, since there are two fission products per fission. A plot of fission yield versus atomic weight (Fig. 9-13) shows that symmetrical curves result with left and right hand limbs that are mirror images (Ref. 7). Since an atom of uranium-235 can apparently fission in some thirty different ways to produce sixty primary fission products (each of which is unstable and may undergo up to three stages of radioactive decay, creating a

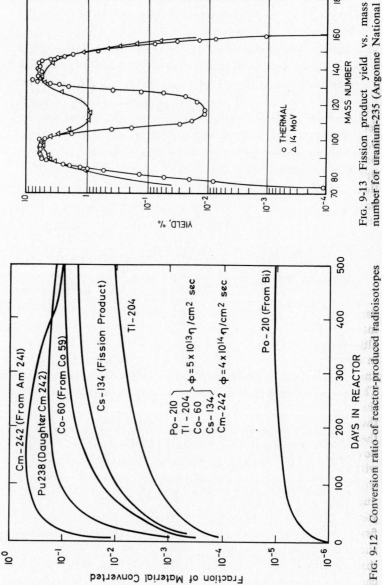

Fig. 9-13 Fission product yield vs. mass number for uranium-235 (Argonne National Laboratory)

FIG. 9-12 Conversion ratio of reactor-produced radioisotopes (The Martin Company)

new radionuclide in each stage), it is obvious that the fission products are a complicated radiochemical system. Furthermore, each of the fission products reacts with neutrons in a reactor at a rate determined by the neutron cross-section and the neutron flux. In addition, some species, formed directly by fission, are also formed later by decay of a parent nuclide. Therefore, the cumulative yields of fission products from thermal fission may be greater than the direct chain yields.

It has been seen above that the rate of disintegration of nuclides of a given species is proportional to A, the number of such atoms present at any time.

If this nuclide is also being formed at a constant rate S, then

$$\frac{dA}{dt} = S - \lambda A$$

A chain of reactions starting with species A, formed at a constant rate S, and with a decay constant λ_A to produce species B which in turn decays to species C, can be indicated as follows:

$$A \xrightarrow{\lambda_A} B \xrightarrow{\lambda_B} C \xrightarrow{\lambda_C} D_{stable}$$

The net rate of formation of species B is then

$$\frac{dB}{dt} = \lambda_A \cdot A - \lambda_B \cdot B$$

For the case of a reactor that has operated for some time to accumulate an inventory of radionuclides and is then shut down so that the primary source, S, becomes zero, the amount of each species present at shut down will be indicated by $A_{(0)}$, $B_{(0)}$, $C_{(0)}$, etc. Then the above relations will have the following solutions for the amount of each species present at some time (t) after reactor shutdown

$$A_{(t)} = A_{(0)}e^{-\lambda_A t}$$

$$B_{(t)} = B_{(0)}e^{-\lambda_B} \quad \therefore_A A_0 \left(\frac{e^{-\lambda_A t}}{\lambda_B - \lambda_A} + \frac{e^{-\lambda_B t}}{\lambda_A - \lambda_B} \right)$$

Solutions of such equations for the other products and for other cases are available in the literature.

Only a few of the several hundred known radioisotopes are acceptable under the criteria established for isotopic sources of thermal energy for auxiliary power units. These criteria include the following:

1. *Specific power.* The isotope should produce enough energy per unit of mass that weight will not be excessive for the application. The specific power is determined by the rate of decay, the energy released per disintegration including in some cases energy from the decay of daughters, and the chemical compound or alloy used.

When the average decay energy is expressed as MeV, the half-life as days, and the fraction of active isotope of atomic weight A per unit mass of fuel material as f, the initial specific power P watts per gram is given by the relation

$$P_0 = \frac{7.75 \times 10^5 \, \text{MeV}_{\text{ave}} \times f}{A \times t_{1/2}}$$

In terms of the decay constant λ, in units of reciprocal days, this relation becomes

$$P_0 = \frac{1.118 \times 10^6 \, \text{MeV}_{\text{ave}} \times \lambda \times f}{A}$$

The specific power for selected isotopes is given in Table 9-1. Usually radioisotopes with specific powers greater than 0.10 W/g will be sufficiently active to produce reasonably sized sources of thermal energy.

2. *Half-life.* Because the thermal energy produced by a radioisotope decreases with time, the half-life should be long relative to the operating time so that large quantities of thermal energy

do not have to be rejected from the system during the initial period of operation.

The variation in relative power as a function of time for a few isotopes of particular interest is illustrated in Fig. 9-14. Values of the half-life together with type and energy of particle emitted during decay are given in Table 9-2. It should be noted that beta-energies are the maximum values and the average beta-energies are a fraction such as 0.4 of these maximum energies. Alpha-particles are emitted at constant energy and hence the values listed may be used without adjustment.

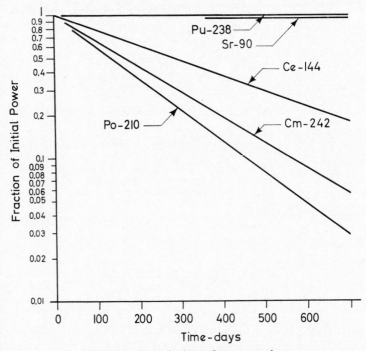

FIG. 9-14   Isotopic thermal power vs. time.

Half-lives in excess of 120 days usually are desired for practical power sources and the nearly constant power of strontium-90 and plutonium-238 sources can be of considerable advantage in the design of a system.

3. *Isotope.* Power sources to be landed on the moon must not interfer with future experiments by radioactive contamination of the surface even in the event of an accidental high velocity impact on the surface. Therefore, a radioisotope that would not be expected to occur in the lunar surface is preferred and curium-242 was selected for the SNAP-11 power source with this requirement in mind.

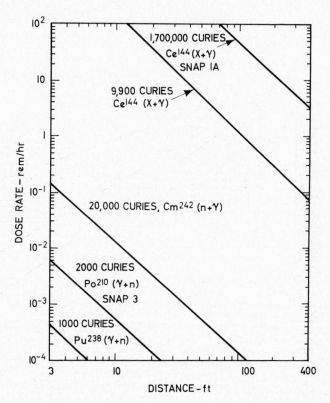

FIG. 9-15   External radiation from radioisotope sources (The Martin Company).

4. *Shielding.* External radiations from the gamma-rays, bremsstrahlung, X-rays or neutrons produced in a radioisotope capsule may require shielding to reduce radiation to levels that are safe

for shipping and ground handling. Shielding may also be required to reduce radiations that may interfer with experiments. On the other hand, shielding must not be so excessive that the intended application of the power source is obstructed.

The major factor, of course, in determining the amount of external shielding required is the choice of the isotope and its purity. Those nuclide that emit only alpha-particles or low energy beta-particles requiring little or no shielding. High energy beta emitters, or nuclides that emit gamma-rays may call for heavy shielding. This requirement can be reduced by selection of light elements for the absorption of energy of beta-particles, or by eliminating even trace quantities of light elements such as boron or beryllium from alpha emitter capsules. The amount of radiation from isotopic sources is shown in Fig. 9-15.

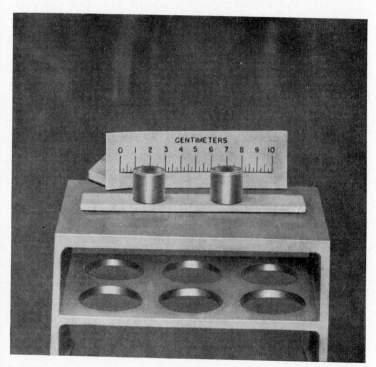

FIG. 9-16 Multikilocurie radioisotope heat sources (Oak Ridge National Laboratory).

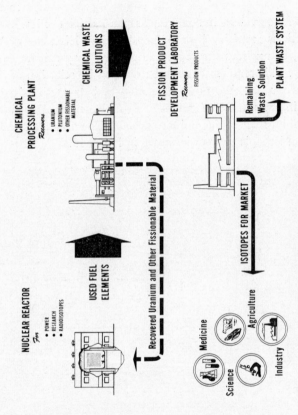

FIG. 9-17   Isotope processing (Oak Ridge National Laboratory).

FIG. 9-18 Welding fuel capsule closure with remote equipment (Oak Ridge National Laboratory).

The half-value thickness of water to reduce the fast neutron dose rate from alpha emitters is about 2.6 in. In the case of a generator containing about 580 curies of curium-242 it was found that 1.6 in. of water is needed as additional shielding during shipment and handling.

Much greater shielding is required for the beta-emitters. The SNAP-1A heat source containing cerium-144 required 9.5 in. of mercury for temporary shielding during ground handling. Since weight of this mercury is about 4000 lb, it is easy to see that shielding can place a penalty on beta-emitters for applications where the shielding weight is a major problem.

5. *Availability and cost of fuel*. The availability of facilities for the separation and packaging of radioisotopic heat sources has governed to a large extent the selection of materials. However the completion of large capacity installations, and the development of new separation processes are making available several isotopes in quantity.

The least expensive materials should be the fission product isotopes which are handled as waste materials and stored at considerable cost. Processes developed for the removal of strontium and other isotopes as part of the waste processing make these materials available in large quantity (Ref. 8).

TABLE 9-1   SPECIFIC POWER OF RADIOISOTOPES

Radioisotope	Fuel form	Power	
		Theoretical W/g	Practical W/cm³
Cesium-134	Cs	6.9	
Cesium-137	CsCl	0.2	0.249
Cobalt-60	Co	12.6	3.8
Curium-242	Cm	122.0	
	Cm-8 Pt		256.0
Curium-244	Cm	2.8	20.0
Plutonium-238	Pu	0.58	
Polonium-210	Po	141.0	1188.0
Promethium-147	Pm_2O_3	0.45	2.0
Strontium-90	$SrTiO_3$	0.45	0.54

TABLE 9-2 PROPERTIES OF RADIOISOTOPES

Isotopes	Half-life	Energy (MeV)			Daughter
		alpha	beta	gamma	
Cesium-134	2.3 years	—	0.65 (70%)	0.605, 0.797	Ba-134
Cesium-137	30 years	—	0.525 (92%)	0.66	Ba-137
Cerium-144	285 days	—	0.309 (76%)	0.70	Pr-144
		—			
Cobalt-60	5.3 years	—	0.312	1.33	Ni-60
Curium-242	162.5 days	6.110	—	0.044	Pu-238
Curium-243	35.0 years	5.780	—	0.227	Pu-239
Curium-244	17.9 years	5.801	—	0.043	Pu-240
Europium-154	1.7 years	—	1.85	0.123	Gd-154
Krypton-85	10 years	—	0.672	0.52	Rb-85
Plutonium-238	89.6 years	5.495	—	0.0434	U-234
Polonium-210	138.4 days.	5.305	—	weak	Po-206
Polonium-208	2.93 years	5.108	—	weak	Pb-204
Promethium-147	2.66 years	—	0.229	0.121	Sm-147
Promethium-146	2 years	—	0.75	0.74	—
Sr-Y-90	27.7 years	—	0.545 (2.26)	weak (1.74)	Zr-90
U-232	74 years	5.318	—	0.057	Th-228

TABLE 9-3 STRONTIUM 90 DECAY CHAIN

↓Krypton-90	(33 sec.)
↓Rubidium-90	(2.7 min)
↓Strontium-90	(28 years)
↓Yttrium-90	(64.3 hr)
Zirconium-90	(Stable)

SEPARATION OF RADIOISOTOPES

The chemical processing of fuel elements from a nuclear reactor to recover uranium and plutonium or other products is a complex operation that requires extensive facilities. Special equipment have been installed at both Hanford and Oak Ridge to separate and package fission products such as strontium and cesium.

The operations used in these separations include precipitation and solvent extraction. Although various novel processes are being developed including volatilization and pyrometallurgy, solvent extraction and ion exchange are particularly effective and give nearly quantitative separations—it is these methods which have become highly developed in the atomic energy installations.

Following separation, the nuclide must be converted to the desired chemical form, dried or alloyed, and pressed into a container—all operations that require large and expensive facilities because the work must be done remotely behind heavy shielding. In addition, a gas-tight system may be required for the processing of some of the alpha emitters, such as polonium-210.

Chemical processing and packaging plants must be designed for remote operation and this equipment is expensive and requires careful maintenance regardless of the production rate. The high cost of special purpose hot cells that may be used only occasionally, can be reflected in an expensive product.

Some of the materials that can be separated and packaged in large quantity at the Fission Product Development Laboratory at the Oak Ridge National Laboratory are shown in Table 9-4.

TABLE 9-4 ANNUAL CAPACITY
ORNL FISSION PRODUCT DEVELOPMENT LABORATORY

Cesium-137	500,000 curies
Strontium-90	250,000 curies
Cerium-144	4,000,000 curies
Promethium-147	500,000 curies

RADIOLOGICAL SAFEGUARDS

The quantity of a radioisotope required to produce an electric output of 100 W can be estimated (Fig. 9-6) at tens of thousands of curies for a typical conversion efficiency and decay energy. This quantity is large compared to the total world production of radium, which was only about 1000 curies up until World War II.

In the case of strontium-90 the total permissible body burden is 20 μ curies; from this it can be seen that the quantity of radioactive material in a small power source is very large compared to a biologically significant dose. Other radioisotopes, such as polonium-210 and plutonium-239, used as energy source, have similar extremely minute body tolerances. It is, therefore, essential that careful consideration be given to the system design and use of nuclear auxiliary power sources so that undue hazards do not result even under the unusual and somewhat unpredictable conditions of rocket launching and re-entry from space.

Fig. 9-19 Radiation measurements on atomic buoy (U.S. Coast Guard).

ISOTOPES IN USE

From the large number of radioisotopes that have been considered for power generation, most candidates have been eliminated
on the basis of the above criteria. The suggestion often is made of
using spent fuel elements with their inventory of mixed fission
products as a source of thermal energy. However, the shielding
required makes their use unattractive for mobile power generators.
Each of the following isotopes has been selected for one of the
SNAP generators on the basis of some advantageous characteristic.

(1) Cerium-144, one of the fission-product isotopes. This nuclide decays to praseodymium-144 with the emission of beta-
particles and gamma-rays. The half-life of this daughter is
175 min, and the decay of the praseodymium-144 (again with
the emission of beta-particles and gamma-rays) accounts for the
release of most of the energy. Since the beta-particles have considerable energy, a large amount of photon radiation is emitted
from the slowing down of these energetic beta-particles (bremsstrahlung). Heavy shielding is required for ground handling and
shipment.

(2) Polonium-210. The neutron irradiation of bismuth produces
polonium according to the reactions:

$$\text{Bi-209} + \text{n} \Bigg\langle \begin{array}{l} \text{Bi-210 } (2.6 \times 10^6 \text{ yr.}) \\[2ex] \text{Bi-210 } (5.0\text{d}) \\ \qquad \searrow \\ \qquad \text{Po-210} + \text{beta} \end{array}$$

Only a small fraction (10^{-5}) of the bismuth is converted to polonium because of the small neutron absorption cross-section of
bismuth and the short half-life of the product, so chemical
separation is required to concentrate the product. The separation
process is difficult contributing to the high cost of this isotope.
Very little gamma-radiation is produced and that is of low energy,
therefore polonium-210 can be used with minimum shielding.
This radioisotope is remarkably energetic. However, polonium is

a low-melting volatile metal that may be corrosive to many container materials. Also, the permissible body burden of the nuclide is unusually low as it is for other alpha-emitters.

(3) Curium-242, an alpha-emitter of 163 day half-life, is of increasing interest for power generators. In addition to the advantageous nuclear properties, this isotope can be produced at a fraction of the cost of polonium-210 with similar characteristics. Curium-242 can be used in elemental form or converted chemically into high density compounds. The alloy of curium with gold or platinum is a preferred fuel form.

Curium is made in a nuclear reactor by neutron irradiation of americium-241 as described previously. The product from 100 days of irradiation in a high flux reactor will contain over 40 percent curium-242 and this composition can be used as a heat

FIG. 9-20 Installation of SNAP generator in TRANSIT IV-A satellite (Johns Hopkins Applied Physics Laboratory).

FIG. 9-21   SNAP-1A generator (The Martin Company).

source without further processing, thus, reducing the production costs. The daughter of curium-242, plutonium-238, may be corrosive to many container materials at elevated temperature (Ref. 9).

The requirement for radioactive material for use on lunar experiments have led to the selection of curium for the SNAP 11 generator.

(4) Strontium-90, Nuclear fission produces nuclides of atomic weight 90 in quantity. The fission product chain is shown in Table 9-3.

The long half-life of the strontium isotope causes it to accumulate in the fuel elements until the time of removal from the reactor for chemical processing to separate the fission products from the unburned nuclear fuel. In the past the mixed fission products have been stored in large underground tanks and the shorter half-life fission products have decayed. Fortunately a simple chemical process for separating strontium from these accumulated wastes has been found. By removing strontium, the danger of possible escape of the stored material is reduced greatly. Strontium-90 in separated form is available for heat sources. Expensive, remotely operated facilities required for the purification and encapsulation of this hazardous material in kilocurie quantities are operated at Oak Ridge and Hanford.

The use of strontium-90 is limited to applications where heavy shielding can be accommodated.

(5) Plutonium-238. Although plutonium is usually considered

Fig. 9-22 Vacuum tests (The Martin Company).

a weapons material or a nuclear reactor fuel, a different plutonium isotope with a half-life of 86.4 years is an attractive heat source. Because the rate of decay is very low, generators can be operated for years without much change in power level. Plutonium-238 emits a high-energy alpha-particle and only a small amount of gamma-radiation so that little external shielding is required. There are facilities suitable for the fabrication and encapsulation of plutonium heat sources at the Mound Laboratory. Since the

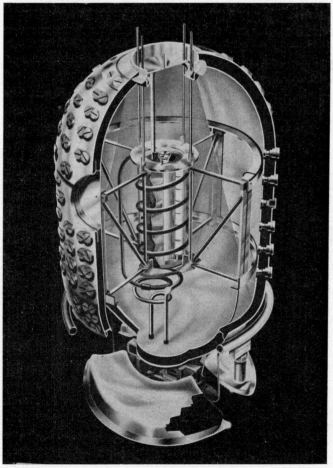

FIG. 9-23   SNAP-1A generator (The Martin Company).

alpha-particles become helium, which creates a pressure in the source, provisions for free volume or venting must be made for the gas in the capsule. Molten plutonium will alloy with many metals. Tantalum liners which resists plutonium are required in containers. The daughter of plutonium, uranium-234 with its long half-life (2.5×10^5 years) contributes little to any further release of energy.

RADIOISOTOPE POWER APPLICATIONS

SNAP-1A GENERATOR

Development of an isotope generator capable of producing 125 W of electrical power for one year was begun in 1956 at the Martin Company under contract to the Atomic Energy Commission. Intended for operation in space, this generator had to satisfy various requirements, one of them the rejection of heat in the space environment. The original concept included a mercury-turbine power conversion system. Fortunately, as mentioned in Chapter 1, thermoelectric generators of reasonable efficiency became available. These made it possible to produce practical generators of unusual reliability (Ref. 18).

The outer shell of the generator, 34.1 in. in length by 24.0 in. in diameter, consists of an inner skin of stainless steel which serves as the thermal element hot junction, and an outer skin of aluminium which is the cold junction. The insulation between these two skins is hinged at the bottom of the unit so that a part of the hot stainless steel inner liner can be exposed in order to radiate excess heat directly into space.

The thermoelectric units fit between the hot inner skin and the cold outer surface. A total of 277 lead telluride couples, each 0.375 in. in diameter, produce an output of 28 V at 4.46 A with an efficiency of 6.75 percent for the bare thermocouple. Good thermal contact between the thermocouple surfaces is maintained by spring pressure. Electrical interconnection is made at the hot junction by a copper jumper strap and at the cold junction by copper wires attached to adjacent solder lugs.

The fuel capsule supported in the center of the shell by struts is made from a block of Inconel-X, 11 in. long by 3.75 in. diameter, containing seven 1.0 in. diameter holes which, after loading, are closed with a threaded closure plug welded in place. The fuel, ceric oxide, is pressed into pellets inside stainless steel tubes, that are loaded into the fuel tubes in the capsule. The top of the capsule fits over locking pins and supports the remote handling lug.

The fuel capsule was designed to meet the requirement that fuel be dispersed during re-entry. This led to the selection of ceric oxide CeO_2, for the fuel form because of its high density (3.7 g per cm^3), and its adaptability to hot cell work. The addition of silicon carbide to the ceric oxide was found to promote dispersion or burnup. By adding 10 percent SiC, the fuel was dispersed in particles of less than 10 microns in plasma jet tests.

A summary of SNAP-1A characteristics is given in Table 9-5.

For a conversion efficiency of approximately 5 percent, an output of 2500 W of thermal energy is required from the radioisotope source at the end of one year. Since the necessary quantity of fission product cerium-144 (some 880,000 curies producing an

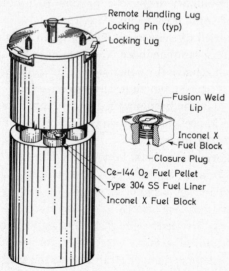

FIG. 9-24 SNAP-1A fuel capsule (The Martin Company).

TABLE 9-5

SNAP-1A	Design Characteristics
Power output	125 W (e)
Duration	365 days
Voltage	28
Current	4.46 A
Efficiency	5.0% actual
	50% Carnot
Hot junction	1050 °F
Cold junction	335 °F
Thermoelectric material	Lead telluride
Radiator surface	14.5 ft²
Shutter radiator area	3.5 ft²
Shield (mercury)	4000 lb
Isotope inventory	880,000 curies, initial
Fuel form	CeO_2
Half-life	285 days
Flyaway weight	200 lb
Length	34.1 in.
Diameter	24.0 in.

initial thermal power of 6500 W) was available, this isotope was selected. The thermoelectric materials at the start of this program were in a preliminary stage of testing and since the greatest amount of available data related to lead telluride, this material was chosen for energy conversion in this system. Its use restricted the maximum hot-junction temperature to approximately 1050 °F, and in order to obtain the desired overall conversion efficiency of 5 percent, the cold-junction temperature was limited to 300 °F.

Thermal analysis indicated that the use of radiation, alone, to reject heat would require a radiator surface area of about 14.5 ft². One of the several designs considered was a fluid heat-transfer system in a closed loop to carry the heat to the external surface of the vehicle for radiation into space. This design was discarded, however, in favor of the more simple radiative boundary design that dissipates heat only through the generator surface.

This quantity of cerium-144 (a beta-emitter) would produce a substantial radiation level, so shielding would be required for handling and installing the generator. Mercury was chosen for the shield material; about 9.5 in. of mercury would be needed for reducing the radiation level to less than 200 milliroentgens (mr) per hour at 1 m. This shielding was considered adequate for limited ground-handling operations. However, the difficulty of shielding cerium-144 and the availability of other isotopes that did not present this ground-handling problem, led to the abandonment of the SNAP-1 generator for space application⸏

SNAP-3 GENERATOR

The first of the nuclear auxiliary power generators developed to demonstrate feasibility and to obtain operating experience under the joint Atomic Energy Commission–Air Force space power program was a 2.4 W electric power unit fueled with polonium-210. A unit was publicly demonstrated at the White House on 16 Jan. 1959, and since then, several SNAP-3 generators have been produced and used in demonstrations and tests (Ref. 19).

The choice of polonium-210 as the radioisotope was determined by its availability and the requirement that external radiation be minimum without heavy shielding. This radioisotope, produced at the Mound Laboratory and used previously in a similar demon-

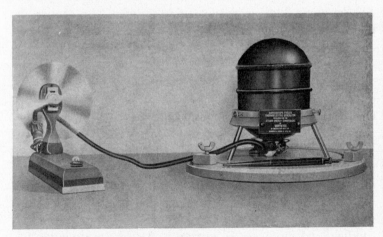

FIG. 9-25 SNAP-3 nuclear electric power device (U.S. Atomic Energy Commission).

stration generator, has a half-life of 138 days; it produces 5.3 MeV alpha particles and some soft gamma (0.80 MeV) radiation. However, since only 0.0012 percent of the disintegrations produce a gamma-emission, this source of external radiation is small. Some neutrons are produced when alpha-particles interact with light nuclei such as boron, hydrogen, beryllium nitrogen or fluorine which may be present as impurities. The external radiation measurements for a 2100-curie polonium-210 source are shown in Table 9-6. The polonium was encapsulated in an inner welded

TABLE 9-6   RADIATION MEASUREMENTS FOR A
2100-CURIE POLONIUM SOURCE

Location	Gamma mr/hr	Neutron mr/hr
Generator surface	400	1200
One meter distance	6	

canister with 0.030 in. stainless steel walls and a similar outer canister. Each generator contained some 1000 curies of material. The canisters were placed in a molybdenium container (Fig. 9-26) designed for a minimum safety factor of at least nine for containing the helium released by the polonium in its decay process.

As mentioned, thermoelectric generators of reasonable efficiency became available at the time this program started, and the development of lead telluride couples made possible the early delivery of these radioisotope generators. The Minnesota Mining & Manufacturing Co. provided 27 insulated thermoelectric couples constructed as shown in Fig. 9-27 for each unit. The radioisotope source in the middle heats the hot-shoe ring. From this the heat flows through the thermoelectric couples to the cold junction at the outer surface cooled by convection and radiation. The 27 couples are connected in series to produce a total voltage of s.5 V at zero load, and 2.5 V at maximum power. Table 9-7 3hows the operating characteristics for a generator.

Later models of this generator which produced a maximum

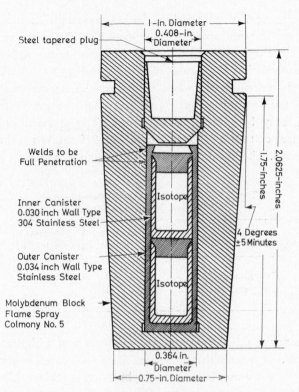

FIG. 9-26 Polonium canister in SNAP-3 generator (The Martin
Company).

TABLE 9-7   OPERATING CHARACTERISTICS SNAP-3 GENERATOR
MODEL 3M1C1, 1959

Overall size	4.75 in. (diameter)
	5.5 in. (height)
Heat source	1495 curies polonium-210
Thermal power	48 W
Electrical power	2.4 W
Efficiency	5 percent
Hot junction temperature	720 °F
Cold junction temperature	175 °F
Weight	5 lb
Specific power	2000 Wh/lb (140 days)

FIG. 9-27   Cutaway model of SNAP-3 generator (The Martin Company).

power of 4 W at 4 V with an efficiency of 5.75 percent were tested
extensively to establish their feasibility in operations. Tests included vibration, acceleration, shock, and operation in vacuum, and
proved that generators of this type can be made rugged enough
to withstand missile launch and flight conditions.

SNAP-7 GENERATORS

A series of isotopic generators fueled with strontium-90 in the
form of strontium titanate is being developed for the U.S. Coast
Guard and the Navy to use in navigational aids and automatic
weather stations. SNAP-7A and E are 5 W systems; the other
SNAP-7 units produce 10–30 W.

The Coast Guard has developed a buoy powered with a SNAP-7A generator. The power system consists of the strontium-90 heated generator, a voltage converter, and a small, rechargeable storage battery. A test buoy with this power system was launched in Curtis Bay in the Chesapeake on 14 December 1961. The unit operated unattended for nearly a year before a decrease in generator output required overhaul to restore the thermocouple contact surfaces. Since this type of generator is expected to have an effec-

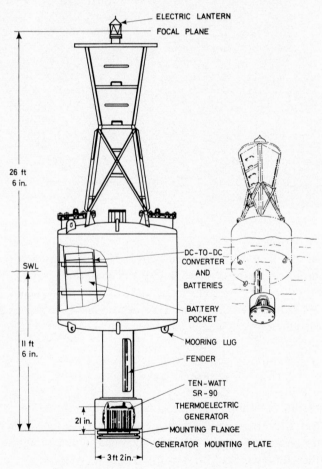

FIG. 9-28   Atomic-powered buoy (The Martin Company).

tive life of more than ten years, its use will greatly simplify the maintenance of the many remote lights, lighthouses, buoys and beacons for which the U.S. Coast Guard is responsible. Heavy shielding of depleted uranium reduces external radiation and contributes to the ruggedness of the unit. The generator weighs 1870 lb—contrast this with the 2500 lb of batteries which must be recharged every year or two required for a large buoy. SNAP-7B will have a 30 W output and will be used by the U.S. Coast Guard to power a land-based navigational light (Ref. 20).

FIG. 9-29   Nuclear generator for buoy (U.S. Coast Guard).

A SNAP-7C generator has been installed in an automatic weather station near McMurdo Sound in Antartica. The entire unit is buried in snow—only the whip antenna and the weather-sensing instruments are above the surface. This station, designed to operate unattended for two years, will transmit data automatically every 6 hr. The 10 W generator, 19 in. in diameter and 21 in. high, also is shielded with depleted uranium. A similar station has been operating on an island north of the Arctic Circle since August 1961 (Ref. 21).

An experimental electronic navigational beacon powered with the strontium-90 fueled SNAP-7E generator, is being developed for the Navy; this unit must operate at a depth of 15,000 ft.

It is likely that many other applications will be found for these generators where remote, unattended operation is required for a year or longer, particularly for navigational aids and communications systems.

SNAP 9

Plutonium-fueled generators for satellite power are in successful operation on a TRANSIT Satellite. This generator was the first step in the development of SNAP-9A which will be used in the Navy's full-scale operational navigational system (and for other space applications). Plutonium-238 was selected because of its long half-life (86.4) years, its relatively high-power density, and its minimum shielding requirements. Since the thermal output of this heat source decreases only 4 percent over a 5-year period, there is no need for thermal controls or other moving parts (Refs. 23, 24).

The plutonium fuel is sealed in a tantalum container with welded closure. The inner container is placed in a Haynes-25 impact-resistant capsule which in turn is placed in a salt-water-corrosion-resistant Hastelloy C capsule. Helium at 1 atm of pressure in the containers provides adequate heat transfer to the outer surface without metal-to-metal contact. The rate of heat transfer could be regulated with this helium pressure.

The thermoelectric material used is lead telluride cast into elements 0.25 in. in diameter and 1.0 in. long. Eighteen pairs of elements produce an electrical output of 1.5 W at 1.5 V when operating with a hot junction temperature of 900 °F and a cold junction temperature of 300 °F. The elements are spring-loaded at their cold junctions to maintain thermal contact with the heat

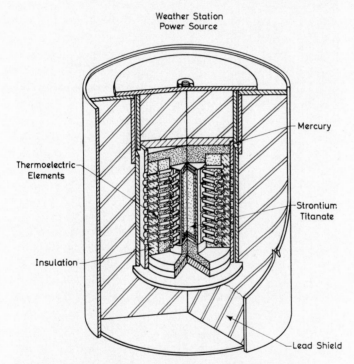

Weather Station
Power Source

Mercury

Thermoelectric
Elements

Strontium
Titanate

Insulation

Lead Shield

FIG. 9-30   Weather station power source (U.S. Navy).

source and to allow for thermal expansion. A rigid insulation is used in the areas around the elements to provide support, and fiberglass felt is installed in non-structural areas. Radiant heat transfer is reduced by a reflecting surface of gold at the back and end of the fuel capsule.

The characteristics of the first model of this type of generator is given in Table 9-8.

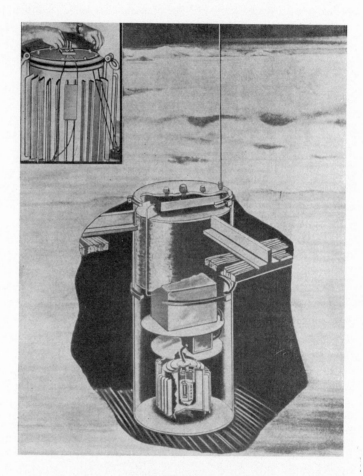

FIG. 9-31 Nuclear power weather station installed in Antarctic
(U.S. Navy).

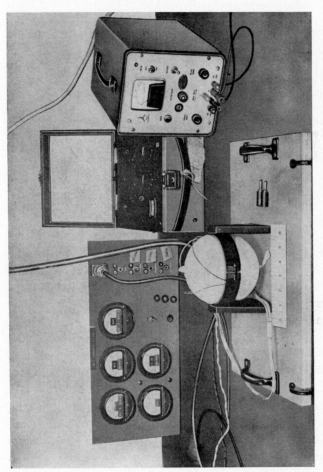

FIG. 9-32 SNAP-9 generator (Applied Physics Laboratory of Johns Hopkins University).

TABLE 9-8   SNAP-9 MOD 1 GENERATOR

Height	4.5 in.
Width	4.5 in.
Length	9.0 in.
Effective radiating area	58.9 in²
Conversion system	18 pairs of lead telluride elements
Heat source	plutonium-238 (85 % pure)
	1110 curies
	75.0 g
Thermal output	36 W
Electric output	1.5 W
Hot junction temperature	900 °F
Cold junction temperature	300 °F
Thermoelectric efficiency	6.4 %
Overall efficiency	4.2 %

SNAP-11

The SNAP-11 generator was developed for the soft-landed lunar spacecraft, Surveyor. Electrical energy will be generated during the lunar day by solar cells in this power system. The radioisotope generator was to provide electrical energy for experiments during the lunar night, and, equally essential, the heat from the isotopic fuel was to warm components which would not function at the lunar surface temperature of around −250 °F. Both sources of electrical energy were to be interconnected to storage batteries through the power distribution systems (Refs. 25, 26).

Curium-242 was selected for the SNAP-11 because of its high specific power (122 W/g) and very low external radiation (radiation could interfere with certain instruments on the Surveyor). This isotope is a high-energy alpha emitter with a half-life of 163 days. The fuel form, an alloy of gold and curium (5 Au: 1 Cm), was chosen for its good heat-transfer properties and for ease of fabrication. Also, the gold serves to dilute the curium, reducing the specific power to a level more convenient in designing the heat capsule. Because curium-242 decays to plutonium-238, it must be enclosed in a thin tantalum liner. Minute holes drilled in the tantalum liner allow the helium that is formed in the decay of curium-242 to escape into the hollow center of the cylinder. The helium pressure in this space will build up to 7870 psi at the end of the useful life of the generator (240 days after encapsulation). The tantalum shell is not made to withstand this pressure, because a heavier tantalum liner would not burn up during re-entry. Instead, the tantalum capsule is placed inside a heavy Hastelloy C container. The Hastelloy C has excellent high temperature strength and is resistant to sea water corrosion, yet will burn up readily under re-entry conditions. The remainder of the heat source is made of tungsten because it is a good thermal conductor and because tungsten is an efficient gamma shield.

A system for heat rejection provides reasonable operating temperatures during the life of the generator. The radioisotope will produce 752 W of thermal energy at encapsulation, 655 W at launching, and 475 W at the end of life. The design electric power to load is 25 W.

Lead–telluride thermoelectric elements also are used in this generator, and 31 couples will produce an open circuit potential of 5.44 V. The thermocouples are sealed and the space inside the generator shell is filled with helium to reduce sublimation of the lead telluride at high temperatures. Some of the operating characteristics of this generator are shown in Table 9-9.

TABLE 9-9   SNAP-11 OPERATING CHARACTERISTICS

Diameter	12 in.
Design life	3 months
Hot junction temperature	1000 °F
Cold junction temperature	370 °F
Number of couples	31
Conversion efficiency	5%
Design power	25 W
Minimum power	18.6 W
Weight	30 lb

SNAP-13

To demonstrate its feasibility, a low-powered, radioisotope-heated thermionic generator is being developed. The design will conform to the SNAP-11 specifications so that the SNAP-13 can be used as an alternate generator for the Surveyor (Ref. 25). As shown in Table 9-10, a major reduction in weight may be obtained with the thermionic system having a cesium vapor diode heated by curium-242. There also are design studies being made on generators for space applications with outputs up to 500 W.

FIG. 9-33   Generator on Surveyor (The Martin Company).

TABLE 9-10 RADIOISOTOPE POWER GENERATORS

Designation	Use	Power W	Size (in.)	Weight (lb)	Isotope	Isotope's half-life	Generator life
SNAP-3	Demonstration device	2.5	4-3/4×5-1/2	4	Polonium-210	138 days	90 days
Undesignated	Satellite power	2.7	4-3/4×5-1/2	4.6	Plutonium-238	89.6 years	5 years
Undesignated	Axel Heiberg weather station	5	18×20	1680	Strontium-90	28 years	2 years minimum
SNAP-7A	Navigational buoy	10	20×21	1870	Strontium-90	28 years	2 years minimum
SNAP-7B	Fixed navigational light	60	22×34-1/2	4600	Strontium-90	28 years	2 years minimum
SNAP-7C	Weather station	10	20×21	1870	Strontium-90	28 years	2 years minimum
SNAP-7D	Floating weather station	60	22×34-1/2	4600	Strontium-90	28 years	2 years minimum
SNAP-7E	Ocean-bottom beacon	7.5	20×21	1870	Strontium-90	28 years	2 years minimum
SNAP-7F	Oil Platform	25	20×9-1/2	27	Plutonium-238	89.6 years	5 years
SNAP-9A	Satellite power	21–25	20×12	30	Curium-242	162 days	90 days
SNAP-11	Moon probe	12	2-1/2×4	4	Curium-242	162 days	90 days
SNAP-13	Demonstration device	5–10	—	—	Mixed fission products	Variable	Up to 10 years
Undesignated	Demonstration device						
SNAP-15	Military Application	0.001	—	—	Plutonium-238	89.6 years	5 years
SNAP-17	Communications satellite	30	—	30	Strontium-90	28 years	3–5 years
SNAP-19	IMPS	25	—	22	Plutonium-238	89.6 years	1–3 years
SNAP-21	Undersea application	10	—	506	Strontium-90	28 years	5 years

Reproduced from "Power for Isotopes", USAEC Pamphlet by R. L. Mead.

IMP GENERATOR

A 40 W radioisotope electrical system is being developed for the IMP (Interplanetary Monitoring Probe) scientific satellites for use in 1964. The first IMP Satellites will use solar cells, however, there are problems with this power source when the satellite is not oriented toward the sun and also solar cells are affected by the radiation environment of space. The IMP satellites are to measure radiation and magnetic fields between the earth and the moon. An operational IMP must be in orbit at all times during the Apollo manned flights.

REFERENCES

1. The Martin Company and Electro-Optical Systems, Inc., "Radioisotope System Design". by J. B. WEDDELL, W. M. BOWES, W. R. CORLISS and G. P. SIX, *Energy Conversion Systems Reference Handbook*, W. R. MENE-TREY, ed., U.S. Air Force Report WADD TR 60-699, Sept. 1960.
2. R. I. SARBACHER, *Encyclopedic Dictionary of Electronics and Nuclear Engineering*, Englewood Cliffs, New Jersey, Prentice-Hall, 1959.
3. Monsanto Research Corporation, Mound Laboratory, *Internal Report on Radioisotope Generator covering work during December* 1953.
4. Monsanto Research Corporation, Mound Laboratory, *Thermal Battery Using Polonium*-210, by K. C. JORDAN and J. H. BIRDEN, Report MLM-984, Miamisburg, Ohio, June 1954.
5. G. T. SEABERG, "Nuclear Power in Space" (prepared for delivery at the International Symposium on Aerospace Nuclear Propulsion, Las Vegas, Nevada, Oct. 1961) *AEC News Release*, No. S-23-61. U.S. Atomic Energy Commission.
6. "New Developments in Radioisotope Production and Application in the United States", *AEC News Release*, No. S-21-61.
7. C. R. RUSSELL, *Reactor Safeguards*, Oxford, Pergamon Press, 1962.
8. U.S. Atomic Energy Commission, *Possible Requirements for Radioisotopes as Power Sources*, by W. H. McVEY, TID-12711, Washington, D.C., April 1961.
9. Monsanta Research Corporation, Mound Laboratory, *Catalog of Polonium and Curium Sources*, 1959.
10. National Bureau of Standards, *Maximum Permissible Body Burdens and Maximum Permissible Concentrations of Radionuclides in Air and Water for Occupational Exposure*, Handbook 69, Washington, D.C., June 1959.
11. National Committee on Radiation Protection and Measurements, *Exposure to Radiation in an Emergency*, Report No. 29, January 1962.

12. National Bureau of Standards, *Permissible Dose from External Sources of Ionizing Radiation*, Handbook 59, Washington, D.C., Sept. 1954.
13. U.S. Atomic Energy Commission, *The Effects of Atomic Weapons*, S. GLASSTONE, ed., Washington, D.C., September 1950.
14. U.S. Atomic Energy Commission, *Handbook of Federal Regulations Applying to Transportion of Radioactive Materials*, Washington, D.C., 1958.
15. U.S. Atomic Energy Commission, *A Summary of Transportation Incidents in Atomic Energy Activities*, Washington, D.C., December 1957.
16. R. V. BATIE, "Shipping of Radioactive Material at the National Reactor Testing Station" (unpublished).
17. H. A. KNAPP *et al.*, "Cost and Safety Considerations in the Transportation of Radioactive Materials" (unpublished).
18. U.S. Atomic Energy Commission, *Direct Energy Conversion and Systems for Nuclear Auxiliary Power (SNAP), A Literature Search*, by S. F. LANIER and H. D. RALEIGH, Washington, D.C., Aug. 1962.
19. U.S. Atomic Energy Commission , "SNAP Fact Sheet", *News Release*, June 1962.
20. U.S. Atomic Energy Commission, "World's First Atomic-Powered Buoy To Be Launched Tomorrow", *News Release*, No. D-345, Washington, D.C., Dec. 1961.
21. U.S. Atomic Energy Commission, "Atomic Generator to Power Navy's Antarctic Weather Station", *News Release*, No. D-271.
22. U.S. Atomic Energy Commission, "AEC Selects Contractor to Develop Deep-Sea Nuclear Power Generator", *News Release*, No. E-126, Washington, D.C., April 1962.
23. U.S. Atomic Energy Commission, *United States Aerospace Nuclear Power Programs*, by C. G. CAPOEN, Washington, D.C., Oct. 1961.
24. D. G. HARVEY and J. G. MORSE, "Radionuclide Power for Space Mission", *Nucleonics*, Vol. 19, April 1961, pp. 69–72.
25. U.S. Atomic Energy Commission, *The Practical Application of Space Power in the 1960's* by J. R. WETCH, H. M. DIECKAMP, and G. M. ANDERSON, Report TID-6312, Canoga Park, Calif., Feb. 1961.
26. U.S. Atomic Energy Commission, "AEC Selects Contractor for Nuclear Generator for NASA Unmanned Lunar Program", *News Release*, No. E-66, March 1962.

CHAPTER 10

ENERGY STORAGE

INTRODUCTION

Applications of energy storage are as varied as the uses of power. They extend from the transient storage of a minute amount of electrical energy in an electronic circuit to the accumulation of hydraulic energy for peak power loads in a city. Most mobile power systems require stored energy. An automobile engine converts stored chemical energy into mechanical energy. Small industrial trucks operate from electric storage batteries. The stored kinetic energy of a flywheel is required for the smooth operation of an internal combustion engine. Energy must be stored in the power system of a spacecraft to provide for operation in the shadow of the earth. Since the performance of many vehicles is limited by their energy storage capacity, the accomplishment of more advanced objectives depends critically on the development of improved means for energy storage.

There are differences of many orders of magnitude between the amounts of energy stored in various ways per unit of material. For example, the stored potential energy that is released by fission of an atom of uranium is 2×10^8 eV. The combustion of a molecule of octane releases some 50 eV. The capacity of a molecule of iron in a steel spring to store energy is some 2×10^{-5} eV. Some values in more convenient units of the capacities of various energy storage devices are given in Table 10-1.

Each type of energy storage device has characteristics that are advantageous for some applications. The steel spring and the capacitor have low specific energy storage capacities, yet these are the most widely used energy storage devices. The classes of energy

372

storage devices are listed in Table 10-2 along with their general
properties. Several of these devices will be discussed in more
detail in this chapter.

TABLE 10-1   CAPACITY OF ENERGY STORAGE DEVICES

Gasoline (lower value)	5600 Wh/lb
Silver oxide–zinc battery	55
Lead–acid battery	15
Flywheel (uniformly stressed disc)	10
Compressed gas (spherical container)	9
Compressed gas (cylinder)	7
Flywheel (cylindrical)	7
Organic elastomer	2.5
Flywheel (rim-arm)	0.9
Compressed liquid (ether)	0.1
Compressed steel	0.03
Torsion spring	0.03
Spiral spring	0.02
Coil spring	0.02
Capacitor	0.002

TABLE 10-2   CLASSES OF ENERGY STORAGE DEVICES

Type	Form	Regeneration	Power level	Output
Chemical	Fuel	Possible for H_2 and a few others	High for combustion, Low for fuel cell	Heat Electricity
	Battery primary	no (by definition)	Limited	Electricity
	secondary	yes	Limited	Electricity
Electro-magnetic	Capacitor	yes	Extremely high	Electricity
	Inductor	yes	Extremely high	Electricity
Mechanical	Compressed gas	partly	High	Pneumatic
	Flywheel	yes	Very high	Mechanical
	Spring	yes	Very high	Mechanical
	Hydraulic	yes	High	Hydraulic
Thermal	Latent or sensible heat	partly	Low	Heat

CHEMICAL ENERGY

The energy released in the oxidation of the elements varies systematically with their position in the periodic table as shown in Fig. 10-1. Here it is seen that hydrogen and certain elements

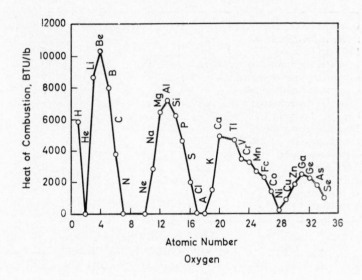

Oxygen

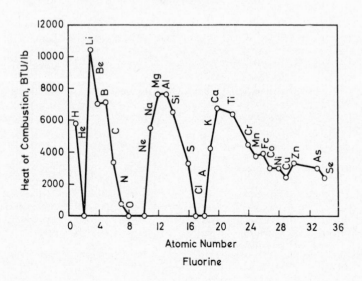

Fluorine

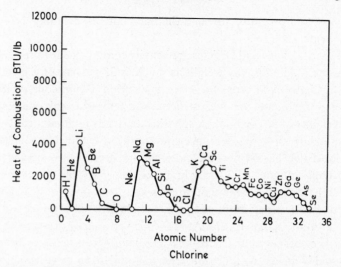

FIG. 10-1 Heats of combustion of elements plus oxidant vs. atomic number (F. W. Lauck, C. Busch, O. A. Uyehara and F. S. Meyer, "Automotive Propulsion after 2063 A.D.". *SAE Journal*, Vol. 70, No. 12, Dec. 1962).

in the second and third groups have high heats of combustion. Lithium, beryllium, boron, magnesium, aluminum and silicon are notable. Most of these high energy fuels are water reactive releasing considerable energy in producing hydrogen. Therefore, if these water reactive elements are to be used in reversible systems, such as high performance secondary batteries or fuel cells, a nonaqueous electrolyte is essential. Fused salts, organic solvents, ceramics, and ion exchange resins are possible electrolytes.

The heat of reaction varies according to the type of oxidant as seen also in Fig. 10-1. The heats of combustion on a mole rather than a pound basis are more nearly the same for the reactions of chlorine and fluorine with fuels.

FUEL STORAGE

Power sources, based on chemical energy, require some form of fuel storage. This fuel storage system can be a major weight factor for long duration power applications. Components of the system may include tanks with insulation and structural members, pumps, and pressure, flow and thermal controls including auxiliary heaters.

Fuel tanks on road vehicles are heavily constructed for practical reasons. The tank may weight as much as 35 percent of the contents. Lightweight tanks for space applications can be constructed from a thin metal skin with structural stiffening at tank openings and points of attachment. A spherical tank has minimum surface and weight. For example, a cylinder with a length to diameter ratio of two has 54 percent more surface area than a sphere of the same volume. Also the cylindrical skin must be thicker than for spheres at the same unit stress levels from internal pressure.

Fuel tanks operating under appreciable internal pressure must be carefully designed. The ASME code for unfired pressure vessels specifies design procedures and values for the maximum allowable stress according to the material of construction for industrial tanks. Cylinders for liquified gases under pressure or compressed gases are conservatively designed for commercial use and are relatively heavy. The weight of a typical propane cylinder equals the net weight of its contents in the smaller sizes. Special pressure vessels are constructed for the aerospace storage of fuels and gases. These special vessels are made with high strength materials and the designed with much lower factors of safety than are allowed in industrial practice. Great care is exercised in design, fabrication and testing.

Useful relations for estimating the minimum required thickness of shell plates for thin-walled tanks under internal pressure are

$$t = \frac{p \times D}{2 \times \sigma} \quad \text{(cylinder)}$$

$$t = \frac{p \times D}{4 \times \sigma} \quad \text{(sphere)}$$

where p is the net internal design pressure (psi), D is the internal diameter (in.), σ is the maximum allowable stress value including any factor of safety (psi) and t is the plate thickness (in.). The value of pressure used is the maximum difference between internal and external pressure. Furthermore the pressure at any height within a tank is the sum of the over pressure and the hydrostatic head. This pressure may increase, if the tank is accelerated. Although the above relations only apply approximately to thin-walled tanks, they are useful for preliminary estimates and parametric studies. These relations should not be used for design purposes or applied to heavy tanks. Also it should be noted that thin-walled vessels can fail under an external pressure that is much lower than the design internal pressure.

TABLE 10-3 MATERIALS OF CONSTRUCTION AT 75 °F

	Ultimate tensile strength psi	Yield strength psi	Specific gravity
Aluminum 5083	42,000	18,000	2.70
Beryllium	95,000	45,000	1.85
Copper	33,000	10,000	8.9
Glass filament	210,000		2.54
Inconel K annealed	155,000	100,000	8.2
Magnesium alloy	30,000	18,000	1.74
Molybdenum TZM sheet	135,000	110,000	10.2
Steel—Stainless 301 heat treated	75,000	30,000	7.8
15.7 PH heat treated	225,000	200,000	7.8
Titanium 6 Al 4V	130,000	120,000	4.5

Using the relations for thin-walled tanks, it can be shown (see Ref. 3-2) that the ratios of tank weights to fuel weights (no ullage) are given by

$$\frac{W_t}{W_f} = \frac{3 \times \varrho_t \times P}{2 \times \varrho_f \times \sigma} \quad \text{(sphere)}$$

$$\frac{W_t}{W_f} = \frac{2(B+0.69) \times \varrho_t \times P}{(B+0.33) \times \varrho_f \times (\sigma - P)} \quad \text{(cylinder with ellipsoidal ends)}$$

where ϱ_t and ϱ_f are the densities of the tank material and fuel respectively and B is the length to diameter ratio of the cylindrical tank. There is a practical limit to the application of these relations at low pressures since metal sheet of 0.025 in. thickness is about the minimum that can be fabricated into tanks. Also the weights of openings and attachments are not included.

Much effort has gone into the development, of lightweight propellent tanks for rockets. These are made from high strength steel or titanium or from fiber glass filaments precisely wound for maximum effectiveness.

COMPRESSED GASES

Storage of gaseous hydrogen, oxygen and other gases at high pressure may be advantageous for small installations. The equipment associated with cryogenic storage such as insulated tanks and transfer equipment is not required and the storage system is simple.

The ratio of the weight, W_t, of a thin-walled spherical container to the weight, W_g, of a compressed perfect gas of molecular weight MW of the same volume at the temperature T^0R is

$$\frac{W_t}{W_g} = \frac{27,800\,\varrho_t{}^*T}{\sigma\,MW}$$

It is noted from this relation that the ratio is independent of the storage pressure and the volume. Also the tank weight decreases with decreasing temperature so that the storage of compressed gases at low temperatures can be an efficient and practical method.

In some equipment, compressed gases can be stored in tubular structural members. Also where environmental conditions permit, fiberglass containers with internal bladders offer weight advantages. However, high-strength steel or titanium tanks are used for many purposes.

CRYOGENIC STORAGE

New insulating materials have been developed that permit the storage of liquified hydrogen and oxygen for long periods (months). These storage systems are used for the transportations of liquified

* lb/in³.

gases, for rocket propellant tankage, and for fuel storage in auxiliary power units. Cryogenic storage has made possible the hydrogen rocket for space exploration.

The design of a minimum weight cryogenic fuel storage system requires optimum compromises on the insulation, the construction materials, equipment size, working pressure and other factors. The transfer of heat into the liquid will cause evaporation and pressure build-up, if the container is not vented. Usually in a system of minimum weight, the volume of gas produced by evaporation equals the use rate so that an equilibrium pressure is obtained without loss of material. However, for long duration low use-rate storage, some gas venting may be preferred. By using the refrigerating effect of the vented gas, an overall weight saving may be obtained. Usually the design of the storage system requires detailed analytical studies to find the optimum conditions.

INSULATION

Methods of insulation shown in Fig. 10-2 include (a) high vacuum, (b) high vacuum with radiation shield, (c) high vacuum with radiation shield cooled by cold gas, (d) powdered or layered insulation in vacuum, (e) powdered insulation with gas cooled radiation shield, and (f) storage of liquid hydrogen in a vessel within the liquid oxygen tank. High vacuum insulation is at a pressure less than 10^{-6} mm of mercury. Some properties of insulating powders for low temperature applications are listed in Table 10-4.

Heat transfer in a high vacuum can be considered to depend entirely upon radiation effects. The rate between concentric spheres is then

$$Q_r = \frac{\sigma A_1 (T_2^4 - T_1^4)}{\dfrac{1}{\varepsilon_1} + \dfrac{A_1}{A_2}\left(\dfrac{1}{\varepsilon_2} - 1\right)}$$

where $\sigma = 0.1713 \times 10^{-8}$ Btu/hr ft^2 °R^4; A_1 is the surface area of the inner sphere, ft^2; A_2 refers to the outer sphere; ε is emissivity.

Coatings with emissivities of approximately 0.03 can be obtained with silvered surfaces or metal foil. Theoretically, a radiation shield between the inner and outer shells will reduce radiation heat transfer to one-half the value obtained without the shield. However, the additional weight of the shield may negate some of

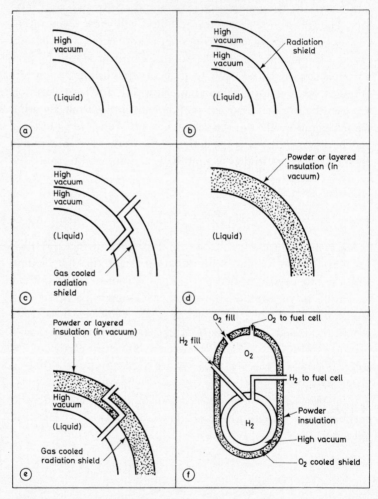

FIG. 10-2   Dewar insulation systems. Reproduced from W. R. Menetrey and J. Chrisney, "Chemical Systems", *Energy Conversion Systems Reference Handbook*, WADD TR 60-699.

this advantage. A further reduction in radiation can be obtained by cooling the radiation shield with gas vented from the container.

A major advance in low temperature insulation has come from the use of powders or layered insulation that have the effect of multiple radiation shields. These are so effective that the primary mode of heat transfer then becomes thermal conductivity through the insulation. The heat transfer is given for this situation by the relation

$$Q_r = \frac{4\pi k \times r_1 \times r_2 (T_2 - T_1)}{(r_2 - r_1)}$$

where k is the thermal conductivity of the powder, Btu/hr ft^2 $^\circ$R/ft; and r_1 and r_2 are the radii of the inner and outer spheres respectively (ft). The heat transfer rate now can be reduced by increasing the thickness of the insulation. Reflective evacuated

TABLE 10-4   PROPERTIES OF LOW TEMPERATURE INSULATION

Insulation	Density (lb/ft^3)	Temperature ($^\circ$R)	Thermal conductivity Btu/(hr)(ft^2) ($^\circ$R/ft)	Manufacturer
Pearlite	6.0	540–37	0.00041	Silbrico Corp., Chicago, Illinois
Silica Aerogel (Santocel, 85-5590, Al powder 15-450 percent)	6.0	540–37	0.00035	Monsanto Chem. Co. Everett, Mass.
Max. efficiency type S1-1	2.5	540–37	0.000080	Linde Company Tonawanda, N. Y.
Max. efficiency type S1-4	6.8	540–37	0.000025	
Max. efficiency type NRC-1	2.2	540–37	0.000052	National Research Corp., Cambridge, Mass.

W. R. Menetrey and J. Chrisney, "Chemical Systems", *Energy Conversion Reference Handbook*, WADD TR 60-699.

382   ELEMENTS OF ENERGY CONVERSION

insulations have been developed with mean thermal conductivities about 10 percent of those found in the best powder insulations. The thermal conductivity refers to the mean value between the specified temperature limits. In order to calculate the heat transfer through the insulation, it is necessary to have a relation between conductivity and temperature at low temperatures. A linear function may be assumed with zero conductivity at absolute zero temperature and the average values given in Table 10-5 for the midpoint temperature.

The required insulation thickness depends upon the capacity of the tank, the properties of the insulation and the allowable boiloff rate as given by the following relation

$$\beta = \frac{7200\,k(T_2 - T_1)}{\varrho_f H_v r_1} \left(\frac{1}{t_{\text{ins}}} + \frac{1}{r_1} \right)$$

where β is the percentage boiloff per day; H_v is the heat of evaporation (Btu/lb); and the insulation thickness is t_{ins} (ft). Some typical values of insulation thickness for cryogenic storage are shown in Fig. 10-3.

Heat conduction through supports and piping must be considered in the design of cryogenic equipment. In well designed

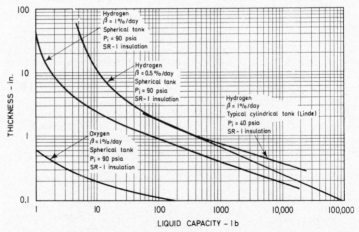

FIG. 10-3   Insulation thickness for cryogenic storage. W. R. Menetrey and J. Chrisney, "Chemical Systems", *Energy Conversion Reference Handbook*, WADD TR 60-699.

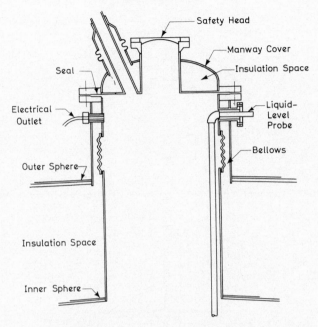

FIG. 10-4 Manway design. Arthur D. Little, Inc., *Handbook for Hydrogen Handling Equipment*, PB 161835, Contract AF33(616)-5641, February 1960.

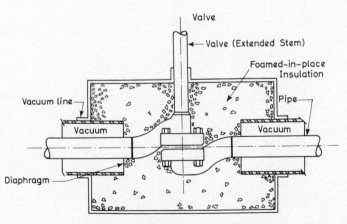

FIG. 10-5 Typical cryogenic valve developed from off-the-shelf components. Arthur D. Little, Inc., *Handbook for Hydrogen Handling Equipment*, PB 161835, Contract AF33(616)-5641, February 1960.

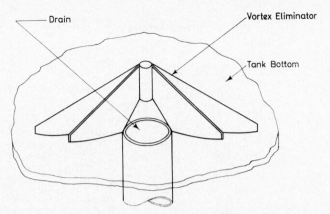

FIG. 10-6 Vortex eliminator. Arthur D. Little, Inc., *Handbook for Hydrogen Handling Equipment*, PB 161835, Contract AF33(616)-5641, February 1960.

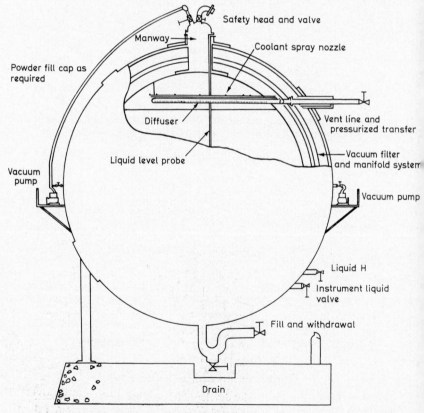

FIG. 10-7 Typical ground storage vessel for liquid hydrogen. Arthur D Little, Inc., *Handbook for Hydrogen Handling Equipment*, PB 161835, Contract AF33 (616)-5641, February 1960.

FIG. 10-8 Storage tank for 100 tons of liquid hydrogen (Linde).

FIG. 10-9 Tank car and truck for liquid hydrogen service (Linde).

equipment this heat conduction amounts to less than 5 percent of the total heat flow. Heat conduction is reduced by making the supports and piping of metals with low conductivity and by

FIG. 10-10   Cryogenic container for 150 l. of liquid hydrogen (Linde).

making these members as long as possible. Bellows are used extensively as shown in Fig. 10-4 to allow for thermal contraction. A cryogenic valve installation is illustrated in Fig. 10-5.

Construction of a ground storage vessel for liquid hydrogen is shown in Fig. 10-7. Vessels for storage, shipment and handling of liquified gases are shown in Figs. 10-8, 10-9, 10-10, and 10-11.

Lightweight cryogenic storage tanks have been developed for spacecraft. Typical system weights for hydrogen and oxygen storage are shown in Figs. 10-12 and 10-13. In a zero-gravity

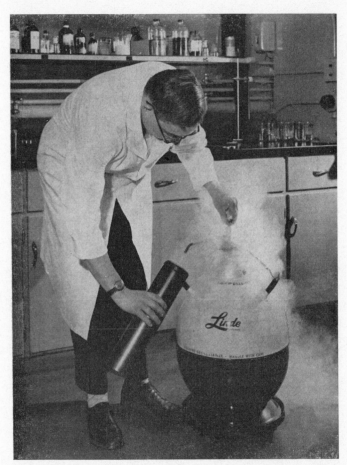

FIG. 10-11 Transferring liquid nitrogen (Linde).

environment, phase separation to withdraw pure liquid may be a problem. This can be avoided by supercritical storage at a temperature just above the critical temperature. Only one phase is present under this condition. There is little weight penalty for supercritical storage of liquid hydrogen in small containers.

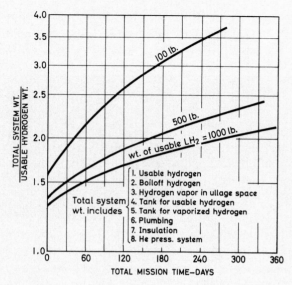

F<small>IG</small>. 10-12   Hydrogen system storage weight (Northrop).

Materials for use at low temperatures must be selected carefully since many metals become brittle. In addition to adequate ductility and impact strength at low temperatures, other desirable properties are low heat conductivity and low coefficient of thermal expansion.

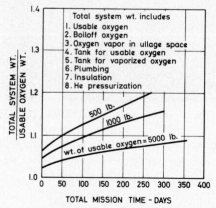

F<small>IG</small>. 10-13   Oxygen system storage weight (Northrop).

STORAGE OF THERMAL ENERGY

Energy can be stored as the latent heat of some phase change resulting from heating a material with appropriate physical properties. Possible changes of state for the storage of thermal energy include fusion–solidification, evaporation–condensation, solution–crystallization, adsorption, wetting, and change of crystalline phase. There are also reversible chemical reactions such as the decomposition and formation of metal hydrides that involve large changes in enthalpy. These and other effects have been investigated for various energy storage applications.

Thermal energy storage is used for many purposes. Hot water can be provided economically by operation of the heater during off-peak power periods to store thermal energy. Many power systems during the night store steam and hot water under pressure to meet the morning peak power demand. Here the steam boiler is a highly effective energy storage device. More recently, thermal energy storage has been proposed to provide power and thermal control during transit of a satellite through the shadow of the earth. These studies have shown that thermal energy storage can be made competitive with other energy storage systems for many applications.

Closed cycle heat engines or static conversion generators can be used to produce mechanical or electrical energy from stored thermal energy. The effectiveness of thermal energy storage depends to a large extent on the minimum temperature at which the heat can be used. This is usually the minimum operating tem-

TABLE 10-5   TYPICAL OPERATING TEMPERATURE LIMITS

	Lower	Upper
Thermionic generator	2400 °F	3500 °F
Gas turbine	1000	1800
Stirling engine	900	1800
Thermoelectric generator	400	1200
Rankine cycle engine	250	1800

perature of the energy conversion device. Some typical values of operating temperatures are listed in Table 10-5.

A wide range of materials have been studied to provide efficient thermal storage over these temperature ranges. Any thermal energy remaining at the minimum operating temperature usually can not be used unless there is a requirement for heat flow for thermal control.

SENSIBLE HEAT

Thermal capacity involving no phase change is by itself an inefficient method of energy storage. Large quantities of material are required and the temperature varies with time during addition and withdrawal of heat. The heat capacity of many solid elements is approximately a constant on a mole basis (Law of Dulong and Petit). Therefore the light elements and their compounds are preferred for heat storage. Some typical values of thermal capacity of various substance are given in Table 10-6.

TABLE 10-6   SPECIFIC HEAT

Material	Melting point °F	Ave. temp. °F	Specific heat Btu/lb °F
Aluminum	1220	900	0.27
Beryllium	2462	900	0.51
Copper	1982	900	0.10
Hydrocarbon	—	900	0.50
Magnesium	1114	900	0.32
Lithium	367	360	1.10
Lithium hydride	1256	900	1.41
Sodium	207	200	0.30
Iron	2800	900	0.16
Water (liquid)	—	212	1.01
Water (steam)	—	212	0.47

HEAT OF FUSION

The entropy of fusion per atomic weight is approximately a constant for many materials of interest for thermal energy storage. Therefore the heat of fusion per atomic weight and the melting point are related by

$$\frac{\Delta H_f}{T_f} = \Delta S_f = \text{constant}$$

The heat of fusion of compounds can be estimated by this rule as the sum of the values for the constituent atoms. It is seen that light atoms and their compounds with high melting point would be expected to have large values of latent heat of fusion per unit mass. Some typical values for materials of interest for heat storage are shown in Fig. 10-14 as a function of melting point.

Many substances have sufficiently large values of latent heat of fusion to be of interest for energy storage. However containment

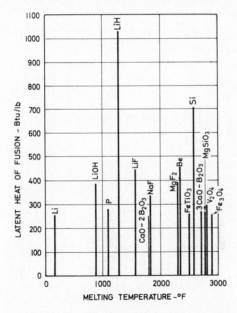

Fig. 10-14   Latent heat of fusion vs. melting point. C. W. Stevens, Electro-Optical Systems, Inc., "Solar-Thermal Energy Sources", *Energy Conversion Systems Reference Handbook*, WADD TR 60-699.

of high temperature molten materials in a heat transfer system is usually difficult. Also in the case of lithium hydride, the material has a low density so that the volume of the energy storage system becomes large. Furthermore there is a loss of hydrogen from lithium hydride by diffusion through the walls of the metal container at high temperature.

HEAT OF VAPORIZATION

The heat of vaporization is usually much greater than the energy of transformation for other phase changes. An exception occurs near the critical temperature where the heat of vaporization approaches zero. The energy content is a function of pressure and temperature. Some typical values of heat of evaporation at atmospheric pressure and of the corresponding energy content per cubic foot of vapor volume are tabulated in Table 10-7. The

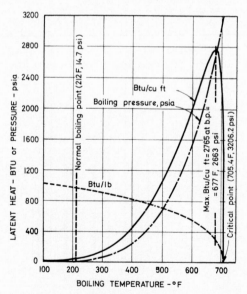

FIG. 10-15 Latent heat of evaporation of water. C. W. Stevens, Electro-Optical Systems, Inc., "Solar-Thermal Energy Sources", *Energy Conversion Systems Reference Handbook*, WADD TR 60-699.

exceptional properties of lithium and of its compounds are noted again. The latent heat of vaporization of water as a function of boiling temperature is shown in Fig. 10-15. Ammonia has similar characteristics. It is seen that the energy content per unit volume increases to a maximum value just below the critical point. However, the energy content per unit mass decreases as the temperature increases. There is therefore a tradeoff between weight and volume. Also control of the pressure and corresponding boiling temperature permits variations in system parameters not available to other changes of state. This is a useful and important characteristic in some applications.

TABLE 10-7   HEAT OF VAPORIZATION OF VARIOUS SUBSTANCES AT NORMAL BOILING POINT

Substance	Normal boiling point, °F	Molecular weight	Heat of vaporization	
			Btu/lb	Btu/ft³ᵥ
Aluminium	3270	27.0	3580	35.5
Ammonia	−28	17.0	589	31.8
Cesium	1240	132.9	230	24.6
Glycol	386	62.1	344	34.6
Lithium	2400	6.94	8500	28.3
Lithium hydride	*	7.95	8250	—
Magnesium	2012	24.3	4640	62.5
Mercury	672	200.6	125	32
Methanol	149	32.0	474	34.2
Nickel	5260	58.7	2790	39.2
Potassium	1400	39.1	920	26.5
Rubidium	1292	85.5	378	25.5
Sodium	1617	23.0	1960	30.3
Sulphur	832	32.1	123.5	28.1
Water	212	18.0	970	35.6
Sodium chloride	2570	58.5	1260	33.4
Lithium fluoride	3040	25.9	3540	35.9
Lithium chloride	2480	42.4	1530	30.3

* Probably decomposes at temperatures under boiling point. C. W. Stevens, Electro-Optical Systems, Inc., "Solar-Thermal Energy Sources", *Energy Conversion Systems Reference Handbook*, WADD-TR 60-699.

THERMOCHEMICAL REACTIONS

Heat is evolved or absorbed in a large variety of reversible chemical reactions. Some, of possible use in power systems for energy storage are listed in Table 10-8. The thermal decomposition of water to hydrogen and oxygen and the thermal decomposition of lithium hydride are appreciable only at high temperatures. These reactions absorb unusually large amounts of energy per unit mass. The reaction of sodium sulfate to form the decahydrate might be considered more properly as hydration.

TABLE 10-8 HEAT OF REACTION

Chemical reaction	$-\Delta H(67\ °F,$ 14.7 psia) Btu/lb
Li (s) $+0.5\ H_2$ (g) $\to$ LiH (s)	4900
Mg (s) $+H_2$ (g) $\to$ MgH$_2$ (s)	1272
NO (g) $+0.5\ Cl_2$ (g) $\to$ NOCl (g)	529
H$_2$ (g) $+0.5\ O_2$ (g) $\to$ H$_2$O (g)	5780
CO (g) $+0.5\ O_2$ (g) $\to$ CO$_2$ (g)	2760
Na$_2$SO$_4$ (s)$+10\ H_2O$ (l) $\to$ Na$_2$SO$_4 \cdot 10H_2O$ (s)	310
CO (g) $+H_2O$ (g) $\to$ CO$_2$ (g)$+H_2$ (g)	380

C. W. Stevens, Electro-Optical Systems, Inc., "Solar-Thermal Energy Sources", *Energy Conversion Systems Reference Handbook*, WADD-TR 60-699.

CAPACITORS

Electrical energy can be stored conveniently in capacitors. They are used in many electric circuits in much the same way that springs are used in mechanical devices. Also both springs and capacitors store energy by producing a strain in a material as the result of an externally applied stress. In the capacitor, this stress is the potential gradient across the dielectric material. This displaces electrons in atoms, moves ions and charged groups in lattices, and aligns asymmetrical molecules. These processes are reversible and the stored energy can be returned as electrical energy nearly instantaneously. There is of course a limit to the stress the material can withstand. This is the dielectric strength or breakdown voltage.

The energy stored in a capacitor is given by

$$W_e = \frac{CV^2}{2}$$

where W_e is the stored electrical energy in joules, V is volts, and C is the capacitance in farads. The capacitance of a parallel plate capacitor (neglecting edge effects) is

$$C = \frac{KA}{4\pi d} \times 1.1 \times 10^{-12} \quad \text{(farads)}$$

The area of one side of the electrode plate is A cm^2 and the separation is d cm. The relative dielectric constant K is very nearly unity for air. Values vary greatly for many materials with temperature, frequency, voltage, and humidity. The dielectric constants for several materials are listed in Table 10-9.

TABLE 10-9   DIELECTRIC
CONSTANTS AT 25 °C

Air	1.0
Compressed gas	1
Mineral oil	2.1
Styrene	2.6
Lucite	3.0
Mica	7
Water (pure)	80
BaSr titanate	2,000

The materials providing the highest energy storage capacities are the organic polymers because of their high dielectric strength. For a maximum voltage of 500,000 the energy storage capacity with allowances of 30 percent for electrodes and connectors is about 0.002 Wh/lb.

The capacities required in electronic circuits are usually small (micromicrofarads) and capacitors of convenient sizes are made from a variety of materials. However the size and cost of capacitor banks for the storage of appreciable amounts of energy become very large. For example a capacitor bank to store a kilowatt-hour of electrical energy would weigh more than 500,000 lb. A conventional storage battery to store this same amount of energy would be less than 100 lb. Capacitor banks are therefore only used where very high energy rate rather than energy quantity is important. Capacitors can be discharged in microseconds.

INDUCTORS

Current flowing in an electrical conductor produces an electromagnetic field surrounding the conductor. When the circuit is opened, the magnetic field collapses, inducing a potential in the conductor tending to keep the current flowing. The effect is accentuated, if the conductor is wound into a solenoid or toroid

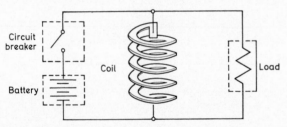

FIG. 10-16   Inductor energy storage (R. B. Colten, private communication).

(Fig. 10-16). More energy can be stored in an inductor than in a capacitor of the same weight by a factor of about a hundred.

The energy stored in an inductor is

$$W_e = \tfrac{1}{2}LI^2$$

where W_e is the stored electrical energy in joules, L is the inductance in henrys, and I is the current in amperes. Thus to store 10^8 joules in an inductor carrying 10^6 amperes requires an inductance of 0.0002 henry.

The inductance of a cylindrical single-layer solenoid is

$$L = \frac{12.57 \, N^2 A K \mu \, 10^{-9}}{b}$$

where N is the number of turns, A is the cross-sectional area of the solenoid in cm², μ is the permeability of the core ($\mu = 1$ for air), b is the solenoid length in cm, and K is a function of the diameter to length ratio ($K = 0.688$ when the length and diameter are equal). Thus a twelve-turn coil, 2 m in diameter and 2 m long would have an inductance of 0.0002 henrys.

The voltage generated when the stored energy is released is determined by the relation

$$E_t = L \frac{dI}{dt} - IR_{\text{internal}}$$

where $\frac{dI}{dt}$ is the rate of change of current flow. A large inductor such as that just described, discharging with a high rate of change of current flow and with low internal resistance can produce a transient potential of several million volts. Attention must be given therefore to high-voltage insulation in the discharge circuit. Also the charging power source usually must be protected by opening a switch before energy discharge.

Switching heavy currents in short time intervals remains a difficult problem limiting the performance and applications of inductors. In disconnecting the power supply after charging the inductor, a by-pass circuit may be required to reduce the switching problem. This by-pass circuit permits the current to continue for a brief interval thereby reducing the rate of change of current flow. Fast-acting mechanical switches have been developed for connecting the inductor into the load. Expendable high-voltage fuses are used in the switching circuits. These fuses can be made from a wire immersed in oil in a tube.

The large power losses during charging and storage can be reduced greatly with superconductors operating at low temperatures in liquid helium. Since the losses are low, a much smaller charging generator can be used and long storage times become feasible. A superconducting inductor circuit is illustrated in Fig. 10-17. After the required current is flowing in the inductor coil, the internal switch is closed and the charging generator is disconnected. A current persists in this superconducting internal

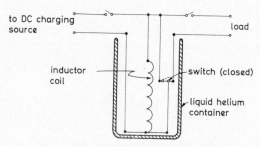

FIG. 10-17   Energy storage in superconducting inductor circuit.

circuit with only very small losses during the energy storage period. The energy is discharged by closing the switch to the load and opening the internal switch.

APPLICATIONS

Inductors are preferred for energy storage where large amounts of energy must be discharged within a short period of time down to a millisecond. Capacitors must be used to obtain much shorter discharge periods of the order of a microsecond. Rotating generators store kinetic energy and are used to produce heavy power pulses of durations in the order of seconds. The typical applications of batteries are for periods of minutes. Stored chemical fuels can provide power for several hours of operation of an internal combustion engine. Radioisotope and nuclear fission power sources are designed to operate for periods of hundreds of days before refueling is required. It is the hope of the future that nuclear fusion power sources will be developed in very large uniss perhaps designed to operate for decades.

REFERENCES

1. F. W. LAUCK, C. BUSCH, O. A. UYEHARA and F. S. MEYER, "Automotive Propulsion after 2063 A.D.", *SAE Journal*, Vol. 70, No. 12, Dec. 1962.
2. W. R. MENETREY and J. CHRISTNEY, "Chemical Systems", *Energy Conversion Systems Reference Handbook*, WADD TR 60-699.
3. A. D. LITTLE, Inc., *Handbook for Hydrogen Handling Equipment*, PB 161835, Feb. 1960.
4. C. W. STEVENS, "Solar-Thermal Energy Sources" *Energy Conversion Systems Reference Handbook*, WADD TR 60-699.
5. R. B. COLTEN, private communication, 1964.
6. H. C. EARLY and R. C. WALKER, "Economics of Multimillion-Joule Inductive Energy Storage", AIEE Paper 57–79, July 1957.
7. P. R. WIEDERHOLD, "Energy Storage for High-Power Discharge", *Astro and Aero Engr.*, pp. 104–6, May 1963.
8. R. C. CLERK, "The Utilization of Flywheel Energy", SAE paper 711A, June 1963.

INDEX

MADE IN GREAT BRITAIN